THE LOGIC OF SELF-DESTRUCTION

THE LOGIC OF SELF-DESTRUCTION

The Algorithm of Human Rationality

MATTHEW BLAKEWAY

MEYER
LEBOEUF

First published 2014
Meyer LeBoeuf Limited
Genesis 5 , Church Lane, Heslington, YORK YO10 5DQ

ISBN 978-0-9927961-0-5 Hardback
ISBN 978-0-9927961-2-9 Paperback
ISBN 978-0-9927961-1-2 ebook

A BIC catalogue record for this book is available from the British Library.

Typeset in Garamond by Ellipsis Digital Limited, Glasgow
Printed and bound in the UK by Clays Ltd, Bungay.

CONTENTS

PREFACE –
WHAT DOES THIS BOOK DO?

Can a simple idea explain something of enormous complexity? This book started with the simple idea that humans perform tactical deception with their emotional behaviour and this confuses how they understand their emotions. Then I realised that misunderstood emotions cause us to perform self-destructive actions. Gradually, the ripples of this realisation spread out to explain the most complex problem that mankind has ever encountered: understanding ourselves. Figuring out how planets orbit or trees grow is a cinch in comparison. Before I knew it, the whole thing grew into a giant multi-disciplinary argument, and I realised that if we assume that a human is a robustly logical computational device, we can account for everything it does. Demonstrating this became my obsession, like trying to solve a Sudoku puzzle. So, this book sets out to explain all the absurdities of human nature by logic.

The argument is rendered tricky by some of the ludicrous explanations of apparently random human actions that have been floating around for the past three millennia. Just as we put the concept of the soul in the trash, I have to cope with cabbies telling me about their subconscious, so I guess it will take another couple of centuries to undo that damage. It will take even longer to stop Supreme Court Judges talking about free will.

Before you start reading, it would be beneficial to give you some idea of the structure of this book, because it isn't possible to state the argument in a linear fashion. I've delved into evolutionary theory, mathematics, philosophy and history, and I can promise that you will lose the plot before realising that an apparent detour was indeed necessary. The argument is anchored around a sequence of thought experiments that explore, firstly, the relationship between emotional behaviour and our concepts of emotion; and secondly, how distorted concepts of emotion cause us to derive a self-destructive action. An actual emotion (as distinct from our idea of it) has its origin in evolution by natural selection, and the point of it is to drive a survival-enhancing action; so disrupting the emotion causes it to drive actions that are not survival-enhancing, and hence (ultimately) self-destructive. The thought experiments are logical in structure, but in an odd way – they lead us to think using distorted concepts, so they explore the rational consequences of misconceptions.

You should assume that I am armed only with logic. Logic dominates because science can neither distinguish real behaviour from pretend behaviour nor determine what happens to a human when self-referencing leads to a circular causality. Beyond logic, the rest of this book is stolen knowledge. Apologies to all historians and evolutionary theorists for being a shameless purloiner of their stuff! However, knowledge is increasingly vested in experts who are becoming more and more specialised, and occasionally we need to take a diagonal slice across multiple fields to find new connections. The goal in doing this is to create a new synthesis of how everything fits together. The result here, I hope, is a radical new conception of human nature that is internally consistent and compliant with current science: *everything* in the human sciences reduces to logic and evolutionary theory.

PART I:
THE HUMAN ALGORITHM

I have no use for knowledge that is not preceded by a sensation.

(André Gide, The Fruits Of The Earth, 1897)

Instinct is sympathy

(Graffiti, Williamsburg Bridge,
New York City, 2012)

SCENARIO A:
THE WRONG FEELING

When the woman was a little girl, her mother would put her to bed. Her mother reassured her and told her that she would always be there for her. The girl would drift off to sleep, but often she would be woken up in the middle of the night. Her father came home when the bar closed, and that was when the shouting started.

She would hear her father shouting, but not her mother. Her mother's voice was muted, as she was trying not to wake her, but her father didn't care. She couldn't tell what her mother was saying, but it sounded like she was soothing him. It sounded like she was trying to reason with him. She couldn't tell what her father was saying because his speech was so slurred. Once in a while, after the shouting, the banging would start. She almost never heard her mother cry out, but she would hear the thud against the wall in the passage. These sessions never lasted long. Her father would eventually stalk off to bed and slam their bedroom door behind him. Then the girl would go back to sleep.

On weekends, her father didn't need to go to the factory, so he would lounge around the house in the morning. He started drinking not long after breakfast, and by lunchtime his eyes were drifting in and out of focus. After lunch, her mother would lay her hand on her father's shoulder, but he would brush her aside and go out. And so the pattern continued.

The girl's mother tried to protect her. What her mother should have done was teach her to recognise her father as a bad man. But she thought she loved him. Her mother tried to protect her by concealing her suffering. Her mother put on a "brave face", but the girl did not know this. How could she? If her mother had told her that it was a "brave face" she would have revealed her concealment for what it was.

So the girl grew up in an environment where she was denied the ability to recognise her mother's feelings relating to her father. Her mother suppressed the outward signs associated with her fear and her anxiety, and the girl was unable to recognise the causal link between her father's behaviour and the feelings that resulted in her mother. Her mother suppressed the behaviour caused by these feelings so they were not visible to the girl.

When the girl grew up, she went out to bars with her friends. There wasn't much else to do in her town. She and her friends didn't have much money, so they would buy cheap beer and have a laugh. No one in the girl's town was rich, so it was rare for men to buy her drinks. However, one day it happened. He was heavy and brutal, but she thought him manly. He bought her another drink, and they agreed to meet a few days later. She wasn't used to the attention and she liked it.

When they met next, she thought she should be a bit careful so she did not drink too much, but he put away a fair bit. However, he didn't appear drunk. As they left the bar, he grabbed her roughly. She smelt the liquor on his breath when he kissed her. She submitted to him, and she had a feeling she had not experienced before.

They went back to his place. When he mounted her, he gripped her arm so that it hurt, and when he climaxed his face contorted into a look of rage. He collapsed on her, and his weight forced the breath from her lungs, and then he fell asleep. She looked at him sleeping, and felt at peace. The feeling that she had felt earlier had resolved itself somehow, and she thought that perhaps that this feeling was love. She was confused by the feeling, but then she had been told that love could be difficult.

She stayed with the man. He didn't have a good job, and neither did she, so it made sense to move in with him. Why pay rent for her

own place, when she could live at his? It wasn't long before he
shouted at her, and it wasn't long after that when he first hit her; but
she didn't leave. She believed she loved him; so why would she leave?

As an all-seeing narrator, I can look into the girl's head and see her
feelings. Furthermore, I can compare those feelings with the feelings experienced by women who have seen the behaviour that her
mother concealed. In real life, of course, this is not possible. What I
find is that the feeling the girl experienced when the man grabbed
her was the same feeling that another woman would recognise as
fear. However, normal women are not subject to the suppressed behaviour of the girl's childhood. In the girl's world, her mother had
suppressed the outward signs of fear. How then could the girl recognise the feeling for what it was?

Our ability to understand an emotion is based on two distinct
causal links: firstly, circumstances in our world cause us to
experience a feeling (which is private to us); and secondly, this causes
us to behave in a certain way, or display a facial expression (which is
on public view). The girl lived in a world where the second stage
broke down, and so her concept of the emotion was corrupted. She
had never seen that part of the emotion that is normally on public
display.

The girl was incapable of refuting her belief that she was in love
with the man, because she lacked the understanding of the link
between the feeling and the cause. If she lacked this understanding,
how could she evaluate her belief that the feeling she felt was love?
She lacked the conceptual framework. Sure, she had a word for fear,
and she had a word for love, but these words did not reference the
correct feelings and emotions.

Casual acquaintances of the girl might have said that what she felt
for the man was not love. But the girl's casual acquaintances are not
in our hypothetical world, so how could they know what she was
feeling? Who really knows what love is supposed to feel like, and
how can anyone be certain that their idea of love feels the same as
someone else's idea?

HOW DOES A HUMAN WORK? –
A MULTI-DISCIPLINARY APPROACH

A human action is determined by a brain algorithm. This algorithm might be very complex, self-reference and run continuously in a loop but that doesn't stop it being an algorithm. A human action could be as diverse as picking one's nose or launching a cruise missile, but we mustn't let a little detail like that put us off. I am going to try to demonstrate that a human is a robustly logical computational device, and I am going to do it with an old mathematician's trick of going into the problem backwards: I am going to demonstrate that self-destructive actions are rationally derived. I will start by looking at hypothetical people who have a very limited set of stimuli and work out how this would affect how they act. The problem with non-hypothetical people is that they have a vast array of stimuli and this makes them annoying to a simple thinker like me. In the opening Scenario, we looked at a hypothetical woman who only had one emotion (fear), the behaviour for which was uniformly suppressed. This led to her misidentifying this emotion, with disastrous consequences. My contention is that all the weirdness of human nature logically derives from the fact that humans perform tactical deception with their emotional behaviour. I am going to demonstrate that there are four binary atomic-level modules as to how a person can derive a self-destructive action. And once we have mastered this at a binary atomic level (which requires uniform behavioural manipulation), we can progress to the probabilistic (when behavioural manipulations are not uniform); then we can build molecules within an individual. Finally, we can aggregate individuals into whole societies.

I'm focussing on self-destructive actions and I am going to let the non-self-destructive ones speak for themselves. After all, if someone eats when they are hungry and sleeps when they are tired, what's to explain? Firstly, I want to look at some of the conventional ways of tackling this question and explain the problems that arise. It is the problem with these methods that leads me to an unconventional hybrid argument.

THE LIMITATIONS OF SCIENCE

All scientists have to deal with dirty data: astronomers have to battle with light pollution and dust in the atmosphere, and chemists have to deal with impurities in their compounds. However, dirty data does not necessarily devalue the results of their experiments. Scientists have to devise strategies to get around dirty data. For example, astronomers can avoid their problems by building telescopes on top of remote mountains or in space.

Occasionally, dirty data intrudes into the process of a scientific experiment in such a way that it invalidates the result. A chemist might be mixing two chemicals in an experiment, and the result is something different to what he expects. Further examination reveals that the first chemical had an impurity in it and the second chemical reacted, not with the first chemical but with the impurity. When this occurs, the experiment is corrupt and the result worthless. The chemist has to throw away the findings and recreate the experiment without the cause of the corruption.

Psychology has its own special form of dirty data: Homo Sapiens. Data does not get dirtier than this. Impurities in a chemist's compounds are nothing compared to the lying, cheating, conniving source of a psychologist's experimental data.

Not all experiments conducted in psychology have these problems. Babies, chimpanzees and laboratory rats are generally not lying, cheating or conniving, but these only provide psychologists with the raw material for experiments on subjects that cannot talk or do not experience a full range of emotions.[1] It is the talking subjects that lie, cheat and connive. So, when psychologists conduct experiments on human emotions, how can they ever be certain that their experimental results are not corrupt?

Some experiments in psychology involve observing human behaviour. However, we often affect behaviour or suppress it. The psychologist might try to conduct experiments by observing behaviour from a secret observation post. However, behaviour is affected by many factors other than the presence of psychologists with clipboards. For example, cultural influences can affect behaviour in permanent and imperceptible ways.

When you summon a bicycle rickshaw driver in Old Delhi, he will drop his head, smile sheepishly, not look you in the eye, etc. This is a behavioural representation of social subordination, but you won't see this in a London cabbie. Generally, in Western societies, we believe that all men are born equal and we reject class in favour of meritocracy. Therefore, the body language relating to subservience has been universally suppressed in the West, but we are no longer conscious of this act of suppression. This is an interesting comparison, because it implies that a shift in political ideology can lead to the suppression of a particular form of behaviour within a culture. Suppression of the behaviour impairs our ability to identify it – just like the woman in Scenario A; so when your puppy leaves a brown steaming thing on your carpet and you express your displeasure, the puppy will drop its head and wag its tail and come to you with a plaintive expression on its face. This is the behaviour of subordination – just like the rickshaw driver. To Western eyes (where this behaviour has been suppressed among humans) it looks as if the puppy is "acting innocent", or displaying its "guilty look". However, to act innocent is to affect a form of behaviour; and puppies cannot act without a concept of their own behaviour. This seems implausible. A guilty look implies a concept of its own morality, which is also difficult to explain in an animal with no language.

Now go into a top restaurant in the West – the sort where the wine waiters wear white tie and tails. The wine waiter affects subservient behaviour when you discuss the wine list with him. If you are a Westerner and you live in a culture where the body language of subservience has been completely suppressed, then you don't know how to react to that body language. This makes you feel an unaccustomed sense of power, and so you order a very expensive bottle of wine.

Sucker!

The wine waiter is affecting a form of behaviour that has been completely suppressed in the rest of society – an unusual double bluff.

Would a wine waiter in an expensive restaurant in India fake a subservient manner with his customers? Why bother? Wealthy Indians are exposed to beggars and street hawkers constantly. Every day they see the body language of subservience, and they reach compassion exhaustion shortly after they go out into the streets; so they are relatively unaffected by subservient behaviour. The waiter is therefore going to achieve nothing by faking it, but he may behave that way naturally.

So where does this leave our researching psychologist? He is thinking that by observing your behaviour without your knowledge, he is getting to look at you in your natural habitat. No such luck! Why? Because there is no such thing as a pure natural habitat, unless you stumble upon a tribe in the Amazon untouched by civilisation. Your natural habitat consists of a cultural environment that has changed your behaviour in ways of which you are not even conscious. All data that a researching psychologist can gather is tainted at source. There is no clean data.

If we cannot counter this problem, then psychological theories on emotion must either be suspect or need to be justified other than by a scientific experimental process. Psychologists are aware of this problem. They try to work scientifically, but the data on human emotional behaviour is a blizzard of random chaos, so they have given up taking it seriously. I am arguing that humans constantly perform tactical deception with their emotional behaviour; so this randomness is exactly what we should expect. Random data makes scientists queasy, but it is precisely what gets mathematicians excited. Sorting it out requires us to abandon experimental science and venture into the murky world of thought experiments.

THE TROUBLE WITH PHILOSOPHY

Philosophy is often rather tritely considered to be the study of the "fundamental questions", whatever those might be; but these days is mostly concerned with disentangling how thoughts, language, experience and actions all dovetail together. In the first half of the twentieth century, there was a tradition of philosophical scepticism regarding psychology. Ludwig Wittgenstein thought it a complete waste of time,[2] Karl Popper followed this up by directly attacking Freud for being non-scientific[3] and Gilbert Ryle said that he didn't understand what psychology was trying to achieve.[4] Let me take Wittgenstein as an example, because he looked at feelings, language and psychology more thoroughly than any other – themes to which I will return.

Wittgenstein stumbled on philosophy by accident while pursuing engineering. He went to Cambridge to study under Bertrand Russell. Russell, considered at the time to be one of the most pre-eminent philosophers of his day, observed "an unknown German appeared .. . obstinate and perverse, but I think not stupid."[5] However, Wittgenstein's intellect and rigour was so ferocious that he started demolishing the theories that had been Russell's life work. Wittgenstein went from being Russell's protégé to becoming his successor without obtaining an undergraduate degree, promptly quitting Cambridge University and writing the *Tractatus Logico-Philosophicus*.[6] This was the start of a revolution in philosophy: the fascination with the nature of knowledge ran out of steam, and attention was diverted to language and logic.

The *Tractatus* was quite unlike anything that had been written before. It was a sequence of extraordinarily dense numbered paragraphs. Paragraph 1: "The World is all that is the case" gives a sense of the rather cryptic nature of the *Tractatus*. The numbering system incorporates a hierarchy of supporting assertions, but there are only seven core statements. So Wittgenstein appeared to have reduced the whole of philosophy down to a supremely minimalist framework.

The book deals with the relationship between facts (i.e. the world or the universe); statements (which describe the world in language); and thoughts (which, expressed in language, are logical pictures of facts). Logic is not about how the universe works, but about how language works. Logic is somehow embedded into the structure of language. Since (as he assumed) thoughts are expressed in language, we can only analyse them using logic; so this informs the way we view the world. Language, however, has its limitations; hence the final statement of the book: "What we cannot speak about we must pass over in silence."

Wittgenstein considered that *Tractatus* dealt with all the problems of philosophy, some of which had been troubling mankind since ancient times. Since he thought he had done all that there was to do in philosophy, he quit. He was thirty-two at the time, so he retired almost twenty years before I even got started. However, the *Tractatus* addresses its central themes by making the assumption that it is possible to construct a logically perfect language that models reality, and where thoughts are logical pictures of facts. But this doesn't really permit us to explore psychological problems. Wittgenstein came to realise that spoken language is not logically perfect.

Abandoning his original work, he returned to philosophy with the intention of starting from scratch. Wittgenstein's friends and acquaintances included many of the greatest thinkers of the day, and he was amazed when a crowd of intellectuals met his arrival at Cambridge station. John Maynard Keynes, the famous economist, announced Wittgenstein's return in a letter to a friend: "God has arrived. I met him on the 5.15 train."[7]

Philosophical Investigations[8] describes language as a collection of word-games bound by rules. Language fits normal life perfectly, but when applied to philosophy, words have to be given very precise meanings to avoid confusion. Words used in the word-games of normal language have very imprecise meanings. They morph from one meaning to the next depending on the context, i.e. the word-game being played at the time.

He demonstrates that when word meanings are forced into logically perfect context (such as in the *Tractatus*), philosophers actually create the problems they seek to solve. Being demonstrated to be mere wordplay therefore solves the problems.

Wittgenstein addresses matters of psychology in *Philosophical Investigations*. He compares physics with psychology:

> Seeing, hearing, thinking, feeling, willing are not the subject of psychology *in the same sense* as that in which the movements of bodies, the phenomena of electricity etc. are the subject of physics. The physicist sees, hears and thinks about, and informs us about these phenomena, and the psychologist observes the *external reactions* (the behaviour) of the subject.[9]

In other words, a physicist can observe the subject of his study directly, but a psychologist can only study second-order effects of his preferred subject of study. This is the same idea as an emotion requiring two causal processes. An external stimulus causes an invisible brain event (for which there is a conscious experience), and this is represented in the physical world through behaviour.

> The confusion and barrenness of psychology is not to be explained by calling it a 'young science'; its state is not comparable with that of physics, for instance, in its beginnings. . . . For in psychology there are experimental methods and conceptual confusion. . . . The existence of the experimental method makes us think we have the means of solving the problems which trouble us; though problem and method pass one another by.[10]

Wittgenstein also re-addresses matters of logic. The *Tractatus* assumes that a logically perfect language can be constructed, but in *Philosophical Investigations* he says that we require perfection of logic, but ordinary language is not up to the job. "The crystalline purity of logic was, of course, not a result of investigation: it was a requirement."[11]

Logic is therefore an unobtainable ideal of ordinary language. We want the truth of our assumptions to lead through our logical argument to the unavoidable truth of our conclusion. If our assumptions are correct, we want the conclusion to be irrefutable based on the structure of the argument. However, sometimes the structure of the language isn't as rigid as we would like and this can disrupt the process.

Irrefutability is the ideal of a logical argument.

Wittgenstein's *Philosophical Investigations* got around the problem of the *Tractatus* by dropping the assumption of a logically perfect language. But it still leaves one problem: it assumes that all thought occurs in language. Thought does not occur in language, but in a brain; and a brain does not couch all thoughts in language.

If we put a laboratory rat in a maze that contains pushable buttons, each of which has a different probability of delivering an edible reward, the rat will work out which button has the highest probability of producing a reward.[12] It will then focus on pushing that button. Wittgenstein would have absolutely no explanation as to how a rat without words for numbers or mathematical concepts appears to compute gambling odds. To say that the rat isn't thinking would be to construe thought in an unreasonably narrow way.

CLUES FROM MATHEMATICS

At first glance it seems to be a contradiction that mathematics can explain how something can do mathematics without understanding it. The mathematician who achieved this astounding realisation was Alan Turing, and the theoretical device he invented was named a Turing Machine in his honour. A Turing Machine is an imaginary machine that can perform logic and mathematics by a series of purely mechanical processes. Calling it an imaginary machine makes it sound like it is something fictional, but Turing defined it in a rigorous mathematical fashion. He then described a Turing Machine that could simulate other Turing Machines – a device that became known as the Universal Turing Machine – and mathematicians went scurrying off to try to devise the simplest Universal Turing Machine possible.

Computers are now such an integral part of our daily life that it seems difficult to imagine that once nobody understood how this could be possible, but when these ideas first surfaced in the 1930s they were met with drop-jaw astonishment. Turing's work was an essential step in the invention of the computer, and he is rightly considered to be one of the greatest thinkers of the twentieth century. Turing and the mathematician Alonzo Church proposed what is now known as the Church-Turing Thesis: anything that is mathematically calculable can be computed by an uncomprehending machine. In other words, all of logic and mathematics can be performed robotically. No mathematician has ever managed to prove this, but today computer scientists shrug their shoulders and treat this thesis as their first assumption.

If a computer is a metal box with wires in it that can do mathematics and logic without understanding them, could a rat be a furry box with neurons in it that performs the same feat? There is of course one key difference: The furry box does not need any human input to perform its uncomprehending reasoning, and the metal box will only solve a problem that it is given by a human. However, the rat gets its input from nature – it is hungry, and this is the problem that it seeks to solve by nosing around whatever environment it finds itself in. Hunger is the driver of the rat – it *is* the urge to act.

Understanding ourselves is the most complex problem in the known universe. Addressing this problem requires us to mix science, philosophy, and mathematics together because none of these disciplines on their own provides the answers. Psychologists and neuroscientists think of themselves as scientists, but they are constantly raiding the philosophical and mathematical toolkit (for example, by exploring problems of free will and consciousness) because otherwise they couldn't do their jobs. We are gradually unravelling how humans work, and inching towards the conclusion that a human brain is nothing more than a biological computing device. A human brain is the most complex object that we have yet encountered in the universe and, although we have made great strides in understanding it, it is hardly surprising that understanding ourselves is the most complex problem that we have ever addressed.

THE PROBLEM OF BELIEF

Psychologists and brain scientists might be achieving great things, but there is one problem where they are making no progress: nobody can explain belief. How is it possible that Argentinians believe that dancing the tango will make them happy, when paradoxically dancing it properly requires you to act as if you are very sad?

Nineteen people thought that they would be doing a great service to mankind if they flew planes into skyscrapers. Attempts to explain this usually state that they were irrational or brainwashed. But is irrationality an absence of causality or a form of causality that we haven't worked out yet? If there was no causality, how come all nineteen of them seemed to have the same thought at the same time? And if they were brainwashed, how does brainwashing work? If I am to explain human nature, I cannot avoid delving into its darkest corners.

There is no human action that is not dependent upon a belief. I used to think that taking a pee was not dependent upon a belief, and I wish to express my gratitude to the New York City police officer that rectified this misconception by ticketing me for public urination. Psychologists are aware of this problem. Steven Pinker says "Psychology banished mental entities like beliefs and desires altogether and replaced them with stimuli and responses. The other social sciences located beliefs and desires in cultures and societies rather than in the heads of individual people."[13] If psychology does not explain belief and sociology treats belief as brute fact, then we have a large gap in our understanding of ourselves. This book aims to fill that hole. I will start by describing how a human calculates an action at the simplest possible level, ignoring the impact of belief. I will set out a logic of self-destruction that demonstrates that self-destructive acts are rational. This serves as a model of how all actions are calculated because, as I hope to demonstrate, all actions have a small part of self-destruction in them and all belief is ultimately destructive to the very people who believe it. I will do this without resort to any concept that I cannot explain causally. Therefore, I will place such notions as free will, minds, evil and souls into the trashcan where they belong. My argument will draw upon evolutionary theory, philosophy and mathematics. But my technique is going to involve a sequence of thought experiments. They incorporate Wittgenstein's notion that sometimes we think in language that isn't logically consistent, but they don't necessarily assume that all thought is verbalised. However, I describe thought using ordinary language because writing this book in quasi-mathematical hieroglyphs would be tiresome and reading it would be worse.

By shifting the scientific context, understanding human nature becomes a giant logic puzzle, and thinking this way is not inhumane. Science, philosophy and mathematics can combine to understand humans without reducing humanity to a collection of walking, talking biological machines, or needing to assume that they are a God-made piece of magic.

A VERY PRIVATE MISCONCEPTION

Let us return to the abused woman in Scenario A.

She thought that she was in love with the man. Based on the structure of language, this was irrefutable to her. A thought that is irrefutable by the person who has that thought is a belief to that person. Does this belief therefore have a critical feature that is in common with a logical conclusion? Could it be said to be a logical conclusion?

This Scenario is written from the perspective of an all-knowing narrator. [Uh . . . Me!] As an all-knowing narrator, I can "see" her thoughts and feelings. What I am able to do is to construct a misconception causally. She is not irrational, but is in a rational trap that results from the misidentification of her own emotion. A Wittgensteinian would say that she is drawing the wrong conclusion because she is thinking in a language where the words have had their meanings distorted. However, these thoughts do not need to be verbalised. Her belief is irrefutable based on a very private misconception. She is employing a rational process that is private to her alone.

So the woman in Scenario A believes she is in love. What is the difference between this and really being in love? In Scenario A, I created a clear distortion. It is therefore easy to see that the woman's feeling is not love. However, in real life this is never possible.

In order to determine when someone is experiencing true love, we would need to have a benchmark. This could not be a benchmark measured in feeling because we cannot see anyone else's feeling. It would have to be a benchmark measured in behaviour. However, in the Scenario, the problem started as a result of manipulated behaviour. How can we have confidence in a behavioural benchmark if it is possible that some people in our reference group are faking or suppressing the behaviour?

Some of the people might be manipulating their behaviour deliberately, but more likely they will be manipulating unintentionally. This could be because of circumstances unique to their make-up or it could be due to cultural influences. Once cultural influences get in the way, it could be that all of our reference sample of subjects have corrupted behaviour. At that point, the whole idea of creating a benchmark is thrown into confusion.

It could be said that people affecting behaviour will reveal subtle clues. However, the subtle clues are generally just another form of behaviour. To analyse this, we need a benchmark of the subtle clues, and this is subject to the same problem that we originally had. How can we distinguish the subtle clues from any other form or behaviour?

The problem seems intractable.

THE LANGUAGE OF FEELING AND EMOTION

To look at the problem further, we need to explore how we form concepts of and language for feelings and emotions. From there we can examine what happens when this process goes wrong.

SHARE THE FEELING!

I thought that it would be educational for me to try an experiment. I wanted to know what it was that made a psychology researcher tick. My experiment is deliberately amateurish because I am a philosopher, and scientific research makes philosophers nervous. This is what I did: I went to my local paint shop and collected a range of colour sample cards of similar colours. I selected two different colour cards: one had shades that were slightly different but of the same level of darkness; the other had shades that were the same, but different levels of darkness. I took two of each colour card, and using scissors cut one set of the cards such that each colour was separate. At this point I had two sets of identical colour cards, one complete in their colour groups and one as separated cards.

I got some of my friends together and I laid out one grouped card and put the separated cards face down. I asked them to try to remember the colours off the grouped card giving them numbers (1 at the top, etc.), and then I turned it over. I then turned one of the separated cards face up and asked them to identify the number of the colour.

What I found is that short-term memory of colour shades is very poor, but is stronger for differing degrees of darkness. For similar shades, the ability to correctly identify the correct colour after only a short interval (a few seconds) was not much better than a random guess. So we can distinguish very similar shades of colour when they are next to one another, but our memory only recalls distinct colours in broad terms. From this we can conclude that our ability to come up with different names for colours cannot arise because we can remember them.

We all often assume that we can remember or visualise colours, only to find that we can't.[14] A common error is to pick a paint colour from a card, only to find out that it looks terrible on the wall of the living room. When this happens, our first reaction is to think that the paint shop has given us the wrong colour, but when we hold the colour card up against the wall, we see that they sold us the right colour, but we failed to imagine what it would look like on the wall.

This is essentially why we are able to have names for colours. We can share the experience of seeing a colour with another person, and we can constantly return to revisit the experience by looking at the colour again. Remembering is not a requirement of colour language.

The ability to share the experience is essential to the naming process, because words are for communication, and only take on true meaning when more than one person understands them and uses them with a common reference.

The ability to revisit the experience is essential, since we do not have to rely on memory to be sure that the same name is always being used to refer to the same colour.

SHOW ME THE FEELING!

Imagine this scenario: you go to your doctor and say, "Doctor, I have a terrible pain in my abdomen"; the doctor says, "What pain is it?", and you say "It is pain number X43." The doctor looks up pain number X43 in his book and says, "Ah! You have an inflamed appendix."

If we could do this, it would be wonderful. We would all be

healthier because incorrect diagnosis would never occur. Being a doctor would be as easy as being a motor mechanic.

Why can this not occur?

We can distinguish many shades of colour, and name many of them. We can also distinguish many types of pain. If a pin is stuck into your hand or finger, even with your eyes shut you know that it is a sharp object and where it is pricking you. However, our vocabulary for pains is extremely limited. We could not name our pain 'X43'. Why is this?

Our ability to have multiple names for colours does not derive from an ability to remember the experience of seeing them. We have multiple names for colours because we can compare each other's experience of seeing a colour, and more importantly we can go back and check the experience of seeing a colour when our memory fails us. With pain, this does not work.

We can neither compare our experience with other people, and we have no means of going back and checking the experience; at least not without constructing some inhumane experiment. Without this ability, we cannot name pains. As a result, our vocabulary of pain is a tiny fraction of what it is for colours.

Let's take an example. My personal perception is that there is a difference between the pain of my toe being stamped on and being stubbed. Surely, it must be possible to devise names for each of these two pains? Let us consider the problems. Firstly, remember that the experience of pain is imprecise (as with colours). But, curiously, when I feel one of the pains I always know immediately whether it is caused by stamping or stubbing. We could say therefore that there is a difference between remembering and recalling. I can remember pains, but not recall them – recalling would somehow involve invoking a reliable mental image of the feeling. However, if I can't recall what they feel like, I need to be able to revisit the pain to remind myself whenever I want to use the name for the pain and this is tricky to arrange. Secondly, you and I cannot experience the same pain simultaneously, but we can each observe one another's body language when we experience the pain. The problem here is that whether you stub your toe or it is stamped on, there isn't a difference in your wincing body language. For us to be able to separately name the pains, we would need to be able to distinguish our own pains and each other's. However, we can't distinguish each other's unless the body language is distinct.

This gives us some clue as to the limits of language for pain. We have no pain names, but we have a few descriptive words: 'sharp pain' or 'dull pain', and the important thing to note is that these broad categories *can* be distinguished by behaviour.[15] Sharp pain gives rise to a clenching of the face and a reflex flinch away from the source of pain, or a rapid clutching of the painful place with the hands. Dull pain gives rise to a miserable appearance, and a nursing of the painful place with the arms but no extreme body movements. We have other words for 'pain', for example 'hurt' and 'agony', but these are largely synonyms. 'Sharp' and 'dull' is almost the limit of our descriptive language, and compared to the huge range of language we have for colour, that is minuscule.

There is another problem with pain language, and that is our inability to compare pains. For example, we can say that two colours are similar, but can any of us really say whether having our thumb slammed in a door is more like a toe trodden on or a toe stubbed? This is partly a memory problem, and partly the impracticality of revisiting the trodden vs stub comparison. We cannot compare pains side by side.

To summarise: our language for pain cannot be more diverse than the body language that results from it.

The difference between our ability to talk about colour and our relative inability to talk about pain is important. Wittgenstein explored this in *Philosophical Investigations*. This piece of philosophy has come to be known as the "private language argument". The essence of this argument is that the idea of a language that necessarily only one person understands is incoherent. This means that we cannot have language for experiences that are private.

What then does the word 'pain' mean? Or to put it another way, what does the word 'pain' refer to?

The word 'pain' can only have meaning to the extent that we are all sure we are using the word the same way. We use the word as if it directly refers to the sensation. However, we can have no certainty that our sensations are the same, although we can have certainty that our behaviour is the same. The word 'pain' therefore could be said to refer not to the *sensation*, but to a Thing X associated with a particular form of behaviour. The reference of the word is indirect. The word does not refer to the sensation – it refers to whatever causes the behaviour; this, we presume, is the sensation.

So our ability to form a concept of pain is based on two causal processes: 1. The stubbing of our toe causes a feeling; and 2. It separately causes a behavioural response – a flinch. This is why the word 'pain' does not refer directly to its intended object.

ACT OUT THE FEELING!

Let us consider how the words 'taste' and 'smell' came about. With pain, we can teach a child the word 'pain' because the child reacts to its own pain, and we rush to its assistance. The child's behaviour and everyone else's similar behaviour is essential to our ability to have the word 'pain'. However, when a child smells something, it does not usually have any visible behaviour.

When you teach a child the word 'smell', you put a roast chicken by your face and the child's and make a big show of closing your eyes and going "Mmmm! Nice smell!" The absence of natural behaviour means that we have to invent behaviour. I need to make a distinction here between *fake* behaviour (that is behaviour that we affect with the intention to decieve) and *pretend* behaviour which is behaviour that we put on solely for the purposes of teaching feeling-words to small children. We would also teach small children by holding our nose and going "Poo! Nasty smell!" in the appropriate circumstances. I cannot think of another way of teaching a small child smell words. We need pretend behaviour because of the absence of visible natural behaviour. However, once the word is learned, we no longer have a use for the pretend behaviour, and so we drop it. Generally, pretend behaviour is only used with small children. (Exception: you are trying to ask for the toilets in a country where nobody speaks your language.)

Let's imagine, hypothetically, that humans have no natural flinch response when they feel pain. Would it be possible to teach a child the meaning of the word 'pain' by means of pretend behaviour? Firstly we have the problem that sometimes a child will fall over and hurt itself, and other times it will fall over and feel no pain; and because the child has no flinch we will be unable to tell the difference. Imagine that we try to teach this child the word 'pain' by falling over ourselves and then putting on some show of pretend behaviour. The child might learn to put on the same pretend behaviour when it fell over, but the distinction would not be made between falls that hurt and those that don't. There is no way for us to be able to tell the difference, and therefore no way for us to be able to teach the child; so the pretend behaviour isn't going to help.

Pretend behaviour works as a means of teaching the word 'smell', but would not work for the word 'pain' in the absence of a human flinch response because of a critical factor: the smell of roast chicken affects you and the child simultaneously. It is a feeling you share. You both have the sensation caused by the same source; so the child can relate to the pretend behaviour. With pain, the source of your pain isn't a source of pain for the child; so the child isn't going to be able to relate to pretend behaviour that comes from your pain.

Taste and smell therefore have certain similarities to colour. We can share the experience with someone else (when we taste each other's dishes in a restaurant), and to some extent we can return and revisit tastes at a later date. However, this latter factor is constrained because unlike a colour card when we can be fairly sure it is exactly the same colour; we cannot be sure that this roast chicken tastes exactly like the one we had last week. For most of us it doesn't particularly matter if this chicken tastes the same as last week's. However, this presents a small problem for restaurant critics and wine connoisseurs; because describing this is their job. They need to be able to convey these small nuances, and to do this they need special language.

If we look at the taste words of normal people (i.e. not wine and food writers), we find a very limited vocabulary; for example: 'salty' and 'sweet'. However, something surprisingly obvious arises: each of these words describes tastes that relate to a single chemical – NaCl or $C_{12}H_{22}O_{11}$. This is important to our ability to name them because their chemistry never changes. They are like the paint shop colour card, and we can be confident that they never change; so we are not reliant upon memory for the naming process. However, the taste of chicken or a particular wine is not definable chemically in such a simple way. The unreliability of memory becomes an obstruction to our ability to create the applicable language.

Writing a review of a restaurant or a wine is a particular art. It is not that the fundamental ability of developing language for these things is lacking, because it isn't. It is just that it is an area of language that most of us don't particularly need to develop.

From this example, however, comes a particularly useful observation: the relationship between language, memory and sensory experience. Certain cultures have languages with more elaborate vocabulary for a certain part of the colour spectrum, and people in those cultures can demonstrate better ability to recognise colour in those spectrums. For example, certain African tribal languages have relatively more emphasis on vocabulary for browns than European languages.[16]

Language helps us to remember sensory experience. It provides an anchor to memory. Listen to a wine expert talking. To the uninitiated, their talk sounds pompous and pretentious. However, this is a jargon that they have developed to describe the particularly sensory experience that is important to them. When they describe a wine as "an oaky little Chardonay with hints of dirty old socks" they are using creative language for the purpose of unusual description. However, the language is not merely descriptive. The language anchors their memory; without it they would be unable to compare their current experience with their historic experience.

A wine expert friend of mine tells me that he thinks that language is what really distinguishes the true expert from the amateur, not taste. So the expert has a superior tongue, not because of its taste buds, but because of the language he can produce with it. The inventive language that wine experts create is essential to their business, but it is also a form of technical jargon: only they understand it (which is why it sounds a bit pompous to the rest of us).[17] A restaurant critic for a popular newspaper cannot resort to jargon and still expect to have a readership. It is a worthwhile exercise to read some restaurant reviews. (And reviews of really bad restaurants are much funnier!) You will find that, because the average man in the street has little language for tastes, restaurant reviewers almost never describe tastes. Instead they use metaphors: "It smelt stoutly of fatty, shredded incontinence pads, and came with two thin slices of bread that were so hard Captain Bligh wouldn't have served them", and "the raw scallop was a raw scallop, like chewing a dolphin's cold adenoid".[18] Neither of these descriptions are actually descriptions of taste at all. They are either metaphors of physical texture, or a taste comparison to something that neither you nor the reviewer has eaten. However, I expect you got the picture!

In summary, taste and smell are a halfway house between colour and pain. We can share the sensations and can compare our experience with others, but our ability to revisit them to check our memory is limited. Language is an aid to memory, but taste and smell language can never be as precise as colour language because (other than simple chemical tastes) we cannot independently check memory: even the greatest wine expert cannot be completely sure that two bottles of wine with identical labels taste identical unless he or she sips the two alternately within a very short timeframe. A gap of only an hour or so would be sufficient for some doubt to arise.

TYPES OF FEELINGS

It is possible to get quite tangled up trying to distinguish between sensations, feelings and emotions. Generally, a sensation is a feeling that has a clearly identifiable cause and which we detect through a sensory organ. These include taste, pain, etc. but there are some unusual sensations, such as the feeling of needing to urinate. The meanings of 'feeling' and 'emotion' are not so obvious, and sometimes these words are used interchangeably. One possible distinction is that feeling is the subjective experience of emotion, but this leaves emotion in its pure sense somewhat undefined. Looked at this way, an emotion is a pure state (love, pity, fear) and the feeling is triggered by the emotion. However, there is a high degree of interchangeability between these concepts. For example, it could be argued that hunger could be a sensation, a feeling or an emotion. Certainly, hunger can trigger an emotion, but precisely what emotion this would be is not clear. An important question is whether we can correctly identify emotions in their pure state.

I am concerned with words and concepts and how these can be used in rational thought. Therefore, I need to understand how we identify our feelings and emotions and how we learn the words for them. Perhaps the best way to explore this is to make a comparison between 'pain' and 'happiness'. The former is generally considered to be a sensation and the latter is an emotional state. I have already discussed that we understand the word 'pain' purely because we can see the behaviour that results from it. How does this compare with the behaviour that results from happiness?

It is perhaps helpful to make this comparison in tabular form:

	Pain	Happiness
Behaviour	Grimace, clutching at painful place, or nursing of injured body part.	Smiling, energised, relaxed demeanour.
Identifiable cause	It is easy to identify the cause of pains resulting from injury, but less so for ones resulting from illness (e.g. abdominal pain). However, pain generally has a single cause.	It is very difficult to determine the precise cause of happiness. Happiness is caused by a wide set of circumstances, and it would be unusual that all these circumstances could be identified.
Immediacy of behaviour	There is generally no time-lag between the cause of pain, the sensation and the onset of associated behaviour.	Very vague connection. Anyway, if you cannot determine the cause of the emotion, how could you possibly determine whether the onset of the associated behaviour is immediate or not?
Duration of behaviour	Lasts only as long as the sensation lasts.	Behaviour will tend to come and go, and what matters is the frequency of the behaviour over the long term.

Clearly, the behaviour associated with pain is much more immediately connected with the sensation itself. Happiness behaviour is more loosely connected with the emotion and the causal links are very difficult to determine. This is one reason why almost nobody is confused about what pain is, but almost everyone is very easily confused about happiness.

So, even if we look at the normal process of learning language for sensations and emotions, happiness is much more difficult to understand than pain. However, fundamentally, there is no difference here in terms of how we learn the meaning of the word: the word refers indirectly to whatever is the cause of the behaviour.

FAKE THE FEELING

So far, I have been describing how language, feelings and behaviour are supposed to fit together. Now let us look at what happens when the normal process goes wrong. Once we start performing tactical deception with the behaviour, the indirect reference of the behaviour either points to the wrong place or fails to point at all.

In Scenario A, we raised the possibility that the behaviour normally caused by an emotion can be suppressed. This caused the girl to have a disoriented perception of an emotion that became embedded in her language. It became embedded in that she gave the word 'love' to the wrong emotion. Furthermore, she had no mechanism to correct this.

The behaviour relating to an emotion can be affected as well as suppressed. We also need to look at the possibility of this occurring. The more likely it is to occur, the more likely we are to be confused. Again, let us make this comparison with respect to pain and happiness:

	Pain	Happiness
Incentive to affect	Common in children to gain sympathy/affection. Very rare in adults. (Exception: you are tripped in front of the goal.)	Considerable incentives to fake in certain cultures, caused by the desire to appear attractive, popular, accepted by peers, etc. In other cultures, this incentive is almost entirely absent.
Ease of affectation	Very easy. ("The referee didn't see that! Is he blind?")	Easy, but to be convincing you have to keep it up over long periods of time, and this becomes tiring. At some point the affectation becomes habit.

Incentive to suppress	Very rare. (Exception: you are dying of cancer, and you think that this will be the last time your grandchildren will see you alive.)	Very unusual, but can occur in specific circumstances. (Examples: Your pay rise was much more than you expected, but you cannot let your boss know you think this. You have just spent a wonderful afternoon with your lover, but cannot let your spouse know.)
Ease of suppression	Almost impossible (the above exception requiring great courage).	Can be difficult, but possible with practise. However, if we cannot suppress it, we can always lie that we are happy for a reason other than the real one. ("I'm just happy to see you, darling.") This is further cause for confusion.

This gives us another clue as to why understanding emotions is much more difficult than understanding sensations.

Pain has both an immediate connection (regarding time) between the cause of the sensation, the sensation itself and the behaviour, and the incentive to affect or suppress the behaviour is very limited. From this we can conclude that it is very unlikely for someone to be confused about pain (unless they play soccer).

There is a further problem for us to consider: in Scenario A, the woman became disoriented because the suppression of the behaviour was systematic over a long period of time. With pain it is difficult to imagine circumstances under which long-term suppression or faking might occur. However, suppression sometimes occurs in people with long-term pain: you just have to get on with your life. With happiness behaviour, it is easy to imagine that someone might fake it over the long term. It is quite conceivable that the faking of happiness could become systematic.

It is less easy to imagine a circumstance where the suppression of happiness could occur over the long term. [They love their job in the funeral parlour!] However, in some strictly religious communities, the outward show of all emotions can be discouraged, and the British "stiff upper lip" is a form of emotional behaviour suppression. Again, these would have a disorienting effect. Later, I will explore how these situations arose. Generally speaking, we have a tendency to affect positive emotions and suppress negative ones. However, it doesn't always work this way round, and I will consider examples that work the other way around, in particular the faking of negative emotions.

For humans, emotion is the core motivator. We aspire to achieve positive emotions (such as happiness) and this is a life-long project. We also seek to avoid negative emotions (such as anxiety). Everything else that we think we want is ultimately subservient to these goals. We want money, solely because we see it as a means to happiness.

The problem is that to achieve these aims, we need to understand what the individual causes of emotions are. If we live in a world where people affect the behaviour associated with an emotion, we deduce a false cause. When we live in a world where people suppress the behaviour associated with an emotion, we are unable to identify the emotion, so its cause is not even considered.

These problems are less likely to arise with positive and negative sensations (pleasure and pain) because the cause is pretty immediate and less likely to be concealed. I am seeking to demonstrate that exposure to affected and suppressed behaviour results in disoriented perceptions of emotion. This leads us rationally to derive self-destructive actions. In Scenario A, the woman was disoriented by the suppression of behaviour by her mother – a third party. What I want to show now is that the suppression of behaviour by the agent himself causes self-destructive actions in a completely different way.

SCENARIO B:
THE FEELING THAT WASN'T FELT

The man sat in the corner of the bar and sipped his beer. He was waiting for his friends to arrive. They would hang out, drink, talk football and make crude passes at women. They were The Guys, the in-crowd. They thought they were pretty cool. But that wasn't how other people saw them.

The man had grown up in a poor family, and he had not done well in school. His father had mocked him for his stupidity, and his mother had constantly nagged him and his father. When he had been a boy he had longed for the approval of his parents, but it never came. His mother had struggled to keep the family together with little money. His father was constantly trying to exert his authority over the family, despite the transparent lack of respect of his mother.

As a boy, he had tried to do better for a while. He wasn't stupid. But his father's dismissive manner towards him constantly belittled him. Eventually, he gave up trying, and then he could tell that his teachers lost hope too. The views of his teachers seemed to support his father's attitude. When he got angry with his family, his father laughed. He was no match for his father's strength, so he sunk into an internal world. His anger was constant, but there was only downside in letting it show, so he suppressed it.

Suppressing anger became systematic; then it became a habit; and eventually he forgot that he was doing it at all.

By the time he was in his teens, he regularly skipped school, and he dropped out as soon as he was able. The only jobs he could get were menial because he had no qualifications, but he had achieved what he thought was his primary aim in life: to be free of his parents. However, he discovered that this strategy did not bring freedom. He had escaped one degrading environment, only to replace it with another: employers of menial people see no reason to respect their workers, and anyway, menial people are easily replaced.

One might imagine that he would be able to work his way out of this rut by hard work and application. This was not possible because other people would never give him the necessary space. They wouldn't permit it because they could see that there was something wrong. The man suppressed his anger, and so the conventional behaviour of anger was missing. However, although this suppression had become habit, there was an effort involved. The suppression had a cost that was observable to other people: his face carried the strain; it was never relaxed. Other people saw him as a coiled spring. The spring might never come uncoiled, but why should other people take a risk on him? He was like a pit bull that had never bitten anyone – menacing, but not actually dangerous. Could the man see the coiled spring in his face when he looked in the mirror? Of course not! This was how he always saw himself. This was just how he looked: tough, cool, streetwise. Other people were wary of him, but he was proud of what he was.

When other people are angry, we only see their behaviour. We do not see their feelings. When we are angry, we are aware of our feelings, but only vaguely aware of what our behaviour looks like to other people. When other people are angry and we see their behaviour, we recognise it and assume that person is angry. When we are angry and we are aware of our feelings, other people can recognise our behaviour and assume from it that we are angry. In this way, we are able to connect our feelings with the behaviour of others. The word 'angry' becomes part of our mechanism for connecting the feeling to the behaviour.

With the man, this mechanism is not working. Someone might look at the coiled spring in his face and ask why he is angry. He might then recognise that there is more than one way of identifying anger in a man. This could give him a mechanism for recognising his behavioural suppression and ultimately address the cause of his anger. However, why would anyone do this if they were worried that the spring might come uncoiled? The only person who might do this would be a therapist, but men with this background don't have therapists.

As a child he suppressed his anger because it only brought further abuse from his father. He continued to suppress his anger because otherwise he would be fired. Once he had ceased to realise that he was suppressing his anger, the word became separated from the feeling. He had a word for anger, but in his language this word only represented a form of behaviour. However, he did not display this behaviour, so he was unaware that he was angry. You might think he would be aware of the feeling, but without the behaviour he could not identify it. He cannot know that other people don't have that feeling, so why would he examine it? He doesn't have a mechanism to compare his experience with the experience of others.

Anger is a mechanism for combating the negative impact of other people's actions upon ourselves, but in the man this mechanism isn't working. He is therefore unable to rectify his situation. It is rational for him to continue in this self-destructive way because he has no means of recognising it.

THE EVOLUTION OF EMOTION

Emotions are the core drivers of human actions. However, they emerged as drivers of action in the animal kingdom. What I want to do in this chapter is set out how emotions became action drivers for animals, and then explain the key aspects of humans that make their operation different. Finally, I want to set out how they can become distorted in humans and thereby become the origin of self-destructive actions.

EVOLUTION BY NATURAL SELECTION

Evolution by natural selection is the only scientific explanation for the existence of life on our planet. There are philosophical theories such as that preached by Hindu mystics, that the whole of existence and life is an illusion. But this, instead of explaining anything, solves the problem by saying no explanation is necessary. Then there is the non-scientific and non-philosophical theory that some sort of pan-galactic metabeing created life and the universe. This theory merely transforms the problem into new problems that we aren't encouraged to explore: how did the metabeing itself come into existence? If the metabeing built the entire universe in a week, what exactly was he (she? it?) doing for the previous bit of eternity? Why is it that this metabeing happens to be moral? Why should it love us? Was the devil created by the metabeing, or is it a product of natural selection, and if neither, how can we be sure that it wasn't the devil that was the creator?

God may move in a mysterious way, but fortunately evolutionary theory does not.

The idea that the metabeing theory belongs in science is a lie. Proper scientists direct their research efforts towards the bits of their theories that seem incomplete or contradictory, but the metabeing theorists ignore their problems. People who believe this theory have been attacking Charles Darwin for over 150 years. Meanwhile, they are quietly ignoring the fact that the consequence of winning the argument (which seems unlikely) will be to spend the next 150 years attacking modern astronomy for making it pretty clear that the universe wasn't created in a week.

There is another implausible piece of the metabeing theory (at least as expressed in the book of Genesis) that tends to get overlooked, and that is that he also created language at the same time that he created the universe; so believers in this theory will then have to go on to refute linguistics. And the philosophical problems that the metabeing theory throws up are simply mind-boggling – for example, how could intelligence, morality and aesthetic judgement pre-exist all life, all matter and (possibly) space and time? How could the designer also be the creator if he existed purely in a non-materialistic form – this is the design/creation ambiguity that we aren't supposed to question. And lastly, if believing the metabeing theory is supposed to give human life a purpose, what is the purpose from the perspective of the metabeing? If he created us purely so that we could worship him, then he was just mailing himself a Valentine's card. These questions are more difficult than the one the metabeing theory sought to answer in the first place, so why bother? It would be easier to assume that life and the universe has always been here (complete with the fossil record), and so doesn't need a start-point. At this point, we are back with the Hindu mystics – claiming that no explanation is necessary.

There is only one way for the metabeing theory to be consistent: reject the entirety of science and philosophy. Most of its proponents would happily dump them to get rid of all the above questions, which they find embarrassing. But they want to keep the bits of science that brought them the iPhone and the internal combustion engine. This makes them at best intellectually inconsistent and at worst hypocritical. I actually respect creationists who reject all of modern science. There is something deeply honest and organic about them. They are perhaps more at peace with the world than the rest of us. Usually, to find such people, you have to hack through rainforest for weeks on end, but they crop up in some strange places such as rural Ohio and Pennsylvania.

Charles Darwin[19] and Alfred Russel Wallace almost simultaneously formulated the theory of natural selection, but Darwin gets disproportionate credit because he wrote his famous books. However, anybody who troubles themselves with the facts cannot deny that this theory is one of the greatest scientific theories in history. Pieces of the evolutionary jigsaw are still missing, but every year another piece or two falls into place; so the passage of time repeatedly emphasises the genius of the original analysis.

Such was the foresight of the original vision and so comprehensive was Darwin's writing that there has only really been one major change to the theory since: Darwin and Wallace didn't know what a gene was. Gregor Mendel discovered the gene during their lifetimes, but the importance of this wasn't recognised until shortly after they were all dead. It was then left to a generation of evolutionary theorists in the 1960s and 70s to reorient evolutionary theory to a gene's-eye view. The emphasis shifted from the survival of the individual to the survival of the individual's genes through the reproduction of that individual gene carrier. A newly evolved gene must enhance the chances of survival and reproductive success of the individual that carries it, otherwise the gene will not propagate in the next generation.

Darwin coined the term 'natural selection'[20], but Herbert Spencer coined the expression 'survival of the fittest'. Darwin adopted this latter expression, but we need to look closely at what it actually means. Firstly, 'fitness' to a biologist does not refer to the ability of an individual to run a marathon, but to the rate of propagation of that individual's genes in the next generation.[21] Secondly, 'survival' does not so much refer to the survival of the individual, as to the survival of its genes as passed on through reproduction. On a preliminary view, the best way for an individual to preserve its genes is to stay alive itself, but this is only true if we either make assumptions about future opportunities to reproduce or a continuing need to nurture offspring. The best illustration why these assumptions do not always apply is to look at spider species where the female promptly eats the male after being fertilised. The male has a greater chance of passing on its genes if it gives its mate a good meal than if it stays alive and goes on an improbable search for a new female to fertilise. Fitness is promoted by behaviour patterns that are individually self-destructive but enhance the probability that one's genes will survive one's own life.

Let us now focus on the piece of evolutionary theory that is relevant to this book. The genes that give rise to feelings are selected only if the feeling drives an action that promotes biological fitness. The feelings of hunger and thirst serve the sole and very necessary function of making us seek food and water – they drive actions that promote fitness. The strength of the feeling is somehow proportional to the threat to survival, and as the strength of the feeling increases, gradually that feeling becomes our dominant driver. It is reasonable to say that things necessary for gene survival (eating, drinking, mating) cause feelings that are pleasurable, and circumstances that threaten survival (lack of food and water, or injury) cause feelings that are unpleasant. Such feelings are sensations, and the genes that gave rise to these sensations were naturally selected because they drive an intelligent animal to pursue actions that promote the survival of its genes, and avoid circumstances that pose a threat. An emotion is something beyond a sensation, and I want to consider how emotions evolved. The genes that give rise to emotions were selected because they drive fitness-enhancing actions.

Have you ever tried to swat a mosquito and been amazed at how they always seem able to fly off just before your hand makes impact?

What is it that makes the mosquito fly off? We might imagine that the mosquito feels fear, and this makes them fly off. However, as explained in the chapter *How Does a Human Work?* we have no basis for knowing this. We tend to judge that certain mammals feel fear because they demonstrate behavioural characteristics of fear similar to humans. Critically, this does not just include flight, but behavioural demeanour (wide eyes, tensed muscles, etc.). With an insect, this comparison is not really possible. Because an insect has an exoskeleton, it cannot make facial expressions, and it is hard to know whether its muscles are tensed.

It is of course possible that an insect does experience fear, but with the absence of the behavioural elements that we associate with fear it is impossible for us to relate to the emotions (if there are any) of an insect.[22] It is therefore natural for us to presume that the mosquito flies away not because of an emotional impetus (fear), but because of a reflex. Whether this is the case with insects or not, it is almost certainly the case if we go far enough back in the evolution of the animal kingdom.

Recognisable emotion (i.e. to a human) appears to evolve somewhere in the vertebrate stage of the animal kingdom, but we can only be certain of it in fairly advanced mammals. Crucially, the evolution of the emotion of fear can be seen purely in terms of evolution by natural selection.

To illustrate the evolution of fear, it is perhaps best to compare ungulates, or hoofed mammals. Ungulates are grazing mammals, and the problem with grazing is that eating grass requires putting your head down. This means that it is easy for a predator to whack you while you eat. The reason that almost all grazing animals form herds is that they take it in turns to lift their heads to survey the horizon for predators. Taking it in turns to look out for predators is of course pointless unless the members of the herd have the ability to communicate alarm, and different families of ungulates do this in different ways.

The family bovidae includes cattle, and the best-known example of cattle in the wild is the wildebeest. What is notable about cattle is that they have not evolved any behavioural expression of fear other than to run. When cattle are afraid, they do not call out and their faces are impassive. Running is the only sign to other members of the herd that one of their members is frightened, and so the only natural response of the herd is to follow suit. Also, when they run, they do so in the same direction. This, in very simple terms, is why cattle stampede. The problem with cattle stampeding is that it is very easy for predators that hunt in packs (lions, wolves, hyenas, dogs) to get themselves a steak dinner. If the whole herd runs the same way, then you just need one member of the pack to frighten them into running towards the rest of the pack where they will be caught. This is essentially how lions hunt wildebeest: some of the pride frightens from upwind and others lie in wait downwind.

The family equidae includes all horses, and the best-known example in the wild is the zebra. Compared to cattle, horses have developed relatively advanced ways of expressing fear. When a member of the herd detects a predator hiding in a nearby bush, it snorts, neighs and runs back and forth looking at the bush. Other herd members will first look at the zebra that is making the commotion, and will then follow its gaze to grasp the problem. Horses have evolved a complete fear emotion, i.e. the feeling (we presume) and the full expression. This permits them to develop much more sophisticated measures to defend against pack-hunting predators. Unlike cattle that all run the same way, alarmed zebras tend to zigzag and run in different directions to each other. By scattering and regrouping later, it makes them much harder to catch because pack-hunting predators will tend to scatter in the pursuit. Zebras' stripes make them hard to focus on when they are zigzagging, but stripes on wildebeest all running together wouldn't work so well. The zigzag strategy only works if all the members of the herd know the initial location of the danger. A zebra has the ability to communicate this to other members of the herd in a way that a wildebeest does not.

The evolution of fear (including the body language associated with it) can be explained in terms of natural selection and survival.

However, although horses express fear with complex behaviour and cattle do not, horses do not obviously express any other emotion. This too can be explained in terms of natural selection. Grazing animals only collaborate in looking out for predators. Therefore, they benefit in being able to communicate fear, but (provided they have bonding mechanisms to keep the herd together) they have little benefit in being able to communicate anything else.

I suspect that fear is the earliest form of emotion in evolutionary terms.[23] However, it is not the only emotion that can be explained purely in terms of natural selection. Robert Trivers, William D. Hamilton and Richard Dawkins are the leading figures in the relatively new science of sociobiology. Hamilton demonstrated that reciprocal altruism[24] (where two species provide a benefit to the other that has a cost to the giver) can be explained in evolutionary terms.

An example of this is a cleaner fish that eats parasites out of the mouth of a host fish.[25] The host fish not only refrains from eating the cleaner fish, but has a mechanism where it warns the cleaner fish of approaching predators. This reciprocal altruism benefits both parties, but only because the cleaner fish tends to stay loyal to one host.

The concept of the 'evolutionarily stable strategy' (or ESS) is a concept derived by evolutionary theorists from game theory to mathematically predict evolutionary outcomes. A Nash equilibrium in game theory is a pair (or combination) of strategies in a game where no player of the game can improve his position by adopting an alternative strategy unless another player also changes his strategy. Biologists use a modified form of game theory to demonstrate that an evolutionarily stable strategy cannot be invaded by a gene mutation that causes an alternative strategy. This has been critical in describing how social behaviour evolves in animals. For the cleaner fish and his host to be an ESS the cost to the giver has to be smaller than the benefit to the receiver. If each party was receiving less benefit than the cost of giving, then the genes that gave rise to the reciprocal altruism would not be selected in either species.

Reciprocal altruism between species is interesting, but for the purposes of this book it makes more sense to look at reciprocal altruism within a species. Let me start with the concept of nepotistic altruism – that is, reciprocal altruism between family members. The sociobiologists point out that natural selection leads not to the survival of the fittest, but to the survival of the *genes* of the fittest, and this means the fittest should be the one who passes on his genes to the greatest number of offspring – as measured by the individual's reproductive success. Nepotistic altruism has an explanation in natural selection because an individual ensures his genes pass to the next generation by ensuring the survival and reproductive success, not only of himself, but of his close relatives. This is because many of an individual's genes are replicated in his close kin, and evolution selects for the survival of the gene, not the survival of the individual. "An individual that assists his brother to be an ancestor may thereby ensure the survival of the gene-pool of the genes 'for' brotherly assistance . . . Parental care is really only a special case of caring for close relatives with a high probability of containing the genes for caring."[26]

Kinship theory[27] explains that we can compute the degree of relatedness (r) of two individuals within a species. This is the probability that a specific gene in one party's genome will also be present in another. Humans are a diploid species, where half of an offspring's genome comes from each parent. For your identical twin, $r=1$; in other words, you have an identical genome to your identical twin. For each of your parents, $r= \frac{1}{2}$ because you receive half your genes from each of them, and for full siblings $r= \frac{1}{2}$ because there is a ¼ chance that your sibling shares a gene that you inherited from your father and a ¼ chance that they share a gene that you inherited from your mother and you have to add these together. Clearly, this means that for half-siblings $r= \frac{1}{4}$. For your grandparents, aunts and uncles $r= \frac{1}{4}$; and for your first cousins $r= \frac{1}{8}$. Generally, the arithmetic is straightforward until we consider non-diploid species or families with incest, where it gets a little messy.

Where an action has a cost (C) and a reciprocal benefit (B), then evolution will tend to select against acts where $Cr > B$. Cost and benefit here should be understood to be cost and benefit in fitness terms – i.e. a cost is a relative decrease in the chances of gene survival in the next generation. Kinship theory is important because if natural selection is concerned with the selection of genes and not individuals; then an individual should have an interest in the survival of a family member proportional to their degree of relatedness. As an example: an animal should attempt to save its drowning full sibling if the chance of being drowned itself was less than ½; but an individual should only attempt to save their cousin if the chance of being drowned itself is less than ⅛.

Kinship theory accounts for some curious aspects of animal behaviour, for example where females mate with many males, siblings will tend to have r= ¼, and where females tend to be monogamous siblings have r= ½. In the latter case, sibling cooperation tends to be higher. An example of kinship theory and nepotistic altruism can be seen in monkey troupes, where the time individuals spend time grooming each other is approximately proportional to their degree of relatedness. Another surprising example is found in ground squirrels. In this species female offspring tend to remain close to their mothers, while male offspring wander off. The giving of alarm calls for predators is altruistic: the benefit (B) is that you warn your relatives (who carry many of your genes) of the approaching predator; and the cost (C) is that you also alert the predator to your own location. Female ground squirrels give warning calls because they can be confident that their close relatives will hear the warning, but this is not the case for males who rarely give warning calls.[28]

Dawkins gives a simple example of how we can use mathematical models of kinship theory to explain altruism:

> I am an animal that has found a clump of eight mushrooms . . . I estimate that they are worth +6 units each . . . The mushrooms are so big that I could only eat three of them. Should I inform anybody else of my find by giving a 'food call'? Who is within earshot? Brother B (his relatedness to me is ½), cousin C (relatedness ⅛), and D (no particular relation: His relatedness to me is

some small number which can be treated as zero for practical purposes). The net benefit score to me if I keep quiet about my find will be +6 for each of the three mushrooms that I eat, that is +18 in all. My net benefit score if I give the food call needs a bit of figuring. The eight mushrooms will be shared equally between the four of us. The pay-off to me from the two that I eat myself will be the full +6 units each, that is +12 in all. But I shall also get some pay-off when my brother and cousin eat their two mushrooms each, because of our shared genes. The actual score comes to $(1 \times 12) + (1/2 \times 12) + (1/8 \times 12) + (0 \times 12) = +19\frac{1}{2}$. The corresponding net benefit for the selfish behaviour was +18: it is a close run thing, but the verdict is clear. I should give the food call; altruism on my part would in this case pay my selfish genes.[29]

This gives us a simple theoretical model of why we are altruistic towards family members. However, animals cannot do arithmetic. If they could do arithmetic (like a human can), they would work out that the optimal strategy would be to eat a couple of mushrooms and *then* give the food call. However, for non-arithmetic animals the only options (in this model) are food call or no food call – selfish act or altruistic act. The model demonstrates that the altruistic act causes the better outcome for the individual's genes in terms of biological fitness, so, over evolutionary time (that is hundreds or thousands of generations) the genes that create the driver to give the food call will be selected. What is this driver? We can just call it 'instinct', or we can be more specific and say that the driver is a guilty feeling whenever we secretly eat food within earshot of our relatives. We can now see how sympathy and guilt have their evolutionary origins. Sympathy and guilt are action drivers. They make us behave altruistically, especially towards kin. Kinship theory can also account for some complex social arrangements. As Trivers explains:

Consider parents with two offspring. Imagine that the first offspring is considering an altruistic act toward the second. It is only selected to act altruistically whenever $B > 2C$ [because for full siblings $r = 0.5$]. The parents are equally related to the two offspring and would therefore enjoy a gain in reproductive success whenever one offspring acted altruistically towards the other at B > C. There must exist situations in nature when C < B < 2C. In such situations parents are selected to socialize their offspring to act altruistically, while offspring are selected to resist the socialization.

A similar argument applies to selfish behaviour. The offspring is selected to act selfishly toward a second offspring whenever C < 2B. But parents are selected to discourage all selfish acts in which C > B. Since there must be situations in which B < C < 2B, we expect to see conflict between parent and offspring over the selfish tendencies of the offspring.[30]

Trivers is using a mathematical modelling approach to demonstrate the evolutionary origin of a parent-offspring conflict that every human parent of more than one child must surely recognise.

Reciprocal altruism extends beyond nepotistic altruism, and this too can be explained in evolutionary terms. Dawkins creates a simple model for demonstrating why non-nepotistic altruism can be an ESS.[31] Assume an animal needs to groom itself for parasitic ticks, but cannot groom the top of its head, and assume that the animal eventually dies if it is not groomed. (Situations like this are not uncommon in the animal kingdom.) The species will become extinct if nobody grooms anybody else.

Now imagine that we divide the population into 'suckers' and 'cheaters'. A sucker will groom the top of anybody else's head without expecting the altruism to be reciprocated. A cheater will accept altruism but never bothers to reciprocate. Initially cheaters will succeed because they can always be groomed, and don't have to waste energy grooming others. This should cause cheating to spread throughout the population. However, as the percentage of cheaters grows, then it makes finding a sucker to groom you difficult, and then even the cheaters won't be groomed, and eventually nobody will be groomed and the ticks will start to kill off the population overall. In other words, cheating will only survive if the ratio of cheaters remains below a certain threshold. A population solely comprising cheaters is not an ESS.

Now imagine that a new type of individual enters the population: a 'grudger'. This type of individual acts like a sucker until it remembers that someone it has groomed in the past acts like a cheater, and then it will act like a cheater towards such individuals. The grudger optimises the strategy because it only wastes energy grooming a cheater once. It therefore wastes less energy than a sucker, and it also has a much greater chance of being groomed itself than a cheater. We can build computer simulations of mixed populations and see how they shift over time. This enables us to simulate thousands of generations of natural selection. The pattern is roughly as follows:

- Initially cheaters do well and suckers do badly so cheater numbers increase and the numbers of both suckers and grudgers decline.
- When the numbers of suckers decline sufficiently, there is nobody to groom the cheaters, so the cheaters start to die off.
- Eventually, the grudgers start to take over because they are always groomed, but never waste time grooming cheaters more than once.
- Once grudgers dominate the population, cheaters can no longer survive.

Thus grudgers will eventually come to dominate the population. It appears that, given the simple assumptions made here, 'grudger' is the ESS. Thus we have an evolutionary basis for the emotion of gratitude.

We need to remember this is only the case because the cost of grooming someone else is less than the benefit of being groomed. If we take another set of assumptions, for example if we assume that the ticks are not a nuisance to the species (i.e. the benefit of being groomed is very low) then it is probable that cheater is the ESS. By playing around with the assumptions, we can work out mathematically that there might be other ESS's, and it is possible that there could be a stable mix of cheaters, suckers and grudgers all coexisting together. However, we can work out certain general conditions that are necessary for same species non-nepotistic altruism to be an ESS. These include: 1) Individuals live long lives; 2) Individuals have effective memories of who has acted altruistically towards them; 3) Individuals tend to stay in relatively stable groups for long periods; 4) Offspring remain dependent upon their parents for long periods. In such circumstances non-nepotistic altruism has advantages to survival and becomes an ESS.

In fact, many animals live in groups where altruism works as a hybrid of nepotistic and non-nepotistic altruism. For example, in a pride of lions there might be several adult females but only a couple of adult males. Female offspring remain with the pride, but male offspring are evicted when they mature and spend time living alone before trying to oust the males of another pride. Lions raise their young collectively, i.e. they don't know which lioness gave birth to which offspring. However, it is possible to build a statistical model for each pair of lions in a pride, and work out the average degree of relatedness of all the lions to one another within the pride. It is actually slightly below ¼, or the degree of relatedness of half-siblings or grandparents. Over time, natural selection would ensure a degree of altruistic behaviour within the pride that was in equilibrium for this average degree of relatedness.

This gives us a theoretical framework to account for the evolution of many emotions that act as drivers of social functioning, since these apply not only to humans but to other advanced animals that live in complex social groups. The psychologist Jonathan Haidt has compiled a natural history of emotions that exactly corresponds with what the work of Trivers would predict: sympathy or pity drives altruistic acts without immediate hope of return; gratitude drives bonding with people who show altruism to us; shame drives us to return favours; and guilt deters cheating.[32] These emotions are action drivers, each of which drives a set of actions that enhances biological fitness. We therefore have an evolutionary explanation for what philosophers call the 'moral emotions'. Importantly, we can see evidence of the operation of these emotions in chimpanzees and other advanced mammals.

As shown by Dawkins' theoretical example, reciprocal altruism requires the evolution of mechanisms to detect cheaters, and this can account for the evolution of anger. Anger as a mechanism for punishing cheaters can be observed in chimpanzees, which throw temper tantrums in a fashion very similar to the way humans do.[33] This is why the study of primatology is so important to our understanding of ourselves. Trivers further refines this analysis by making the distinction between 'gross cheaters' (who return no altruism) and 'subtle cheaters' (who return altruism only sufficiently to avoid detection as cheaters). He points out that this accounts for the fluid relationships between friends where altruistic pairings shift when one party detects subtle cheating in his soon-to-be ex-friend.[34] Again, all of the behaviour that this theory would predict has been observed in chimpanzees, and clearly provides clues to the origins of such relationships in humans.[35]

Sociobiology is not the only newly emerging science that provides clues as to the evolution of emotions. Evolutionary psychology is the discipline that explains human behavioural characteristics purely in terms of evolutionary theory. Evolutionary psychology could be said to be an extension of sociobiology applied solely to humans. Martin Daly and Margo Wilson are evolutionary psychologists who have focussed on homicide and male violence. "Should a more aggressive type of male appear in a population of long-lived pacifists, for example, and should the new type tend to fertilise more females but die younger than the old, then that new type will supplant the old by natural selection, and male life span will decline."[36] In a society where competition exists for mating partners or resources, conflict arises. Daly and Wilson demonstrate that male violence is generally prompted by threats to fitness (i.e. the ability to pass on genes) and is directed at the threat. Individuals who gain a reputation for violent retaliation are very unlikely to be the victim of opportunistic exploitation by either females (who might deceive a male into assisting in raising another male's offspring) or rival males (who might steal his females).

The reason that violence is a particularly male trait also has an evolutionary cause. To understand this, we first need to understand the concepts of 'sexual selection' and 'parental investment'. The concept of sexual selection is the process of choosing mates: in mammals it is generally the case that females choose males and males will mate with almost any female. Darwin was the first to explain this[37], but its significance was ignored for almost a century. In mammals, the female invests much more in parenting than the male, since she has to carry the foetus in her womb and then suckle the newborn infant. The female investment in parenting therefore can take months or years, but the male investment can be limited to a single teaspoonful of semen. For example: Moulay Ismail Ibn Sharif, a seventeenth-century Moroccan King, fathered more than 850 children.[38] Needless to say, he couldn't invest in the care of his offspring because he was too busy conceiving their siblings. Female mammals do the selecting because reproduction places a much greater burden on them – it matters more to them that they get the right mate because it will be a long time before they get another chance.

This logic would not apply to a species where both parents make an equal parental investment. The greater parental investment of females also makes them the bottleneck in the reproductive process, which is why males compete for females and not the other way around. A successful male can father offspring with many females, but an unsuccessful male will father no offspring, so males have a higher variability in reproductive success. This leads to violent conflict among males. The tendency for successful males to breed with many females is known as polygyny, and if we compare the degree of polygyny across different species key characteristics emerge that are exactly what the evolutionary theory would predict. As the degree of polygyny increases:

- Males become more violent;
- Males become increasingly larger than females to enable them to fight, and they may develop fighting weapons such as antlers or horns;
- Males have an increasingly short life expectancy relative to females. This is partly a result of fighting over mating rights, but also because there is no evolutionary reason for a male who makes no parental investment to survive beyond insemination.

For example, red deer, which are highly polygynous, have substantially larger males, equipped with huge antlers for fighting, and male mortality in fighting is high. In contrast, monogamous antelope species that share parental care exhibit two sexes of identical size, with identical antlers, and almost identical life expectancy.

If this theory of male violence is correct, we should expect female violence to be pronounced in species where the reproductive roles are reversed. And indeed we do! A Polyandrous species is one where successful females are likely to mate with several males. For this reversal of reproductive roles to be possible, we would need to have males making the higher parental investment. This would mean that males were the bottleneck in reproduction, so females would compete for males, males would have the role of selecting mates, and females have more variability in reproductive success. In these circumstances, we find that females are more aggressive. This set of circumstances isn't possible in a mammal because embryos must be carried by the female and the young suckled by her, but neither of these factors apply to birds. Several wading bird species are polyandrous (spotted sandpipers, Wilson's phalaropes and jacanas).[39] In these species, females are larger and more brightly coloured; they aggressively compete for male partners; and crucially, the male incubates the eggs after the female has laid them and then cares for the young. A successful (and therefore aggressive) female can raise several broods with different males, and an unsuccessful female will raise none. Polyandry, together with these resulting behavioural consequences also arises in seahorses and several insect species.

Humans are a polygynous species. Most societies legislate monogamous marriage, but even in these societies males are more prone to have further offspring from second marriages, and it is likely that successful men have more covert reproduction. Every study that is not motivated by some dubious political agenda consistently demonstrates that male humans in every society are more violent than females. This debunks the idea that males are more violent because they are "socialised" differently.[40] Greater male violence can be seen in tribal societies, where violence leads to power and status and dominance of breeding rights over females. However, in advanced societies this effect is masked because the state usurps the legitimate use of violence.[41]

If successful males of a polygynous species (such as humans) breed with more than one female, then some males inevitably fail to breed. A male who is facing complete reproductive failure should (in evolutionary theory) be prepared to adopt desperate measures to pass on his genes. Thus violent and risky behaviour in human males is explainable in evolutionary terms even if a possible outcome is the death of the individual. This explains why human males of low social status are more prone to violence, and why they are most violent at the age at which they are seeking breeding partners – early adulthood. Reproductively successful males subordinate unsuccessful ones, and unsuccessful males need to break free from this subordination to have any chance of breeding.[42] To optimise our biological fitness, men need to have sufficiently violent revenge acts to counteract humiliation. This gives us an evolutionary basis for why human males enact violent revenge as a response to humiliation. This is an important conclusion, and later I will draw upon it to explain some of the most grotesquely violent aberrations in human history.

The evolutionary theory surrounding parental investment and sexual selection also gives us a basis for explaining jealousy. Male animals have a problem of certainty of paternity. Certainty of maternity is not a problem at all for female mammals, but can be a problem for female birds where another female may dump eggs in her nest. Different species cope with this differently: In many species, the male copes by mating with as many females as possible, but makes no parental investment beyond copulation. In species where parental care is shared (most birds, most primates and many rodents) males are jealous because they are selected to resist cuckoldry: The genes of a male who makes a parental investment in another male's child won't pass to the next generation and so aren't selected. The male will either watch the female during her fertile period or will actually confine her and guard her. For male birds, there is a double problem of guarding the female against fertilisation by another male, and guarding the nest against egg dumping. This explains why birds are so intensely territorial during the breeding season – it is necessary for the couple to stay away from all other birds of the same species.

Humans share parental care, so jealousy has an evolutionary basis. However, experiments of infidelity role-playing performed on dating college students produced completely different responses in men and women: men had fantasies about sexual contact between their girlfriend and their rival, whereas women were mainly concerned with their boyfriends investing time, money and attention on their rival.[43] This is absolutely what evolutionary theory would predict. In evolutionary terms, a female whose partner cheats is only having male parental investment in her offspring diluted; whereas a male whose partner cheats is risking raising another male's offspring – the ultimate evolutionary fail, which explains why men react to cheating more severely than women. Cuckoldry is the most serious problem for males, but benefits females, who can take sperm from a strong but uncaring male and deceive a weak but caring male into helping her raise them – the evolutionary slam-dunk for females. Jealousy exists for evolutionary reasons, and the different form of jealousy between the sexes similarly has an evolutionary basis.

To summarise, evolutionary theory, particularly that which has emerged since the 1970s, gives us a basis for explaining the existence of many human emotions. The moral emotions drive actions that promote cooperation in animals that live in social groups. Humiliation, revenge and jealousy drive actions that enhance male fitness, maximising the chances of a male breeding and preventing him from being a victim of cuckoldry.

THE IMPACT OF LANGUAGE

A critical stage in the evolution of emotion is emergence of language.[44] Language is, more than any other thing, what distinguishes humans from other animals. There is a boundary separating thought processes that require language from those that don't. Scientists studying animal behaviour approach this boundary from one side, and philosophers and scientists studying technical linguistics approach from the other. For the most part there is not much disputed territory regarding where the boundary lies.[45] There are two separate (but related) consequences of the development of language in humans; the first is that it permits us to form concepts; and the second is that it considerably increases the potential range of emotions that humans can experience.

There are two separate concepts that humans can form that I want to explore. The first is that we form concepts of abstract space and time. This completely transforms the way that we humans can conceive of ourselves in our environment. It permits us to think outside of ourselves, and imagine being in another place or time. Without this, we could not imagine our future, and without that we would have no incentive (or, possibly, ability) to plan. It has become orthodox thinking among animal behaviourists that animals cannot plan. A squirrel that hides nuts does so instinctively, but has no understanding of the approaching winter, or any knowledge that soon the trees won't bear nuts.

Secondly, humans form concepts concerning emotion and behaviour. The combination of this and the concept of time permits a human to conceive of future emotions. This has a curious effect: it creates a situation where the causality of action is reversed. Let us consider hunger. We don't usually think of this as an emotion, but it is a good example because nobody is confused about what it is.[46] Hunger, like an emotion, is a feeling that is a product of evolution by natural selection: it drives an action that promotes biological fitness. Hunger drives an animal to seek food and to eat. Until it is hungry, it will not perform these actions. So how is this different in a human? A human can conceive of future hunger, and can therefore plan its avoidance. So we take action in advance of our hunger to strategise its avoidance. This creates a reversal of the causality of action. We could say that in an animal, the feeling pushes the action, but in a human the action pulls the feeling. The same can be said of emotions. Fear drives an animal to run away, but for humans, the concept of hypothetical future fear drives a human to strategise its avoidance.

It is common for evolutionary biologists to talk about animals being "survival machines". If a human is solely the product of an evolutionary process, then the fact that a human can self-destruct is an apparent contradiction that this book is focussed on explaining. The apparent contradiction is resolved by looking at the ways that humans strategise emotional outcomes. So whereas we can think of an animal as a "survival machine", we have to think of a human differently. I am going to assume throughout this book that a human is a "machine that goal-seeks emotional outcomes". Goal-seeking is a computer science technique[47] that enables us to calculate backwards, and a human brain is a computer: we seek the output (an action) of a formula that would result from a given input (an emotional goal); since I am exploring the reversal of an evolved causal mechanism for driving actions, this analogy is apt. Goal-seeking emotional outcomes involves humans forming concepts of future emotions, and implicit theories as to what causes them. A human is driven by the need to create for itself an environment that achieves favourable emotional outcomes and avoids unfavourable ones. What I am seeking to demonstrate is that all our actions are determined this way.

*

So if language fundamentally changes how emotions drive human actions, can it also create new emotions? In the previous part of this chapter, I examined emotions that could be said to have evolved by way of natural selection. In other words, they arose because they enhanced the chances of gene survival. Let us compare fear with anxiety. Fear is an emotion that is common in the animal kingdom. But we could consider fear and anxiety to be related. We could also argue that anxiety has an evolutionary origin in that it drives us to evade foreseeable threats before they present themselves to our sensory perception. But could this arise in an animal that doesn't have language?

Generally, we consider fear to be triggered by the perception of immediate danger. I recall a photograph of a zebra that had just been grabbed by a crocodile on a riverbank. The zebra's eyes bulged, its lips were drawn back to reveal its teeth and all the veins in its neck bulged with the tensing of its muscles. Anxiety is generally triggered by the belief in a continuous danger. Define it like this, and already the idea of anxiety in animals is running into problems because it is difficult to understand how belief can arise without language. (Your dog can see you put its food in its bowl, but can we really say that it *believes* it is about to be fed?) Anxiety, in comparison to fear, is more of a slow burn emotion – more constant rather than immediate. In humans, it also has a different body language – furrowed brow, rather than the muscle tensing required of fight or flight. It is difficult to imagine an equivalent to this body language in an animal. Without the body language, we have no way of knowing if they experience the emotion itself.

Does this mean that animals do not feel anxiety in the way they feel fear? We could return to the example of the grazing herd where each member of the herd looks up periodically to survey the horizon for predators. I have argued that their urge to run is caused by fear, but is their urge to look up caused by anxiety or is it just an instinctive habit?

I think this question can be clarified if we look at the difference between fear and anxiety another way. Fear could be said to be a response to a present danger, and anxiety could be said to be a response to a non-present danger. Anxiety has a speculative quality: it needs a "what if . . .?" element to frame impending doom. This transforms the question: can an animal that has no language have awareness of non-present danger? To be aware of a non-present danger, we need to be able to conceptualise sources of danger in abstract time and space. This is surely only possible with language. A child can worry that there is a monster under the bed, but surely a puppy cannot.[48]

Philosophers have long doubted that animals experience anxiety. Wittgenstein asked: "A dog believes his master is at the door. But can he also believe his master will come the day after tomorrow? – And what can he not do here? – How do I do it? – How am I supposed to answer this? Can only those hope who can talk? Only those who have mastered the use of language."[49] Similarly, Kierkegaard said "Time does not really exist without unrest; it does not exist for dumb animals who are entirely without anxiety."[50] And Rousseau argued that an animal cannot have a concept of its own death.

Once we have realised the way in which language expands the possible range of emotions, we can attempt to divide emotions into pre-language and post-language emotions. Clearly, fear is a pre-language emotion. I believe that anxiety is a post-language emotion because awareness of dangers that we cannot currently detect with our senses requires us to have a concept of the danger separate from the perception of the danger itself. This is language-dependent, but difficult to clearly define. Certainly there is a grey area between fear and anxiety and the boundary is not always clear. Hope is almost certainly a post-language emotion because it requires a concept of future.

There is nothing in our experience of happiness that would lead us to believe that it is a post-language emotion. However, in the next section I will argue that it certainly is. This is a surprising conclusion, and makes it clear that we cannot tell from our experience of an emotion whether or not it is pre or post-language. The reason for this is that we can no longer remember what life without a language is like. This is because, among its myriad applications, language is an instrument of memory – humans remember things through the medium of language. Our inability to know this by examining ourselves is why the study of chimpanzees and other animals is crucial to the understanding of humans.

Evolutionary psychology and sociobiology also give us clues as to certain other emotions having origins before the evolution of language. Are there other examples of pre-language emotions that I have not already mentioned? It is difficult to be certain, but one likely possibility is grief. There is evidence that elephants sometimes cover their dead with sticks and leaves, and chimpanzee mothers have been known to carry their dead offspring for days after death.

Certainly, grief is a very old emotion in humans. Translations of ancient poetry give rise to dangers because poets tend to assume an understanding by the reader of the words they use. So-called 'translations' of poetry are often recreations of poetry in modern language from ancient texts. A translation of a word relating to an emotion from a poem therefore runs the risk of not representing the intended feeling (if there was any) of the original poet, and we can have no means of knowing this unless the poet describes each of the cause of the emotion, the feeling *and* the behaviour. This comprehensive description of emotion in ancient poetry is perhaps only found in the case of grief. Certainly, many ancient poems are loaded with it. Gilgamesh, probably the oldest known work of literature, was written approximately 4,700 years ago.[51] It contains extensive descriptions of its central character suffering from grief following the death of his friend. However, as I will explain soon, ancient Chinese philosophers saw grief in a way that makes it sound not completely like an emotion, which illustrates the problems of knowing for sure.

Arguably, the distinction between a pre-language and post-language emotion has little theoretical significance. However, it is important to realise that for pre-language emotions, the story does not end with natural selection because the subsequent emergence of language can further alter these emotional states. Maybe anxiety is a post-language distortion of the pre-language fear emotion; but language changes the fear emotion even when we regard it in isolation. An animal is fearful of anything that chases it, but without a concept of time and space (which are language-dependent) it cannot visualise its own death. A human can visualise its own death, so fear is altered by language: animals fear threats, and humans fear the *consequences* of threats. A zebra fears the lion that is chasing it, but a human chased by a lion fears the consequence of being caught. This transformation occurs simply because a speaking human can conceptualise the consequences, whereas a non-speaking animal cannot.

There is one other sense in which language alters a pre-language emotion, and this is the origin of morality in humans. As I argued in the previous section, the moral emotions are pre-language emotions. But as critics of W.D. Hamilton point out (irrelevantly in my opinion) his explanation of the evolution of altruism explains behaviour that has the effect of altruism without the intent. This is correct. But language gives humans the concept of their own behaviour, and they understood the intent after the behaviour evolved. In other words, altruism (without intent) could be driven by pre-language emotion, and humans observing their own behaviour worked out why they were doing it. This means that the behaviour (without intent) evolved first, and the intent was an ex post facto discovery that was dependent upon language. Chimpanzees have moral emotions without having a morality because without language they lack the intent.

THE IMPACT OF PHILOSOPHY

Evolution by natural selection can explain how human emotions evolved, but can it account for happiness?

Every owner of a dog assumes that tail wagging is the body language of a dog that is happy. Dogs are pack-hunting animals that develop complex behaviour and social structures. This includes behaviour demonstrating dominance and subservience. Dominance and subservience are necessary for enforcing mating rights (of the individual) and territorial rights (of the pack). However, dominance and subservience must be suspended during hunting. Hunting requires teamwork, but no member of the pack can give orders without language. Teamwork requires bonding, and in particular it requires the identification of pack members and the ability to distinguish members of rival packs. It is difficult to explain how the survival of dogs is improved if they have an emotional state of happiness. Simply put: what is the benefit to the survival of the species in being able to communicate a sense of wellbeing to other members of your herd or pack? Observation in the animal kingdom does, I think, provide almost no evidence that animals experience happiness. The laws of survival dictate that any weak member of a pack will simply be left behind to die. Even animals that demonstrate powerful maternal instincts will show little sentiment towards sick offspring. For example, elephants will ultimately abandon orphaned young that can no longer suckle. It therefore seems likely that tail wagging is not a sign of happiness, but is more a sign of greeting. This is not the same as saying that absence of tail wagging is not an indicator that something is probably wrong with your dog. It is simply saying that it is incorrect to say that tail wagging is a sign of an emotional state.

Tail wagging is not a way for a dog to say it is happy. It is a way for a dog to say "let's suspend the dominance behaviour for a minute because I am about to sniff your genitals." In any case, how can humans imagine that they can identify the emotional state of another species that demonstrates entirely different body language? Tail wagging in humans does not indicate happiness, unless they are dancing the samba. It is entirely a coincidence that dancing the samba often precedes genital sniffing in humans.

So if the emotion of happiness does not arise in the animal kingdom, when and how did it first appear?

A baby's first smile is always a memorable moment. Clearly, this is something instinctive – innate. But can it be taken as a sign of an emotional state, or is this bonding behaviour? As bonding behaviour, it has an evolutionary explanation. For an infant to be able to demonstrate wellbeing is difficult to explain in evolutionary terms. To survive, a baby only needs to tell us when something is wrong which, as any new parent knows, they manage perfectly well. Charles Darwin admitted that he could not distinguish between pleasure or joy as emotions, and affection or greeting as bonding mechanisms.[52]

To many of us, smiling is considered to be an indicator of happiness. But could this really be a bonding signal that has become habitual? Certainly, there are places in the world where people hardly ever smile. In parts of China, people will only smile if you smile at them, and this is more of a greeting (like tail wagging) than a sign of happiness.

Searching for the origins of happiness in humans is tricky because we have no way of observing historical behaviour. However, we can find clues in ancient writings. Ancient poetry and drama seems to refer to happiness, but translation problems cloud the issue. A close reading makes it appear unlikely that the poet or dramatist considered a feeling to be involved. For example Aeschylus, writing in the fifth century BC, talks almost continuously of every conceivable grief and lamentation, but only obliquely about happiness. George Thomson's translation of Agamemnon refers to a "happy state",[53] but Anne Carson's translation interprets the exact same passage as a "happy change"[54] which doesn't sound like an emotional state. Thomson's translation is closer to a literal translation, but Carson's is more a recreation of ancient drama in contemporary language. Again, Thomson's translation refers to a "happy life",[55] but Carson's version makes no such emotional reference in translating the exact same passage. However, it isn't clear that Aeschylus ever seems to consider a happy *feeling*. It is therefore difficult to conclude that he sees this as an emotion. Likewise, Euripides writing around the same time delivers negative emotion to the point of overload. Indeed, he took it so far that Aristophanes mocked him.

Looking for clues in poetry is not very reliable because poets simply assume that their readers understand the words they use. It is therefore possible that a word that we think we know how to translate might have had a completely different meaning at the time it was written. What I therefore want to do is to analyse ancient philosophical writings because philosophers need to be more precise, not in their choice of words, but in explaining exactly what they mean by them. Crucially, this is less likely to be lost in the translation process because translators of philosophy must retain the meaning intent of the philosopher, whereas translators of poetry are more concerned with retaining the poetic quality.

My aim here is to demonstrate that happiness is not innate in humans because there was a relatively recent time when it didn't exist. This in turn means that, unlike the emotions discussed in the first part of this chapter, it certainly did not evolve by way of natural selection and, additionally, it is certainly a post-language emotion.

One of the earliest Western references to happiness arises in the *Nicomachean Ethics*[56] of Aristotle (384–322BC). Aristotle wrote the Ethics in 350BC.

Aristotle is seeking to explain human behaviour: we want money because it permits us to buy things; we want health because it permits us to work and live an active life; we want honour because it enables us to interact with our fellow man and have their respect. But is there anything that men want purely for its own sake? Aristotle's answer is that happiness is the ultimate end, since we want it for its own sake. We want other things solely as a means to happiness.

Aristotle's view would seem to be in agreement with how most people would consider happiness today. In my shorthand terminology, a human is a machine that goal-seeks happiness. However, a careful reading makes it clear that Aristotle's conception of happiness is quite different from how we think of it today.

The Ancient Greek word that Aristotle uses is 'eudaimonia'. This word is generally translated as "happiness", but a literal translation means something closer to "living well" or "having a good life".

Most scholars now agree that Aristotle was not referring to an emotional state when he used this word. Rather, *eudaimonia* is an "activity of the soul".[57]

Aristotle sees the soul as divided into two parts – the rational and irrational. The irrational soul is further divided into the vegetative soul (which plants also possess) and the appetitive soul representing the desire to satisfy bodily needs (which is common to all animals). Aristotle distinguishes between intellectual virtue that comes, via the rational soul, from learning; and moral virtue that comes, via the irrational soul, from habit. Aristotle believes that *eudaimonia* comes from developing good habits. In time, one learns to develop pleasure in performing good actions.

For Aristotle, *eudaimonia* is not an emotional state; it is an action. He says that it cannot be measured until close to the end of your life. But *eudaimonia* cannot be an emotion if one cannot know it concurrently with life's experience.

It has been suggested that early languages were too simple to fully convey emotion. That they were structured in such a way that they could only be used to describe material things and their properties,[58] and that this could imply that happiness has always been a human emotion, but the language to describe it only emerged later. However, I don't think this is true of Aristotle. This is made clear when he discusses other emotions; for example he is explicit in stating that shame is a feeling, and not a state of character.[59]

Prior to Aristotle, the word *eudaimonia* occurs several times in Ancient Greek philosophy, but none of these occurrences come with a thorough definition of what it is. Socrates (469–399BC) held a number of beliefs on *eudaimonia* that would also indicate that it was not an emotion: for example, that it was caused by scientific thinking[60] or virtue alone.[61] Again, Socrates does not go on to define this in terms of feeling, but it seems difficult to imagine it as an emotional state if it is solely the result of correct behaviour rather than being correlated to the outcome.

One other Ancient Greek reference connected to happiness is in Democritus (approximately 460 to 370BC). Democritus became known as the "laughing philosopher". However, don't imagine that this is laughing as you and I now know it. The laughing for which Democritus was famous is often translated as 'scoffing', as in "scoffing at the foolishness of men". His contemporary nickname was the Mocker, which seems to support the view that his laughing was not mirthful. This reputation notwithstanding, Democritus wrote several works on ethics, one of which is *On Cheerfulness* in which he says that cheerfulness ('euthumia') is the goal of life: "Cheerfulness arises in people through moderation of enjoyment and due proportion in life."[62]

However, like Aristotle's *eudaimonia*, it is almost certain that Democritus did not think of *euthumia* as an emotion. The principal biographer of the Greek philosophers, Diogenes Laertius, writing some six centuries later summed it up like this: "The goal or summation is *euthumia*, though this is not the same as pleasure (as some have mistakenly understood it to be . . .), but is the state according to which the soul is in a calm and well-balanced condition, disturbed by no fear, superstition or other emotion."[63] This does not sound like a positive emotional state, but an absence of negative emotional states, something that is consistent with my view that the concept of positive emotional states had not yet arisen. Democritus referred to the idea of a calm absence of emotional states as wellbeing ('euesto').

My view that happiness didn't exist as an emotion in ancient times is also supported by early writings from the East. Kung-Fu Tzu means "The Master Kung-Fu", but he is generally known in English as Confucius (551–479BC). He is China's most famous philosopher. Mencius (Meng Tzu, or The Master Meng, 372–289BC) is considered to be one of the principal interpreters of Confucius, although he is clearly a philosopher in his own right. Both lived in Eastern China. As a comparison, the life of Confucius just preceded Socrates and Democritus, and Mencius overlapped with Aristotle. Confucius and Mencius lived during a period of Chinese history known as the Warring States Period. Confucius sought to end the constant civil war by demonstrating that moral behaviour was to the benefit of all people. He set out to demonstrate the correct behaviour of both rulers and the ruled. In effect, Confucius sought to re-establish altruism by reason, since its prior establishment by evolution had become disrupted – perhaps because humans began to suppress their moral emotions.

Confucius was concerned with teaching morality. However, his ethics are based in doctrine. There is really no evidence that Confucius considered human nature to be a distinct concept. In particular, he seems largely unaware of emotion.

The Chinese word 'wen' in Confucius is often translated as 'culture', but more properly means "what beautifies human life".[64] However, Confucius never discusses how this makes one feel. Confucius discusses mourning, but he does not seem to specify what the feeling element of it is. He describes mourning in terms of ritual and considers that breaking from this ritual would result in the mourner not "feeling at ease".[65] However, this is far from a description of the emotion of grief – in fact, the cause of the feeling he refers to is ignoring the ritual, not the death of a family member. And yet, he does have a concept of insincere mourning: "the forms of mourning observed without grief – these are things I cannot bear to see!"[66] This is an important statement because it makes it clear that humans understood that they performed tactical deception with their emotional behaviour in the fifth century BC. But Confucius is not clear what separates sincere from insincere grief – a distinction that we would see in terms of the presence of the feeling. (By way of comparison, ancient European literature tends to refer to grief more than any other emotion.) In ancient China, music was not listened to for pleasure, but was considered to have magical power. Confucius saw his response to music not as an emotion, but as evidence of its magical power.

Happiness gets very little mention in Confucius, and there is nothing to enlighten us as to what he thinks it is. We think of happiness as a positive emotional state, but contentment is more an absence of negative emotional states. With ancient writings, it does not appear that they had any concept of positive emotional states, but in translation, the word 'happiness' is often used when it isn't clear that an absence of negative emotional states wasn't the original intent. For example "The Master said, He who seeks only coarse food to eat, water to drink and a bent arm for pillow, will without looking for it find happiness to boot."[67] A reference to unhappiness also appears, where it is unlikely that the original meaning is how it sounds in translation. The Three Ways of a true gentleman are "He that is really good can never be unhappy. He that is really wise can never be perplexed. He that is really brave is never afraid."[68] The Chinese word 'jen' is generally translated as 'good' but more appropriately means, "possessing the qualities of one's tribe".[69] Arthur Waley compares this with one Englishman saying that another is a "true Englishman" as intended to imply a high form of praise. However, it occurs to me that there is another clear explanation: the sign of tribal bonding being taken as a sign of personal wellbeing. Compare the wagging of a dog's tail as it bonds with its pack members and the perception that this means that it is happy. Humans are, like dogs, pack animals. Happiness and being within your tribe or pack are not the same thing, but could over time come to seem so.

Further evidence of the absence of a concept of emotion at the time of Confucius can be seen in the *Tao Te Ching*. The date of this is uncertain, although it precedes Mencius, and there is uncertainty as to whether its author Lao-Tzu (literally "The Old Master") was a historical figure, so the *Tao Te Ching* might be a collection of sayings from many people. There is a story about Lao-Tzu and Confucius meeting, but it is uncertain whether this is historical fact. However, there is no evidence the writer (or writers) of the *Tao Te Ching* showed any awareness of the concept of happiness. In fact, there is plenty of encouragement in the *Tao Te Ching* to be rather dour. Desire in all its forms, according to the *Tao Te Ching*, is seen as a cause of incorrect behaviour. It teaches that knowledge does not lead to virtue, and that contentment comes from letting things just happen – a philosophy of non-intervention in the natural course of events.

The concept of emotion (at least positive emotion) has not emerged in China, and the concept of feeling is only just appearing. The concept of feeling appears in a more evolved form two centuries later in Mencius, and even then it is not really quite how we understand it today.

The Chinese word 'xin' is often translated as 'feeling', but is also sometimes translated as 'heart-mind'. These alternate translations seem to have little in common, and this highlights the difficulty in translating 'xin', though the term 'heart-mind' "is most adequately understood as a function rather than an organ".[70] This likens it to Aristotle's use of the term, where *eudaimonia* is an action, not an emotion. Crucially, the word 'xin' appears only six times in the *Analects* of Confucius, but 119 times in the writings of Mencius.[71]

Confucius considered that morality could be learned but does not appear to have considered whether men have a nature – either good or bad. Mencius considered that men were fundamentally good; so morality was innate in men. Feeling is important for Mencius because it is the origin of the moral force. It is what we should look to for moral guidance. He does not see it as a source of selfish motivation in humans, but it is starting to emerge as a concept of a human disposition. "Feeling," says Mencius, "guides us more surely than doctrine in charting the most productive course".[72] Mencius is moving away from the Confucian concept of a morality defined entirely by ritual patterns of behaviour, towards a more humanistic morality that builds on natural human responses.

The following is perhaps the most famous passage in Mencius. It gives us an insight into his entire philosophy:

> Each and every human has feelings sensitive to the suffering of others. The former kings had such feelings, and these were manifested in their compassionate governing. Putting such feelings to work in governing, they ordered the world as easily as turning it in their palms.
>
> As for each human having feelings sensitive to the suffering of others, suppose a person suddenly sees a child about to fall into a

well. Each would feel empathy for the child – not in order to gain the favour of the child's parents, nor to win the praise of villagers and friends, nor out of concern for a potentially blemished reputation.

From this we observe the following: without such a feeling of commiseration one is not human, without a feeling of shame one is not human, without a feeling of deference one is not human, without a feeling of discrimination one is not human. A feeling of empathy is associated humanity in its germinal state. A feeling of shame is appropriateness in its germinal state. A feeling of deference is ritual propriety in its germinal state. A feeling of discrimination is wisdom in its germinal state.

People have these four sprouts just as they have four limbs. For one to possess these four sprouts yet consider oneself incapable of developing them is self-mutilation; for one to consider the ruler incapable of doing so is to mutilate the ruler.

For anyone having these four sprouts in him or herself, to realise their enlargement and bring them to 'fullness' is like having a fire catch or a spring break through. If these germinal beginnings are brought to fullness, one might safeguard the whole empire; if they are not, one might not even tend to one's own parents.[73]

This passage is often referred to as Mencius' philosophy of the four tender shoots of human nature. Feeling creates a genuine moral impulse that requires no deliberation before acting. This analogy is important because the Confucian concept of a moral ruler is modelled on his idea of the instinctive protection of parents for their children. Compare Mencius in this passage with the sociobiologists and evolutionary psychologists who came over two millennia later. They argue that natural selection provided humans with the emotions that are necessary for altruism and social cohesion – in essence evolution provides us with the tools required for morality. Mencius is arguing that we should trust in nature. Correct action follows from the impulse that nature provides us.

In the progression from Confucius to Mencius, we can see the beginnings of the human awareness of feeling, but there is still not a concept of positive emotion. Confucius parallels Socrates in equating happiness with virtue without describing what happiness is in any way. Mencius can loosely be compared to Aristotle in seeing feelings as a motivator without having a concept of positive emotion. It remains a great mystery why Eastern and Western thought should be so convergent at this stage of history. The mystery extends beyond Greece and China. At approximately the same time as Confucius and Socrates, Zoroaster in Persia, Isaiah in Judah, and Siddhartha Gautama in Northern India and Nepal were developing broadly similar ideas without there being any evidence that they had knowledge of one another.

Siddhartha Gautama is popularly known as the Buddha. Buddhism teaches that enlightenment or virtue comes from the avoidance of desire or craving, including the desire for continued existence. This is very similar to the *Tao Te Ching*. This could be interpreted for my purposes as the avoidance of negative emotional states without really defining positive ones. The origins of Buddhism are deeply entrenched in the concept of negative emotions. According to the legend (or history, depending on your belief) Siddhartha Gautama lived in luxury in a palace. The beginning of his journey in becoming the Buddha started when he left his palace for the first time and saw old age, sickness, death and finally a monk. Siddhartha Gautama chose the life of a monk and set out on his course of seeking a way to escape from the cycle of suffering – or negative emotional states. Buddhism teaches that enlightenment is the goal, but there is no suggestion that enlightenment is happiness, or even an emotional state at all.[74]

Approximately 100 years after these teachings, Patanjali, the author of the yoga sutras, talked about achieving "bliss" through meditation, ethical practice and the study of philosophy and metaphysics. This might be said to be an early emergence of an awareness of positive emotional states. However, it still isn't clear that this is happiness. Bliss could be seen as an early concept of happiness, or it could also be seen as a form of inner peace – the absence of negative emotional states.

Putting all these strands of ancient teaching together, it seems clear that happiness as an emotion is not something natural or instinctive. It was absent in ancient times, and our concept of it being a distinct emotional state emerged later. This leaves open a key question: what was the process by which happiness came into being? It appears to be the bringing together of an instinctive gesture of greeting or bonding, namely smiling, with teachings of morality and virtue. We could perhaps argue that Aristotle (for example) invented it. But with philosophers from history we can never really be sure whether they were the first to have the idea, whether they copied the idea from someone else, or whether they merely recorded an idea that was already emerging in popular consciousness.

THE EMERGENCE OF BEHAVIOURAL STRATEGY

There is one final point about the evolution of emotion that I want to raise. This is the ability to tactically affect or suppress emotional behaviour. Charles Darwin demonstrated that the expression of emotions through facial expression and behaviour was universal among humans, as was our ability to recognise them.[75] He hinted at an evolutionary basis, without being able to work out the mechanism. Darwin also understood that the tendency to poker face this expression is highly variable from one culture to another. However, although scientists have looked at poker-facing emotional expression, few seem to have studied the habitual affectation of such expressions of emotion. This is also variable between cultures; for example the affectation of happiness is endemic in America, but a Romanian told me that if you smile too much in Eastern Europe people will think you stupid, so Eastern Europeans tend to suppress smiling – the opposite tactical deception.

You might disagree with my view that the emotional range of a zebra does not extend much beyond fear. But could a zebra that is experiencing fear ignore the fact? For that matter, could they fake it? My sorry little philosopher-brain always assumed that the ability to fake or suppress emotion was language-dependent. However, the science demonstrates that this isn't quite true. Experiments with the famous chimpanzee Nim Chimpsky[76] lead to the conclusion that chimpanzees have a basic ability to learn vocabulary but no ability to master grammar.[77] They also show no urge to gobble up language the way a human child does. But the only example of deliberate emotional behaviour suppression that I can find in the scientific literature occurs in chimpanzees. A chimpanzee bares its teeth when it is frightened, and there are recorded observations of a male chimpanzee after a fight pushing its lips shut with its fingers before he turned to face his adversary.[78] This leads us to the conclusion that the ability to do this is dependent upon something other than language, possibly some more basic form of self-awareness. A simple experiment checks this: leave an animal or person in front of a mirror for some time, and then take them away and alter their appearance (e.g. by putting paint on their face), and then put them back in front of the mirror. If they stare at themselves in the mirror after their appearance has been altered this would seem to indicate an awareness of self when looking at the mirror. Humans record a positive result in this test from the age of about 16 months; but several other species provide a positive result (principally the great apes).[79] Note that a chimpanzee can only suppress its facial expressions by using its fingers. Imagining that humans needed to do this would be a pretty good basis for a Ricky Gervais movie. This, I think, makes it inconceivable that a chimpanzee could suppress behaviour habitually or systematically – something that humans constantly do.[80]

The suppression of an emotion could either mean suppressing the behaviour, or it could mean suppressing the feeling that underlies it. However, surely it is not possible to suppress the feeling while letting the behavioural response flow normally. So suppression must start with concealing the behaviour. A person who is experiencing fear can, with an act of will, suppress the behaviour associated with that fear. But they can only do this because they have a concept of the behaviour that they can separate from its performance. This is a concept that is certainly dependent upon self-awareness, and which is greatly strengthened by language. An animal with no concept of self sees danger, and reacts to it. When it does this, it does not see its reaction as a separate entity. Similarly, social animals react to the behaviour of other herd or pack members without seeing this behaviour as a separate concept.

I cannot find an example in the scientific literature of an animal tactically affecting emotional behaviour. Affectation is a more complex tactical deception than suppression because it requires memory of the behaviour. I believe therefore that affectation is unique to humans. The faking of an emotion is similar to suppression: it starts with the faking of the behaviour – for example, pretending to be happy. This requires us to be able to see the behaviour as a separate concept to its cause and the feeling associated with it. This certainly requires a concept of self. It certainly requires a memory of the relevant behaviour, and it may well also be language-dependent.

Emotion is not irrational; it is *pre*-rational. The very first piece of human reasoning started with someone thinking, "Soon I will be hungry." A belief in a future emotion was the original axiom of logic. Originally, the chain went

Belief in a future emotion => Logic => Action

But then somebody realised that the action could be to pretend an emotion: they could go

Belief in a future emotion => Logic => Pretend emotion

and tactical deception with behaviour was born. At this point humanity became horribly confused. The birth of man's problems came at this moment, not when Adam and Eve ate the apple. But worry not! Sorting it out is just a logic problem that I want to persuade you can be solved. A human is a machine that goal-seeks emotional outcomes. Tactical deception with emotional behaviour results in us deducing the identity and cause of our own emotions from falsified data. We then perform self-destructive acts, not because we are irrational, but because we goal-seek emotional outcomes based on false beliefs about the causes of emotions.

False behaviour is the original false assumption from which self-destructive actions are derived.

SCENARIO C:
THE FEELING THAT WASN'T HAPPENING

The Girl That Has Everything is sitting across the table from The Current Man.

I am calling her "The Girl That Has Everything", but really this was how she saw herself. It isn't, as will become apparent, how we are going to see her. Sure, she had the looks, the body, the charm and the high adrenalin career, but she lacked elements of self-awareness. All of us lack elements of self-awareness; and, logically, we don't know what these elements are.

This Scenario, then, is about what The Girl That Has Everything doesn't have.

I am calling him, "The Current Man", but it really doesn't matter what I call him because he only has a walk-on part. I could have replaced him with the man that came before him, or the one that will come after. He is merely the "current" man because I have chosen to write this in the present tense. My choice of tense, like the way that The Girl That Has Everything chooses her men, is arbitrary.

The candlelight is too dim to fully illuminate each of their faces, and this makes it easy to maintain eye contact. They just have to focus on the vicinity of each other's eyes, and the impression is that eye contact is maintained. This creates in each of them the perception of an intimacy that doesn't really exist.

They are most of the way through a bottle of wine, and she knows that they are going to sleep together. At least, she knows that they are going to sleep together unless he messes it up. She isn't going to mess it up. She has done this enough times to perfect the routine.

"You're adorable", she says.

That is all the dialogue that we are going to have in this Scenario. Two words isn't much, but it is enough for us to analyse her language and explore what it is that The Girl That Has Everything doesn't have. "Adorable" literally means "capable of being adored". It refers to a capability of a hypothetical someone else. Therefore, if we take the meaning of her statement in its strict sense, logically The Girl That Has Everything isn't doing the adoring herself. This is a subtle nuance of language that conveys a colossal weight of fact. You might think that her lack of adoration would be something that she couldn't possibly miss. However, she does miss it because she is affecting adoration. She is doing this with her eyes, and with the way she leans forwards to the Current Man as though she is enthralled.

The Current Man might notice her choice of language means that she doesn't adore him, although it is unlikely. However, even if he does, he isn't going to say anything because if he did, he wouldn't get to sleep with her. The Girl That Has Everything thinks she knows that only he can disrupt their sleepwalk into her bed, but the Current Man knows that the right ploy is to say nothing. So the absence of dialogue of the man in this story is not just a literary conceit; it is realistic – practical advice in how to get into the bed of a woman like The Girl That Has Everything.

She knows that one day she will meet a man that will be The One. At least, she thinks she knows. In fact this is merely a belief, and this is not actually a belief about a man, but a belief about a feeling. She believes that if she keeps searching, a man will come into her life that will trigger a feeling in her that she will know is love.

Her belief is mistaken.

This is not because the man does not exist. It is not necessarily because the feeling does not exist. It is because she won't recognise the feeling when it arrives. Sure, she knows the words "adore" and "love". However, her ability to understand what these words mean is because she has seen the look that people have on their faces when they say they have the feeling. Perhaps she knows this just from the movies, or if she is lucky she will know it because she saw it in her parents throughout her childhood.

How then is she supposed to know when she has this feeling herself? Normally, she would know it because when the feeling occurred in her, she would realise that it causes the same reaction in her that she has seen in others. However, she can't do this because she regularly affects this outward appearance when she does not have the feeling. She might also know it by the way the Current Man responds to the way she is looking at him. But how could this occur? If she always fakes adoration of the men she sleeps with, how can she know whether their response is ever genuine? In fact, if they respond genuinely to behaviour that is affected, then are they worthy of respect? How then, could she ever know that the Current Man is The One?

It's not that her encounters with men don't involve any feeling. The feeling that she has is called orgasm, but this isn't the feeling that she is looking for. Certainly, she has been known to fake orgasm, but she has not done this unselfconsciously. Her faking the body language of love is unselfconscious because she has done it for so long, and with so many men. She is no longer aware that she is doing it. It has become habit.

She fakes orgasm for the benefit of her men. However, originally she faked love purely for herself. Certainly, though, her men do benefit. Her faking an unfelt intimacy gives them the green light to proceed to her bed. Mainly though, she benefits short-term from faking love because of her need for denial. This denial is the increasingly desperate need to hide from herself that she is like a bee repeatedly hurling itself at the inside of a window. Her repeated adventures with men will not lead to a stable relationship. Without denial, she would realise that she will continue to do this until her beauty fades.

Ultimately, though, she is The Girl That Has Everything, and her inability to find a nice man with whom to have a loving relationship must be down to some failure on their part; not on hers. She cannot see that the problem lies with herself, and her unselfconscious self-deception.

She is repeating a strategy that she believes will lead to a man who will trigger a certain feeling in her, but if that feeling ever actually arose, she simply wouldn't recognise it.

DISCOVERING THE HUMAN ALGORITHM
BY THOUGHT EXPERIMENT

THE THOUGHT EXPERIMENT SQUARED

The Scenarios in this book are not fiction. They are a form of hypothetical reasoning that philosophers call a "thought experiment". A thought experiment is a methodology for exploring the possible consequences of a given set of circumstances. They employ logic, rather than empirical observation, to challenge established "common sense" modes of thinking to demonstrate that such thinking is absurd. The term "thought experiment" has been in use since the nineteenth century, but obviously people have been doing them (without calling them that) since the earliest days of inductive reasoning. The whole of mathematics is a giant network of thought experiments, and they are the principal methodology by which physics advances.

Consider the most famous experiment in the history of physics: Galileo demonstrated that objects fall under gravity at the same rate irrespective of their mass. He did this by dropping objects of different masses from the top of the leaning tower of Pisa.[81] However, Galileo did not conduct this experiment out of random curiosity. He did it as a demonstration to his sceptical colleagues because he already knew the outcome. He worked this out in a thought experiment. Galileo reasoned that if heavy objects fell faster than light ones, as had been supposed since the time of Aristotle, then two such objects attached to each other as they fell would result in the heavy one dragging the light one faster, and the light one slowing down the heavy one. This would imply that they would fall at a rate in between their two individual rates of descent.

However, attached together they form a body of greater mass than the two individually, so they should fall faster. Thus, the common sense view led to an impossible inconsistency.

Einstein's Theory of Relativity, the most famous theory in physics, is also a product of a thought experiment. It started with an empirical observation: measuring the speed of light from twin orbiting stars, physicists realised that light travelled at a constant speed irrespective of the relative motion of the point of propagation. This caused physicists to put everything they knew about space and time onto the scrapheap, and work out a whole new structure. Einstein's book *Relativity* was his attempt to explain the theory to non-physicists. [That would include me.] He explains much of the theory by a series of thought experiments using a hypothetical train moving along an embankment. He thereby demonstrated that events that are simultaneous relative to the embankment would not be simultaneous relative to the train. So, space and time could not be regarded as fixed and independent.

Mathematics is a network of thought experiments that is ultimately rooted in empirical observation. John von Neumann, the mathematician who originated game theory, is one of the few brave enough to admit that mathematics has an empirical origin. "It is very hard for any mathematician to believe that mathematics is a purely empirical science or that all mathematical ideas originate in empirical subjects."[82] Mathematicians tend to get lost in their world of thought experiment and lose touch with the real one.

Let us consider the most basic statement of mathematics "2+2=4" – that cliché of the irreducible, irrefutable truth. Most of us learn this before we can even read, and yet it is surprisingly difficult to prove, in part because it is irreducible. Wittgenstein attempts to reduce it to logic in the *Tractatus*, and I am not going to pretend that my understanding of his proof is beyond doubt. So how then do we know this simple fact? The human who first figured out how to count was perhaps the most influential human that ever lived, yet we have no clue as to his/her identity. But we can speculate as to what happened in the mind of the first human who ever figured out that two plus two was equal to four. Let us call him Abdul because he probably lived in the Middle East somewhere – perhaps prehistoric Babylon. It was probable that Abdul noticed that if we put two apples in one hand and two apples in the other, then we have four apples in total, and this was also the case with oranges. Initially, Abdul might have found it strange that apples and oranges have this thing in common, but then he started to think about this in his imagination. He started to imagine two apples in each hand, and then he pictured each apple individually morphing into an orange. Once he realised this, he could imagine the apples morphing into anything he so chose, including palm trees or camels; and once he had realised this, he could imagine them morphing into a completely abstract object. He could take the statement "two apples plus two apples equals four apples" and leave out the word "apples". True arithmetic was born of fruit and pure imagination.

If mathematics and physics are rooted in a combination of empirical observation and pure imagination, is it possible that the problems that psychologists try to resolve can be treated in the same way? What I am attempting to do is to reduce the cause of a human action to an atomic level. I am doing this by a combination of empirical observation and imagination. It isn't possible to do scientifically for a host of reasons, among them finding any human who has only one emotion, or concluding with any certainty whether a human is tactically manipulating their behaviour. I therefore follow Abdul in constructing it hypothetically in my imagination. If arithmetic can have such a humble origin, perhaps understanding human nature – the most complex problem that we have – can have a humble solution.

The Scenarios in this book are thought experiments of an unusual kind: they are thought experiments about thoughts – a thought experiment squared. This is something that a physicist or mathematician never has to bother with. Firstly, I have to construct a hypothetical mind in which a concept of an emotion has been corrupted by manipulated behaviour; and secondly, I have to determine how such a hypothetical mind would rationally determine a course of action. To do this, I have to construct a second thought experiment inside the hypothetical mind that was the product of the first thought experiment.[83] This is a technique to enable you to understand non-understanding, which is not an intellectual process but a form of engineered empathy. If we can construct an atom of non-understanding, then we can create molecules of non-understanding, and what I am suggesting is that these molecules of non-understanding are the key to understanding human nature.

If we corrupt the normal operation of human emotions, specific modes of corruption lead to specific rational but self-destructive outcomes, and the agent will be oblivious that this is happening. To demonstrate this, I employ creative logic – I explore what happens when logic starts with mis*con*ceptions that are in themselves the product of *per*ceptions. Logic is a system of inference that was mostly formalised by Aristotle. An example of an Aristotelian syllogism would be:

- All mammals give birth to live young;
- Dogs are mammals;
- Therefore dogs give birth to live young.

The important thing about logic is that it is concerned with the relationship between statements, not facts. However, it permits us to draw correct inferences about facts, since, when the statements are true, they correctly reference facts. However, logic still works when one of the statements is false. For example:

- Fido is a dog;
- All dogs go "meow";
- Therefore Fido goes "meow".

. . . is still impeccably logical. I expect you are thinking that the second assumption is false, and because this is logical, that would mean that the conclusion is false too. However, there is another possible interpretation: because of some oddity in my upbringing (of which there were many), I think that "meow" is the correct name for the sound a dog makes. In this case, the second assumption is factually correct, but contains an error of language. In this case, since it is logical, the conclusion is also factually correct, but contains the same error of language.

I am concerned with rationality, which is related to logic but not quite the same thing. Whereas logic is concerned with relationships between statements, rationality is concerned with relationships between thoughts. Many thoughts can be expressed as statements, but certain thoughts arc not verbalised in a human brain. However, the end goal of logic is a conclusion, which is of course a form of statement. But the end goal of rationality is generally an action, which is of course not a form of thought, but the product of a type of thought that we generally call an intention. We could therefore describe rationality as the logic of human intentions. For example:

- I want to be happy;
- Happiness is caused by dancing the samba;
- Therefore I will dance the samba.

This is clearly rational (whether the thoughts are verbalised or not). However, rationality remains rational (like logic remains logical) when one of the assumptions is false or contains an error of language; so the following is still rational:

- I want to avoid anxiety;
- Stroking the cat causes anxiety [which, for me at least, is false, but for you might be true if you are allergic to cats];
- Therefore I will avoid stroking the cat.

I am exploring rationality in hypothetical minds where emotional concepts have become misunderstood. To do this I use dramatic irony – the technique dating back to the time of Sophocles where the reader or audience knows something is wrong but the protagonist does not. A famous example of dramatic irony in recent times is the movie *The Truman Show*, where Truman does not know he is living in a reality TV program, but the audience both knows this and also knows that Truman doesn't know it.

When you read the Scenarios, you the reader know the protagonist is operating under a misconception but the protagonist does not know this. In this way, I can explore what happens when someone thinks rationally, but where the normal mechanism for understanding emotions and the words for emotions has been corrupted.

Models are often constructed (for example by economists or meteorologists) to permit hypothetical analysis and make predictions. Normally, these models are constructed using mathematics, computer programs and logic. However, I cannot construct a model of human rationality in this way because mathematics, computer programming language and logic all assume that the language in which they operate is consistently functional. I need to drop this assumption, since I am exploring the consequences of inconsistent language and incorrect non-verbalised concepts.

An animal emotion is a driver of an action, but because a human can conceive of its future emotions, he/she determines his/her actions based on beliefs about what causes those future emotions. These beliefs are derived from emotional behaviour that is almost certain to have been altered by some nuance of habitual tactical deception.

What I need to do now is to explore some of the philosophical problems that arise from this process of forming concepts of our own emotions.

QUALIA THOUGHT EXPERIMENTS

When you experience an emotion, you do indeed have an *experience*. 'Qualia' is philosopher-speak for the internal and subjective components of sense perception. For example, if I look at a green object under a red light, the quale (which is the singular form of 'qualia') is the internal experience of how that looks to me. Clearly, I need to consider the nature of the qualia of emotional experience.

The philosopher Daniel Dennett wrote a paper called *Quining Qualia*[84], which is now regarded as a classic. The verb 'to quine' means to deny resolutely, and seems to be a word that Dennett procured by dubious means because he would only be satisfied with a word beginning with "Q". So Dennett is attacking the "obvious" observation that qualia are meaningful things. He does this by producing a dizzying number of contradictions or confusions to do with the way we conceive of qualia, and he manages to do this with slightly Monty Pythonesque humour. Dennett coined the term "intuition pump" to describe a thought experiment structured in a manner to find answers by an intuitive approach. I guess that Dennett would call my Scenarios intuition pumps, but I resist his term because we have not the foggiest clue what intuition is, and assuming that it is a part of our nature is as potentially confusing as thinking that "free will" or a "soul" or a "mind" is part of our nature. I rather think that intuition is a misnomer for thought processes that we cannot introspect – and there are certainly plenty of those.

One of Dennett's thought experiments concerns two fictional coffee tasters for Maxwell House called Mr Chase and Mr Sanborn. One day, Mr Chase confesses to Mr Sanborn:

> I hate to admit it, but I am not enjoying this work any more. When I came to Maxwell House six years ago, I thought Maxwell House coffee was the best-tasting coffee in the world. I was proud to have a share in the responsibility for preserving that flavour over the years. And we've done our job well; the coffee tastes just the same today as it tasted when I arrived. But, you know, I no longer like it! My tastes have changed. I've become a more sophisticate coffee drinker. I no longer like that taste at all.

Mr Sanborn was rather surprised by this remark because he was having a similar thought himself. He replied:

> When I arrived here, shortly before you did, I, like you, thought

Maxwell House coffee was tops in flavour. And now I, like you, really don't care for the coffee we're making. But my tastes haven't changed; my . . . tasters have changed. That is, I think something has gone wrong with my taste buds or some other part of my taste-analysing perceptual machinery. Maxwell House coffee doesn't taste to me the way it used to taste; if only it did, I'd still love it, for I still think that taste is the best taste in coffee. Now I'm not saying we haven't done our job well. You other tasters all agree that the taste is the same, and I must admit that on a day-to-day basis I can detect no change either. So it must be my problem alone.

Now the confusion here is that Mr Chase and Mr Sandborn both used to like Maxwell House coffee, and now neither of them do. However, each claims a different reason for not liking it any more. On top of that, one (or both) of them could be simply wrong, and there is no way that anyone can know, including Mr Chase or Mr Sandborn.

Dennett manages to come up with an example of a contradiction or confusion for practically every type of sensory experience. "So when we look one last time at our original characterization of qualia, as ineffable, intrinsic, private, directly apprehensible properties of experience, we find that there is nothing to fill the bill."[85] From his demonstration that we cannot form meaningful concept of qualia, he concludes: "So contrary to what seems obvious at first blush, there simply are no qualia at all."

I agree with Dennett that philosophers cannot form meaningful concepts of qualia, and yet to conclude that qualia don't exist is to use the word 'exist' in a very narrow scientistic sense. The nature of sensory qualia presents us with a metaphysical problem that we might never resolve, but we can't just deny the problem exists. Suppose someone punched Dennett and he responded by suing them; if the assailant used Dennett's theories in their legal defence, how could he respond? Likewise, I suggest that Dennett never tries to persuade starving people that their hunger qualia don't exist. When I introspect the neurological processes that occur during emotion, it produces a quale that most people call a feeling. I think of feeling qualia as being like a thumb smear of paint on a canvas – there, but not coherent. A phenomenon, like abstract art, doesn't have to be coherent to be worthy of consideration.

However, I have no interest in getting into a dispute with Dennett because we are travelling down different roads. Dennett correctly argues that philosophers cannot form meaningful concepts about qualia. But I am a philosopher saying that normal people *think* that they can form meaningful concepts of qualia. 'Normal people' in this context means people who aren't philosophers, and philosophers when they are off-duty – presumably including Dennett. I am assuming that if Dennett were to be pounced upon by a lion, he would momentarily forget to philosophise and at that point his fear would be real to him. Because concepts about qualia have an impact on what normal people do, we have to look at how their misconceptions arise and understand how this might explain the strangeness of their actions.

Since Dennett started using the taste of coffee as an example, let me continue:

Most mornings, I grind my own coffee (having similar taste in coffee to Mr Chase in later life). And I just *love* the smell of those freshly ground beans. Before I make my coffee, I place my nose over them and breath in deeply. Nothing is better than that smell. But then, after about twenty seconds, I can't smell it anymore.

Now, I could assume that after twenty seconds the coffee simply ceased to smell. Perhaps the smell is made by little creatures in the coffee that get frightened of the sight of my nostrils and curl up into their shells. But wait a minute! There can't be little creatures in there because the coffee has been thoroughly roasted and then put through my grinder. Our conception of science (that inanimate substances cannot change their properties at will) leads me to the conclusion that it isn't that the coffee ceased to smell; rather what happened is that my coffee smellers shut down. If I put the coffee back in its jar and do other things for a couple of hours, I can smell it again.

What seems to happen then is that my coffee-smelling sensors become accustomed to the smell of coffee, and quite quickly I cease to be able to smell it. For me to assume that the coffee ceases to smell would be obtuse, and in any case I can check by asking you if you can smell it. [Yes! Yes . . . We could over-philosophise and assume you might lie, or that you are a zombie programmed by the Evil Deceiver.] So it seems clear that my smell sensors cease to operate after a brief exposure to a smell, and when this happens I assume that the coffee still smells, but this is a belief alone.

Now, the question that I *really* want to ask is: does this also happen to the feeling of happiness? After I have felt happy for about twenty seconds, do I become so accustomed to the feeling that I am no longer able to feel it?

When someone asks me if I am happy, I generally answer "yes" without having to verify that feeling. In this way, I am reporting a belief about a feeling, generally without actually going to the trouble of detecting a feeling. If I look for happiness qualia, I cannot be sure that there are any. So I am going to *do a Mr Sandford* and propose that my happiness is so overwhelming, so overpowering, that it has actually blown the neural fuses that permit me to detect the feeling. How can I question this assertion? The check that I can do with the coffee isn't available to me: I cannot put my happiness back in its jar and see if I can feel it a couple of hours later. It is like halitosis in that nobody can sense it in themselves, but it is unlike halitosis in that nobody else can sense it for you. I *know* that I am happy, even when I can't detect a feeling. At such times, all I have is a belief. The metaphysics of happiness qualia might be like the metaphysics of God: if it didn't exist, we would invent it.

The woman in Scenario C is driven by the aim to achieve love without ever knowing that she has succeeded. The aim to achieve happiness is similarly a core driver of humans. However, when we have achieved it, it is by no means certain that we will have any feeling to let us know with certainty that we have done so. How then do we actually *know* that we are happy? We are driven by the desire to achieve something that is entirely inenubilable. [Admit it!

You are going to have to look that word up. I just did that to prove that I am as good as Daniel Dennett at finding ridiculously obscure words. My word has the added advantage of being practically un-pronounceable, although I couldn't find one beginning with a "Q".]

SCENARIO D:

THE FEELING THAT WAS ONLY IMAGINED

The Man's life is trash. Every day he slaves in a foundry, sweat streaming from his pores until his clothes reek. He works non-stop in filthy conditions for hours until the end of his shift, when he trudges home, head bent, feet scuffing the paving stones. As he approaches his walk-up tenement, discarded food wrappers swirl by on vortices between parked cars. He is trapped here; he knows it.

The people in the Man's world view him as an outsider. They refuse to be downtrodden. Together, they hold their heads up, smile at each other and slap each other boisterously on the shoulder. To their thinking, to submit is to be weak; and they regard the Man as weak. They shun him. To survive, they need to ignore the hopeless-ness of their situation, and they do this by determinedly acting out survival. They do this when they meet each other – forcefully acting out happiness and contentment. And by doing this, gradually they become a tribe. The foundry people stick together and despise out-siders; this includes the bosses of the foundry who they imagine are people who do not understand what life is really about. But if they act happy, then are they happy? Their act occurs whenever they are together in groups. They do it on cue, and eventually it becomes a habit – something they do reflexively once they belong to the tribe.

Acting happy creates a belief in happiness, but if the happiness is affected then there is no feeling attached. However, why would they assume that there is supposed to be a feeling if their understanding of happiness is just a behavioural state? What started as a means of survival became a tribal ritual, and now it has become a symbol of their identity. This identity is the mechanism that permits them to deny the hopelessness of their situation, and so the habitual faking of happiness takes away their incentive to form strategies of escape. Someone who systematically acts out their wellbeing is concealing from themselves the causes of their own wellbeing. How then could they understand that their belief in their wellbeing is something that they have themselves constructed?

The Man refuses to play the game of the foundry people because he still dreams of escape. However, the strongest condemnation of the foundry people is reserved for people who are insiders but who refuse to deny their situation. Among such people we find the Man: the insider treated worse than an outsider. The Man's refusal to conform behaviourally threatens the foundry people by providing evidence of their miserable situation. They need to reject the Man because to pity him is to acknowledge the situation they are denying.

Occasionally, someone from the foundry escapes to a better life. The foundry people nod grudgingly and wish them well, but behind their back they make snide remarks about the betrayal of their roots, and gradually such people are transferred to the world of despised outsiders. Escapees who return to visit quickly learn not to bother eulogising their new life. The foundry people don't want to hear, and accuse the escapee of pretension or disloyalty.

So the Man has a choice of escape or conformity. Conformity seals off escape by creating a false belief in happiness in a place of despair. He can try to escape, and if he fails he can try again; but when he tires of failing, he will eventually have to submit. One day, he will meet his colleagues from the foundry and switch into the easy banter, the joshing, and the physical enactment of roughneck tribal bonding. And then his life will be locked into a cycle of daily grind. He will be held in place by a belief in happiness that is actually a pretence that he and the foundry people conspire together to create. But this belief is merely a behavioural construct, and it traps them into their denial of misery, and therefore self-destruction.

This is the last of what I call the four core Scenarios. In case you didn't spot it, they have a symmetry in that each involves a different aspect on emotional tactical deception. This, in summary is as follows:

Scenario A: suppression in the second/third person
Scenario B: suppression in the first person
Scenario C: affectation in the first person
Scenario D: affectation in the second/third person.

I will keep referring back to this throughout the book. If, at any time, you need a quick reference summary you can refer to the Appendix where they are summarised in a flowcharty kind of way.

BRAIN ILLUSIONS

In an argument of this complexity, there is inevitable debris that gets left on the floor. The time has come to sweep it up. My central theme is looking at how concepts of emotion can become corrupt, but this is confused by the fact that our brains create a number of other illusions that cloud the issue. I need to address this, and this means being thoroughly unscientific, and only marginally philosophical. Writing this chapter fills me with self-loathing [for which I shall suppress the behavioural response].

There are three misconceptions that I need to dispel: firstly, the notion that true biological instinct ever drives a human action; secondly, that we think with a "mind"; and, thirdly, I need to address the confusion surrounding perceptive illusion in general. More specifically, I'll be looking at the question of how our brains create the impression that we can remember feelings and rely upon this memory for identification of emotional states.

INSTINCT AND RATIONAL THOUGHT

Lions and hyenas hate one another with a passion. They hate each other even more than the New York Yankees and the New England Patriots hate each other. [Wait! Do they play the same sport?] Whenever lions and hyenas meet each other, they fight ferociously, but these fights almost never end up with death or injury. They end with one team running away. So which team flees? In almost every case, it is the one with the lower aggregate body mass. The "Brave Lion" idea does not stack-up here.

Imagine you are in a restaurant in New Orleans with your friends, and the waiter brings a steaming plate of Cajun crawfish. Your eyes focus on the plate like a vulture, and pick out the biggest one; then (acting all nonchalant, and perhaps making a remark intended purely to distract) you swoop in before anyone else spots it. When you do this, you make a decision. (You could after all have taken the smallest one.) You can make this decision without using language in your head. This is fortunate, because lions and hyenas also have to make a decision; and they don't have language.

If you hold up two objects, you can look at them and spot whether one is bigger than the other or not, without using language in your head. Now imagine that I hold up two blocks of wood, and I ask you: is this block more or less than 20% bigger than the other? Again, you can look at the two blocks of wood, make a mental comparison and decide without needing to use language in your head.

Now let's imagine that because lions have sharper teeth and retractable claws, they can take on hyenas with a 20% higher aggregate body mass. If you can assess whether something is more or less than 120% of your size without using language, why can't the lion? The problem is this: "the same size as" is something that can be understood if you have *never* had language; but "20% bigger than" is hard to conceptualise if it has never been put into language.

Lions and hyenas work off equality of size because they have never had language. Their simplistic fight or flight instinct has been streamlined by the process of natural selection, and this instinct is possible without language. One lion is going to be more frightened of two fat hyenas than he is of three lean hungry ones if the former has a higher aggregate weight. From the lion's perspective, this is probably the wrong choice. But how can the lion improve on it without language? If the lion gained language, he could work this out. But look what has happened: the simple instinct gained through natural selection has disappeared. A lion with language has to decide when to use the simple rule, and when to use the more subtle assessment. However, this results in the simple rule being ousted as the only outcome determined by instinct. It is now simply another option. Instinct would evaporate the instant the lion could make the decision using language-based reasoning.

Language permits you to second-guess your instinct, and if you can second-guess it, it isn't instinct any more. Humans, who have language, are able to engage in post-language non-verbal thought, so they no longer have true biological instinct. We have behavioural responses to emotional states that can be explained as instinct derived from evolution by natural selection, but once we start habitually manipulating these responses, can we still be said to fully retain the instinct?

Imagine that a female friend of yours says to you: "I have met this guy, but I can't decide whether he is serious or a jackass." And you advise: "Listen to your instincts." What you mean, it seems to me, is to assess how you feel and think of the situation without using language as a medium for reasoning. However, as should now be clear, thinking about how we feel isn't that simple. Human emotion was originally a product of evolution by natural selection, but this process has been corrupted. Language enables us to think conceptually about behaviour and this has led us to tactically deceive ourselves with our own emotional behaviour, and instinct no longer provides a reliable answer.

When the quarterback sees his teammate in open space by third base, he throws the ball without thinking it through in language. This is post-language non-verbal thought: how could he know the point of this throw (as opposed to another one) if he had not learned the rules and strategy of the game? Learning the strategy requires language. The decision on where to throw the ball does not.

So there are three modes of thinking:

1. Instinct, which is non-verbal (and pre-linguistic) decision-making where a fixed pattern of responses follows a set of stimuli in a way that is determined by natural selection;
2. Post-language non-verbal thinking where decisions are made

without verbal reasoning, but based on certain objectives or criteria that were previously verbalised; and

3. Thinking that requires language as part of the decision-making process.

In any situation where we have time for the second and third, we can never be said to truly follow the first. Instinct, in its biological sense, vanishes. [Eureka! And he kicks the puck through the hoop and into the bleachers.]

THE MYTH OF THE GHOST IN THE MACHINE

Discovering what consciousness is should be a scientific problem. We should approach the problem the same way we try to understand gravity or how influenza viruses cause disease. However, the only consciousness that each of us can observe is our own, and to analyse it in an objective scientific manner we would need to be able to observe someone else's. Our initial line of enquiry is bound to be introspection, and it becomes hard to avoid some appeal to intuition. In this way, science collides headfirst with philosophy and creates a problem that leaves the greatest thinkers flummoxed.

We don't need years of study in philosophy to be able to study our thoughts by way of introspection. When you read this book, I hope that it causes you to have thoughts, although it might just trigger a feeling of boredom. Either way, you will doubtless see your response as a conscious one – something that is subjective and personal to you alone. This process of introspection has led people through the centuries to regard the mental world as distinct from the physical one. We make decisions in our mental world (according to the "common sense" view) and this causes our body to do the mind's willing. The philosopher-speak term for this conception of separate mental and physical worlds is "dualist interactionism" (or sometimes "interactionist dualism" by annoying people trying to pretend that their theory is different). In exposing its absurdity, the philosopher Gilbert Ryle rather caustically referred to it as "the myth of the Ghost in the Machine".[86] This became the catchphrase by which people poke fun at such ridiculous explanations.

Most people attribute dualist interactionism to Descartes[87], but this is a mistake. In philosophy, practically everybody from ancient times to the mid-twentieth century believed in the separateness of the mind.[88] The significance of Descartes is that he was the first to examine the problem in the wake of the scientific revolution that followed the discoveries of Galileo. Prior to Galileo, most philosophers couldn't see a problem with mental phenomena causing physical ones. Gilbert Ryle terminated philosophy's belief in a non-physical mind causing the movement of the physical body through "volitions". In other words, the laws of physics and chemistry determine the movement of the body, but this causal chain cannot begin with something that lies outside these laws.

Philosophers tried to wriggle off this hook by making two distinct concepts of mind: the "phenomenal mind" is the mind of experience qualia that we observe through introspection; and the "psychological mind" is the mind that causes the body to act. But this just moves the scientific disconnect to a different place. If your decision to act occurs in your phenomenal mind, then how does this cause the psychological mind to do its stuff? If the psychological mind is all that matters, then what exactly *is* the phenomenal mind?

Scientist have tried to finagle the problem by making use of the same risible distinction: Freud and his followers examined the phenomenal mind, and later the behaviourists focussed on the psychological mind, sometimes going as far as completely denying the existence of mental phenomena. In other words, your experience of your thought is an illusion. Well, as we will discuss in the next section, the brain is certainly a consummate illusionist, but the problem is that we cannot ask what *sort* of illusion it is except through the medium of thought, which is the very illusion that we are trying to analyse. This is a problem that appears intractable.

Contemporary thinkers from both science and philosophy mostly divide the problem of consciousness into the "Hard Problem" and the "Easy Problem". The philosopher David Chalmers coined this terminology[89], but Leibniz was perhaps the first to make the Hard Problem clear:

> Supposing there were a machine, so constructed as to think, feel, and have perception, it might be conceived as increased in size, while keeping the same proportions, so that one might go into it as into a mill. That being so, we should, on examining its interior, find only parts which work one upon another, and never anything by which to explain a perception.[90]

The Hard Problem is explaining how thought generates the *experience* of thought. Somehow, we have a way of seeing our thought as it happens and we are aware of it. Similarly, perception generates the *experience* of perception. This is the Hard Problem because we don't even know what a hypothetical explanation might look like.

Now for the Easy Problem, which is actually not easy at all; it is called "easy" because we sort of know what the problem actually is. It is understanding how unconscious *and* conscious brain processes work. Neuroscience is gradually unravelling all this. For example, cognitive neuroscientists are a grim bunch of people who study people who have had bits of their brains destroyed by tumour, haemorrhage or trauma. They do so to find out what each of them can no longer do. By a process of gradual elimination, they are constructing a map of the brain to determine what each part of the brain actually does (speech, movement, memory, rational thought, etc.). If every conscious thought requires a bit of the brain for us to experience it, we could say that cognitive neuroscientists are gradually exorcising the Ghost from the Machine. However, if cognitive neuroscientists find all the parts of the brain that deal with the human experience of suffering, they could not be said to understand suffering. If suffering were just a physical brain state, then surely we wouldn't need to care about it. I am guessing that even cognitive neuroscientists are capable of suffering, and what is important about suffering is that we *experience* it, not that it is just some neural electronics. We are also learning how neurons work. Although we are still some way from understanding how logical thought can be explained by neural function, it is not inconceivable that eventually scientists will figure this out, but this still won't explain consciousness.

Many philosophers and scientists suspect that the Hard Problem will never be solved.[91] Others argue that the Hard Problem does not even exist.[92] These two views on the Hard Problem seem to have reached a sort of stalemate where nothing will change until someone comes up with a completely different way of looking at things.

There has been a philosophical hoopla about this for about two millennia. So what progress have we made? Precisely none! David Chalmers considers that philosophical theories of consciousness basically fall into eight different categories, and there are another nine (mostly scientific) theories.[93] Seventeen theories is hardly evidence of emerging consensus. If I overdose on my imagination pills, I could probably dream up an eighteenth, but would that actually help?

This book is about how we understand feelings, which are states of consciousness; so I must address the problem. I can either solve it or dodge it. And since nobody else has been able to solve it, dodging looks like the prudent strategy. Why bother being clever when being wily gets you out of trouble with much less effort?

I tend to start these problems by looking at it from an evolutionary angle. Let's consider a hypothetical sensory qualia, because this enables us to avoid the preconception that, if we see it, it must be *True*. Carbon monoxide kills humans, but doesn't have a smell. Imagine that some geological event meant that the earth starts to periodically spew carbon monoxide. A genetic mutation occurs in me that somehow causes a "ding" to go off in my brain whenever carbon monoxide is present. At first, I have no idea what the ding is, but then I notice that whenever the ding goes off people around me start dying, so I learn to run until the dinging stops. I will out-survive other humans, and my offspring will out-survive the humans of their generation, so the ding-gene will propagate throughout humanity. My brain is tricking me to promote my survival, and it is senseless considering whether the ding is representative of a true state of affairs. It is not necessary to understand the metaphysics of emotional qualia to understand that they serve the purpose of driving actions. If these qualia are some sort of brain-synthesised phenomena, and if they prompt actions that promote survival, then the nature of the phenomena is irrelevant. Evolution is concerned with passing on your genes by any means – including, possibly, your deception.

An emotion is a form of yearning that drives an action that enhances biological fitness. Lower animals that seem to lack consciousness have mechanisms to survive, but don't have a *yearning* to survive because yearning occurs in the phenomenal mind. Is not the yearning a prerequisite for more complex survival strategies? The conscious mind is almost certainly a prerequisite of language that again permits the calculation of even more complex survival strategies.

MEMORIES OF FEELINGS

A while ago, I did a survey of a group of friends. [Remember: philosophers don't *get* scientific research!] I asked them to close their eyes and think of an image and tell me whether this image was in colour or not. About a quarter of them told me that they saw the image in monochrome black-and-white while the rest saw the image in polychrome. I have thought about this, and I have come to the conclusion that I don't see the image either way.

Think about how you see with your physical eye. You have this sensation of seeing the whole of your visual field as a colour image; but actually your physical eye flits over what is before you and takes in the most important parts of the image in sequence, and the rest is left to your peripheral vision. There is a physiological reason for this: The light sensors at the back of your eye (the retina) have a concentrated point (called the "fovea centralis"). Here there is a concentration of cone cells, and the rest of your retina has a higher concentration of rod cells. We tend to overlook how hopeless our peripheral vision really is. Ask a friend to put up a number of fingers in front of your face, but just to one side of your focal point, and you won't be able to count them.

Now, let's think about the mind's eye. When I picture a mental image, my mind's eye does the same thing as my physical eye: it flits over the mental image in sequence, picking out the most important details in sequence and the rest is left to the peripheral vision of my mind's eye – which is almost non-existent. There may be a physiological reason why my mind's eye works the same way as my physical eye; namely that the vision circuits of my brain evolved in tandem with my eye, and they are simply set up to process visual data in the way my physical eye sees: a sequence of detailed images in the middle of a fuzzy one. When I conjure up a mental image, I use some of the same brain circuits as when I see a physical image, and these are simply set up to scan the image one point at a time.

So then, how do I see my mental image with my mind's eye? Well, let's say that my mental image is a pastoral scene, rather like a John Constable painting. As my mind's eye flits over the mental image, it picks out the colours in sequence, but my mental peripheral image is entirely black-and-white. So if my mind's eye flits to the sky, my brain says "blue" and when my mind's eye flits to the cornfield, my brain says "yellow". But if I try to assemble all the colours together, I simply cannot do it. This way of seeing with my mind's eye is neither monochrome nor polychrome. I call it "serial duochrome", but our brain tricks us into thinking that we see a polychrome image.

It is instructive to think about the vision of other species because as we go backwards down the evolutionary chain, we can see elements of our incredible visual ability being successively taken away.

Colour vision in mammals evolved about thirty million years ago, before the evolutionary split between New World monkeys and Old World monkeys. The only mammals that have colour vision are humans, apes and Old World monkeys. We therefore tend to think that it is easy to imagine what your dog sees – you just have to look at a black-and-white TV. However, it is quite likely a dog lacks many other elements of our visual capability, though it is difficult to be certain.

When I was a child, I used to go bird watching. I remember that if you want to enter a bird hide in clear view of the birds, then three people should approach the hide, two should enter it and the third should walk on in clear sight of the birds. If everyone enters the hide, the birds know that you are there and stay clear. However, if one person keeps walking, the birds don't know that there is anyone in the hide because a bird cannot tell the difference between three humans and one. Maybe a bird sees humans in much the same way that you see fingers when they are held just off the centre of your visual field. It is certainly astonishing that hawks can spot a mouse from a hundred metres up, but we should not imagine that they see what we see *plus* the ability to see the mouse. A hawk can pick out the *movement* of the mouse so well, in part because it is poor at resolving everything that is stationary. Birds keep their head stationary for brief periods of time and then jerk them to another position. The frequency with which a bird twitches its head (three or four times a second) is a crude measure of how long it takes to resolve a static image. A lizard moves its head only every few seconds. This would imply that a bird resolves a static image several times faster than a lizard, which seems reasonable since it has a more highly evolved brain.

It is almost impossible to imagine what some animals see. Try to imagine what an insect "looks like" to a bat's echolocator on a pitch-dark night. The philosopher Thomas Nagel attempted to describe this.[94] Bat sonar, Nagel points out, is nothing like any sensory experience that we possess, but we must assume that a bat experiences the perception of its sonar. Our imagination might permit us to imagine what it is like for *us* to be a bat, but it does not permit us to imagine what it is like for a *bat* to be a bat: flying on webbed hands, catching insects in our mouths in the dark and spending all day hanging upside-down in a cave. This, in part, is because we lack the neurophysiological systems that a bat has for echolocation.[95] A bat must have a different experience of this because it has a different brain structure.

Some scientists and philosophers argue that only humans have consciousness. I think this implausible, and a better way to think of it is that consciousness is proportional to development. For example, a frog lacks most of our conscious experience of vision because a frog cannot see anything that is stationary.[96] This is fine for the frog because everything the frog eats moves, and everything that eats the frog moves. You can get a frog as hungry as you like, and when you sit it in front of a fly it will do nothing. However, as soon as the fly moves, the frog will zap it with a sticky slurp. What else does a frog need to see? Its sex life is conducted solely through the senses of touch and sound. The way a frog sees therefore accounts for the way it moves: hop-freeze-hop-freeze. The freeze permits it to see any pursuing predator because the predator is the only thing (during that moment of freeze) that is moving relative to the frog. If the frog moved smoothly, its eye would deliver its brain a blur of information that it would not be able to compute (frogs not being too clever).

OK, so now think about how an egret hunts. Egrets are a major predator of frogs. The egret makes a confident stride towards the frog, and then it freezes. From the frog's perspective, danger appears in a flash and then completely vanishes. Now let's break this movement down a bit further: An egret at rest has a long neck coiled in an S-shape. Before the egret starts its stride, it stretches its neck out first like an arrow. Only when its neck is fully extended, does it take the step and it simultaneously recoils its neck; so when its body moves forward its head is motionless. The frog is sitting on its lily pad contemplating all that is beautiful in the world (i.e. insects); and suddenly a pointy head appears without a body attached. The head then vanishes; and then a body appears without a head attached. Then both the head and the body vanish. The frog never sees a complete egret, and now cannot see anything. The frog is thinking "huh?" when a jagging stab comes out of nowhere, and the frog disappears down a slimy tube into oblivion.

Vision can mean many different things, and physical vision may not result in comparable images to mental vision. So let's get back to our mind's eye, and do a simple experiment: I want you to conjure up a mental image of the world's most famous painting – the Mona

Lisa. Imagine you enter the hallowed room in the Louvre where the Mona Lisa hangs, and there is chaos in there. Someone has vandalised the Mona Lisa. Oh no! They have put bright pink lipstick on her mouth. So, you are focussing on your mental image of the Mona Lisa; and now, I want you to apply bright pink lipstick to your mental image. Concentrate now! When you have a mental image of the whole of the Mona Lisa complete with bright pink lipstick, you can open your eyes and write an angry blog-post about how my book is complete nonsense. However, I doubt you can do that (unless you are David Hockney) because your brain tricks you into thinking it can do things that actually it can't.

We have explored the mind's eye. Now let's explore the mind's big toe.

Huh?

Didn't you know that your mind has a big toe? [This is what happens if you do too much philosophy – it's pathetic!] In the chapter *The Language of Feeling and Emotion*, I pointed out that a different pain results when someone stamps on your toe and when you stub it. Now close your eyes and try to remember exactly what stubbing your toe *feels* like. This is your mind's big toe in action. I find that thinking about this is the best way to visualise what an egret looks like to a frog. If I try to recall the feeling, I simply draw a blank.

One of the only times in my life when I have been seriously hurt was when some goon knocked me off my bike with his car. I have often tried to remember what that actually felt like. It isn't that I can't remember anything, because I do. So when I say, "Hey, Brain! Give me a memory of the *feeling*", my brain says, "Sure, Matt! Here you go"; and my brain gives me a mental image of me lying in the road like a rag-doll. "No, Brain! The feeling!" This result is seriously strange because I never saw myself lying in the road; all I saw was the paramedic looking down at me. Not only does my brain convert the feeling in my memory into the body language of the feeling, it converts it into body language that I never actually saw.

Why would my brain do this to me unless it was incapable of delivering me a memory of the feeling itself? Our brain is constantly playing con-tricks on us to make us think it can do things that it can't.

But what is the implication of this for emotional memory? If we think we remember feelings but actually only remember the body language, then the memory is false if the body language was either affected or suppressed. If you live in a culture where people habitually pretend to be happy or suppress anxiety, then remembering the behaviour is going to give you falsely favourable memories of the experience. This would imply that nostalgia has a simple causal explanation. You could be remembering, not a feeling, but a belief about a feeling. Or it could be that you remember a belief in an emotion, where the feeling never actually occurred. How could you ever know?

THE HUMAN ACTION DRIVER

What I want to do now is focus on how our emotional goals have shifted over the centuries and been shaped by philosophy. This has been much more variable than one might expect. It is important to try to visualise what they were in times past because that way we can break the spell that our present goals are some kind of "fundamental truth".

In this chapter, I want to explore how it came about that people are driven by the desire to achieve positive emotional states and avoid negative ones. Emotions are the product of evolution by natural selection, and drive the behaviour of non-speaking animals. In humans, there is a non-evolutionary transition where philosophy and language change how humans understand their emotions and thereby how they determine their actions. Happiness is not innate in humans, but probably emerged from philosophical teachings that were principally concerned with morality. However, we could say that the desire to achieve happiness is our core driver, so there is a transition that needs explaining because we are now driven by something that isn't even innate.

This is a progression that we can trace through the history of philosophical theories because, from the time of the pre-Socratics to the late nineteenth century, most Western philosophers followed the same architecture of reasoning:

(1) Such-and-such is my definition of human nature;

(2) From (1), I can deduce the needs of men, and what drives them;

(3) From (1) and (2), I can deduce a system of morality;

(4) From (1) through (3), I can deduce a political system.

That political ideology requires a notion of human nature was best summed up as follows: "Nor do I know, if men are like sheep, why they need any government: Or, if they are like wolves, how they can suffer it."[97] More precisely, a political ideology and a concept of human nature can be derived from one another by a process of pure algebra: for example, we can take an atom of a political ideology "lowering interest rates, will cause an increase in investment", and derive from this an atom of human nature "a human will respond to the stimulus of low interest rates by investing more." This begets the obvious empirical question: "Well, do they?" The problem is that if you believe the ideology, then the answer to the question is too obvious for the question to be asked, and so it is never investigated. This, of course, is tautological, and the precise nature of this tautology is the focus of the second half of this book.

In the late nineteenth century the classical philosophical architecture changed because a new notion emerged – that there was no such thing as human nature. The theory was that men were born as a "blank slate" or a "tabula rasa" upon which any belief (political or religious) could be written. For example, Karl Marx, who jumped right in at the deep end: "The history of all hitherto existing societies is the history of class struggles."[98] [Oh, get a grip Karl! Can you name a tribal society that has a proletariat? Hmmm?] With that single sentence summarising the entire history of humanity, he completely skipped steps (1) and (2) of classical reasoning. This was no accident, since Marx was a believer in the blank slate, and he believed his political theories were science. The denial of human nature gave rise to some of the worst political aberrations in the history of humanity, as dictators and intellectuals sought to engineer the perfect man and the perfect society, only to wind up with brutal totalitarianism. The causal chain is all too obvious in hindsight: it is a small step from the denial of human nature to assuming the irrelevance of human suffering.

For my purposes here, I am particularly concerned with the examination of step (2) in philosophical history. What I aim to do is to find the origin of the *perception* that the conceptualised emotions of men are the core driver of their actions, and then see if I can find out how the *fact* arose. Trying to figure this out is like trying to find the source of the Nile: the further you get from the sea; the harder it gets. We can find early periods of history when this idea didn't exist (or at least wasn't expressed), but between then and now were periods when everything is a bit blurred. In the chapter *The Evolution of Emotion*, I looked at philosophy from both East and West, but here I will only look at philosophy from the West because this is where the perception arose. This is no coincidence and hinges on one of the critical differences between Eastern and Western thought: Western philosophers have all assumed that the point of life was the attainment of a higher state – for example a positive emotional state.[99] Eastern philosophers have all assumed that the point of life was to escape from the cycle of suffering – the avoidance of negative emotional states.

In *The Evolution of Emotion*, I described how Aristotle's *Nichomachean Ethics* said that man wanted *eudaimonia* as the ultimate end of all his actions, but that *eudaimonia* was not the emotional state of happiness, but a sort of precursor to it. However, shortly after the time of Aristotle, most of the ideas of Greek philosophy got buried under a pile of religious orthodoxy. The Christian World did not emerge from this until the Renaissance about 1,500 years later.

The period in between is often known as "The Dark Ages". It's a bit unfair to regard this period as entirely dark, but the key factor of the Dark Ages is that philosophy and science were completely subservient to theology. By contrast, the Muslim World during the medieval period flourished culturally, producing the best mathematicians and poets, until the Crusades. Following the Crusades, that were actually a military defeat for the Christian World, an unexpected transformation took place where the Christian World flowered with the Renaissance, and the Muslim World slid into a cultural funk.[100]

The writings of Abbess Hildegard von Bingen (1098–1179) can be taken as indicative of the intellectual freezer of the Dark Ages. Hildegard denies the acceptability of secular happiness. She talks at length of "foolish joy" and how to repent from it: "if the men who fail with foolish joy strive to overcome the evil spirits who urged them on to this sin want to flee from this joy, let them restrain their flesh with scourging and fasting in proportion to their sin and according to the wishes of the one who presides over them."[101] She also doesn't hold back on the appropriate punishment for such misdemeanours: "covered by fog and eaten alive by worms"[102], to be precise. [Calm down, Hildegard! It can't be *that* bad.] She contrasts unhappiness not with a positive emotional state, but with "blessedness"[103], and takes despair as evidence that a person does not trust in God. The only positive emotion that she acknowledges is "heavenly joy" which is the ultimate reward for life, so secular happiness is denied. "Heavenly joy" is what I call a super-positive emotion – a mythological emotion so fabulous that mere mortals cannot possibly imagine it.

So when the intellectual ice age thawed with the Renaissance, where did philosophy go?

During the Renaissance it was virtually impossible to justify any opinion without demonstrating that it had a basis in Catholic theology or the writings of the ancient Greeks. Shaking off the religion took another few hundred years. By the seventeenth century, secular values, a critical application of reason, and a search for practical evidence to support beliefs and theories were becoming accepted. Individualism and a preference for plain speaking began to flourish. Freedom of thought and practice were accepted, despite their threat to religious orthodoxy; in part because they yielded huge advances in science and knowledge generally.

*

Perhaps the best place to pick up the journey is Thomas Hobbes (1588–1679). Hobbes is significant because he saw politics as a branch of science. He thought that humans could be treated as agents of cause and effect in an almost mathematical way. [Precisely! You tell 'em Thom!] Hobbes argues that man's natural state would be one of perpetual conflict:

> If any two men desire the same thing, which neverthelesse they cannot both enjoy, they become enemies; and in the way to their End, (which is principally their owne conservation, and sometimes their delectation only,) endeavour to destroy, or subdue one an other.[104]

> Without a common power to keep them all in awe, they are in a condition which is called Warre; and such a warre, as is of every man against every man.[105]

Thus Hobbes argues the legitimacy of the all-powerful nation-state – Hobbes' Leviathan – to subdue men, without which they would be in "continuall feare, and danger of violent death; And the life of man, solitary, poore, nasty, brutish, and short."[106]

Hobbes does not have a concept of emotional drivers for human behaviour, but he has (like Aristotle) a half-formed concept:

> When in the mind of man, Appetites, and Aversions, Hopes and Feares, concerning one and the same thing, arise alternatively; and divers good and evill consequences of the doing, or omitting the thing propounded, come successively into our thoughts; so that sometimes we have an Appetite to it; sometimes an Aversion from it; sometimes Hope to be able to do it; sometimes Despaire, or Feare to attempt it; the whole summe of Desires, Aversions, Hopes and Fears, continued till the thing be either done, or thought impossible, is that we call DELIBERATION.[107]

> In Deliberation, the last Appetite, or Aversion, immediately adhaering to the action, or to the omission thereof, is that wee call the WILL; the Act, (not the faculty,) of Willing.[108]

According to Hobbes, it is usual that the good and evil consequences of acting form such a long chain that we can seldom see the end of it, and deliberation is the process of assessing the net good or evil of action.

> Continuall successe in obtaining those things which a man from time to time desireth, that is to say, continuall prospering, is that men call FELICITY; I mean Felicity of this life. For there is no such thing as perpetuall Tranquillity of mind while we live here; because Life it selfe is but Motion, and can never be without Desire, nor without Feare, no more than without Sense.[109]

'Felicity' is an old-fashioned word that is sometimes interpreted as happiness, but can also mean appropriateness, so we are close to Aristotle's conception where it isn't clear that an emotional state is meant. "Felicity of this life" seems better interpreted as a form of appropriateness, which is not far different from Aristotle's *eudaimonia*.

John Locke (1632–1704) set out the most thorough and plausible formulation of empiricism (the theory that all knowledge ultimately comes from sense-experience). His views on political theory influenced constitutional law of the United States, France and Britain. He moves forward from Hobbes, but still does not see emotions as a core driver of behaviour. He believes in free will, with the caveat that we have no choice in having free will. "To the Question, what is it determines the Will? The true and proper answer is, The mind."[110] Locke goes on to ask what drives the mind to exercise the will in the way it does:

> What moves the mind, in every particular instance, to determine its general power of directing, to this or that particular Motion or Rest? And to this I answer, The motive, for continuing in the same State or Action, is only the present satisfaction in it; The motive to change, is always some *uneasiness*: nothing setting us upon the change of State, or upon any new Action, but some *uneasiness*. This the great motive that works on the Mind to put it

upon Action, which for shortness sake we will call *determining of the Will*.[111]

Locke's philosophy on the drivers of men's actions is very much centred on this concept of uneasiness (which he always wrote in italics as if it was a technical term). Desire is an uneasiness caused by the absence of whatever it is that is desired. *"Aversion, Fear, Anger, Envy, Shame*, etc. have each their *uneasiness* too, and thereby influence the *will*."[112] The will is determined by whatever is the greatest *uneasiness*. "And whenever a greater *uneasiness* than that takes place in the mind, the *will* presently is by that determin'd to some new action, and the present delight neglected."[113] [Huh, John – isn't it the case that if we are *always* determined by the greater uneasiness, then that would be determinism? You know: the belief that free will is a myth. Oh, never mind!]

So Locke does not see us driven by emotions. Happiness is something we judge ourselves to have, but the driver is the *uneasiness*. Locke is not a utilitarian, but he also does not have a naturalist philosophy. He has difficulty seeing how liberty can be trusted with morality determined by man-made rules, and so sees morality coming from God. Although he sees the human driver as the *uneasiness* caused by the passions, his ethics focusses on piety and prudence, presumably because he feels the need for restraint on the fulfilment of desire. Without this restraint, Locke cannot see how man would not run amok – and in this respect his thinking is still rooted in Hobbes.

David Hume (1711–1776) advances on Locke in that he is perhaps the first truly naturalist philosopher. He believes that we can account for morality and human nature entirely in a scientific way without resort to the will of God. The subtitle of his greatest work is "An Attempt to introduce the experimental method of reasoning into Moral Subjects".[114] So Hume is attempting to demonstrate that we can derive morality, and this is dependent upon some conception of human nature that can be gleaned from observation.

Hume also completes the intellectual journey to perceiving humans as driven entirely by their emotions.

> I shall endeavour to prove *first*, that reason alone can never be a motive to any action of the will; and *secondly*, that it can never oppose passion in the direction of the will.[115]

He argues that our actions are determined solely by the desire to achieve pleasure and avoid pain, both of which he considers to be emotions. Our reason assists us in determining what causes these emotions, based on experience.

> 'Tis obvious, that when we have the prospect of pain or pleasure from any object, we feel a consequent emotion of aversion or propensity, and are carry'd to avoid or embrace what will give us this uneasiness or satisfaction. 'Tis also obvious, that this emotion rests not here, but making us cast our view on every side, comprehends whatever objects are connected with its original one by the relation of cause and effect. Here then reasoning takes place to discover this relation; and according as our reasoning varies, our actions receive a subsequent variation. But 'tis evident in this case that the impulse arises not from reason, but is only directed by it. 'Tis from the prospect of pain or pleasure that the aversion or propensity arises towards any object: And these emotions extend themselves to the causes and effects of that object, as they are pointed out to us by reason and experience.[116]

Here, Hume argues that the *only* function of reason is to determine what causes the emotion. "Reason is, and ought only to be the slave of the passions, and can never pretend to any other office than to serve and obey them."[117] Our reason can alter our judgement as to what will bring about pleasure or pain. But this does not alter the fact that it is the aim to achieve pleasure or avoid pain that is the sole cause of the action. [Well done Dave! You got it!]

Hume's position is basically my own starting point. He explores the causes of self-destructive acts, but is unable to determine the root of them. However, he correctly (in my view) realises that their cause is a false judgement, but he is unable to isolate the origin of that judgement.

> 'Tis not contrary to reason to prefer the destruction of the whole world to the scratching of my finger. 'Tis not contrary to reason for me to chuse my total ruin, to prevent the least uneasiness of an *Indian* or person wholly unknown to me. 'Tis as little contrary to reason to prefer even my own acknowledge'd lesser good to my greater, and have a more ardent affection for the former than the latter. A trivial good may, from certain circumstances, produce a desire superior to what arises from the greatest and most valuable enjoyment; nor is there any thing more extraordinary in this, than in mechanics to see one pound weight raise up a hundred by the advantage of its situation. In short, a passion must be accompany'd with some false judgment, in order to its being unreasonable; and even then 'tis not the passion, properly speaking, which is unreasonable, but the judgment.[118]

False judgement, according to Hume, can lead to seemingly disadvantageous choices of action by incorrectly deducing the cause of an emotion.

> I may will the performance of certain actions as a means of obtaining any desire'd good; but as my willing of these actions is only secondary, and founded on the supposition, that they are causes of the propos'd effect; as soon as I discover the falsehood of that supposition, they must become indifferent to me.

Hume understands (correctly in my view) that false judgement leads to false understanding of the causality of emotions, which in turn leads to self-destructive acts. But he does not search out the source of the false judgement.

Hume is not only completing the analysis of emotion as the driver of human behaviour, he is laying the foundation for the philosophy that became known as Utilitarianism. Jeremy Bentham (1748–1832) and John Stuart Mill (1806–1873) argued that not only are humans driven by the desire to achieve happiness, but that the aim of achieving the maximum happiness for the maximum number of people should be the sole basis for morality.

> Nature has placed mankind under the governance of two sovereign masters, *pain* and *pleasure*. It is for them alone to point out what we ought to do, as well as to determine what we shall do. On the one hand the standard of right and wrong, on the other the chain of causes and effects, are fastened to their throne. They govern us in all we do, in all we say, in all we think.[119]

We have been tracking the development of the perception of emotion as a driver through the British empiricists of the Age of Enlightenment. It's worth mentioning that one parallel European train of thought, through Spinoza and Kant, rejected happiness as the measure of good. They thought that pleasure was ignoble and sought to build morality on notions they considered to be noble. This isn't really relevant to my project because it has little to do with emotional drivers. It also has little acceptance today. However, another European development must be acknowledged: Romanticism. Initially a reaction to the Age of Enlightenment, Romanticism curiously came to similar conclusions with respect to emotions being a driver of human behaviour.

The Romantics saw the advances of science as dehumanising. They feared that science would ultimately demonstrate that men were just machines [as indeed they are]. Their reaction to this was an almost violent rejection of rationality in exchange for uncontrolled emotion. Romanticism wasn't a philosophy as such, but, as Charles Baudelaire stated, a "way of feeling". Among the educated and cultured people of France in the eighteenth century, it became fashionable to admire *La Sensibilité,* which was an outpouring of emotion uncontrolled by reason. This is an historic example of the systematic mass affectation of emotion. It is done to the point where it becomes difficult to distinguish the real from the fake, and the emotion from the belief. The emotions the Romantics considered to be of greatest importance were pity and sympathy.

The Romantics idealised the harmony of the pastoral scene; they admired poverty and considered a peasant to be noble. However, there was something deeply hypocritical about this: Romantics were wealthy and educated. The poor had no time for Romanticism because they were too busy trying to survive. But for a Romantic, what was important was to react emotionally when confronted with poverty; one must be overcome with the emotion of pity. Any attempt to actually solve the problems of the poor was seen as boorish. To do this was considered to dehumanise the peasant by seeing him as an economic unit. The trouble with real poor people was that they were . . . uh, human; and this meant that they might argue back or notice that your sympathy was a sham. Better, then, to avoid real poor people and use paintings of them or poems about them as a surrogate instead. Paintings and poems don't argue back, and have the added advantage that you can be overcome with pity without being overcome by the stench of sweat.

The Romantic movement produced one standout philosopher although, true to Romanticism, he occasionally deliberately dispensed with rationality. That man was Jean-Jacques Rousseau (1712–1778).

Rousseau follows the classic pattern of reasoning that I outlined earlier: define human nature, and from this understanding devise moral and political rules for that nature. Rousseau is concerned with the nature of man in his original primitive state. He argues that man is naturally good, and he is concerned with the process by which this natural state became corrupted. Rousseau does not say that man is naturally moral, but that we can speculate as to what man would be like before he had true morality (i.e. self-restraint) and political structures. Rousseau's concept of original man is often summarised as the "noble savage", which is a mistake largely arising from the French word "sauvage", which actually means "wild" as in the sense of "wild horses".

Rousseau's *Discourse on the Origin of Inequality*[120] describes the transformation of humans from primitive to civilised. "Its paradoxical vision of human existence: that what makes us civilised is what makes us miserable, is simultaneously outrageous and obviously right."[121]

Rousseau uses a form of hypothetical reasoning to explore the distinction between "primitive man" and "civilised man". The overarching theme here is the transformation of men from simple beings driven by their instincts to socialised beings driven by their emotions. Innocence lost is irreversible, but Rousseau is certain that primitive man was innocent. This view is an attack on Hobbes, who argued that men need government because otherwise they would perpetually be at war with one another.

The ideological battle between Rousseau and Hobbes – whether primitive man was noble or savage was one of the great intellectual battles of the Age of Enlightenment, and remains one of the foundation assumptions of different visions of human nature. In fact, recent anthropology has demonstrated that most tribes with limited contact with the developed world tend to slaughter each other in wars and feuds with shocking frequency and brutality. Sadly, this supports Hobbes, though evolutionary theory also demonstrates that the moral emotions have evolutionary origins, thereby lending support to Rousseau. This argument is difficult to bring to a close because the idea of the "noble savage" is embedded in many religions (for example, the book of Genesis up to the biting of the apple) and religious beliefs are unlikely to be overturned by science. Belief trumps fact, as I will explore in Part II.

Rousseau's reasoning starts by asking what man would be like if left in his purely natural state. He describes the concept of "original liberty": primitive man lived instinctively and only sought to satisfy his immediate needs of food, water and shelter. As such, he was solitary and peaceful.

Rousseau conceives of the sentiments[122] of primitive humans as consisting of two: *amour de soi* and *pitié*. *Amour de soi* is self-love, but not in a selfish sense; it is the awareness of what gives rise to wellbeing, but only so far as is required for survival. Primitive man, whose behaviour is determined by instinct, is not capable of either altruism or egoism because he is "pre-moral".[123] This is not in conflict with sociobiology and evolutionary theory. Rousseau is making the point that primitive man would act altruistically without having a concept of his actions being altruistic: the distinction between instinctive altruism and the moral altruism of intent is concordant with the science. *Pitié* as conceived by Rousseau is not pity in the modern sense, but the recognition that any fellow-being that behaves like us must have comparable sentiments; a compassion and, perhaps, the recognition of another's *amour de soi*.

> It is this compassion that hurries us without reflection to the relief of those who are in distress: it is this which in a state of nature supplies the place of laws, morals, and virtues, with the advantage that none are tempted to disobey its gentle voice: it is this which will always prevent a sturdy savage from robbing a weak child or a feeble old man of the sustenance they may have with pain and difficulty acquired.[124]

Rousseau was one of the earliest philosophers to realise that language is critical to the ability of humans to engage in conceptual thought and reasoning. He says, "general ideas cannot be introduced into the mind without the assistance of words."[125] Early humans without language could not foresee the future, and therefore did not have the fear of death that becomes such a burden for civilised humans. When such an early human came under immediate threat, they would suffer fear, but would have no such fears in the absence of immediate threats. Self-consciousness is a prerequisite of awareness of mortality, and this is conceptual and dependent upon language. [Rousseau is in agreement here with my distinction made earlier between fear as a pre-language emotion; and anxiety as a post-language emotion.]

Language gives the power of reasoning; this enables humans to break down the concept of *amour de soi* into its cause and effect, which permits us to create strategies to achieve its fulfilment.

It is by the activity of the passions that our reason is improved; for we desire knowledge only because we wish to enjoy; and it is impossible to conceive any reason why a person who has neither fears nor desires should give himself the trouble of reasoning. The passions, again, originate in our wants, and their progress depends on that of our knowledge; for we cannot desire or fear anything, except for the idea we have of it, or from the simple impulse of nature.[126]

Rousseau sees agriculture as the origin of our loss of innocence. He prefaces Adam Smith (often credited as the founder of modern Capitalism) when he says "what man among them would be so absurd as to take the trouble of cultivating a field, which might be stripped of its crop by the first comer, man or beast."[127] But he goes on to conflict with Smith:

The first man who, having enclosed a piece of ground bethought himself of saying 'This is mine', and found people simple enough to believe him, was the real founder of civil society. From how many crimes, wars, and murders, from how many horrors and misfortunes might not any one have saved mankind, by pulling up the stakes, or filling up the ditch, and crying to his fellows: 'Beware of listening to this impostor; you are undone if you once forget that the fruits of the earth belong to us all, and the earth itself to nobody.' [128]

Language gives rise to reason, which in turn gives rise to self-awareness and therefore self-interest; we see our own interest in contrast to those of others. In this way, *amour de soi* turns into *amour propre* or vanity.

Behold then all human faculties developed, memory and imagination in full play, *amour propre* interested, reason active, and the mind almost at the highest point of its perfection. Behold all the natural qualities in action, the rank and condition of every man assigned him; not merely is share of property and his power to serve or injure others, but also his wit, beauty strength or skill, merit or talents: and these being the only qualities capable of commanding respect, it soon became necessary to possess or to affect them. It now became the interest of men to appear what they really were not. To be and to seem became two totally different things; and from this distinction sprang insolent pomp and cheating trickery, with all the numerous vices that go in their train.[129]

Thus mankind creates the possibility of virtue and therefore the existence of vice. Rousseau demonstrates how reason leads to the perception of self-interest that causes men to employ tactical deception with their behaviour.

The British empiricists may have been the ones that ultimately realised that men were driven by concepts of their emotions, but Rousseau was the earliest thinker to realise that *reason* leads men to manipulate their behaviour. Between them, they created the conception of human nature that is my own starting point: we are driven by our concepts of emotion, but we cannot see our emotions because we are surrounded by corruption of the behaviour that is their only external evidence.

Rousseau presages the theory of *the logic of self-destruction*: reason permits the advancement of civilisation, but this is the origin of man's problems. "All ran headlong to their chains, in hopes of securing their liberty; for they had just wit enough to perceive the advantages of political institutions, without experience enough to enable them to foresee the dangers."[130] In a civilised society, "the arts, literature and the sciences . . . fling garlands of flowers over the chains which weigh them down. They stifle in men's breasts that sense of original liberty, for which they seem to have been born; cause them to love their own slavery, and so make of them what is called a civilised people."[131]

In this chapter, I have sought to describe how our perception of emotion has changed. I have written almost exclusively of philosophy; however, I have not been *philosophising*. My argument is that animals are driven by instinct, which includes emotions in an un-corrupted state; whereas humans are driven by emotional objectives that depend upon concepts of emotion. What I have been trying to find is how this transformation took place. Science cannot answer this question because we have no way of observing historical behaviour, and fossil evidence isn't much help.

I have been using philosophical writings as a sort of historical record of awareness, tracing the development of a human driven solely by the aim of achieving emotional outcomes. However, I have to admit to a chicken-and-egg problem here. The scientist has the problem of being unable to observe historical behaviour; I have the problem of being unable to know which came first – the fact or the perception. Is it that humans have always been driven by emotional objectives, but that Hume and Rousseau were the first to notice this? If this hypothesis is true, then why was Aristotle incapable of noticing it, and why don't animals function the same way? If, as I have argued earlier, the emotion of happiness did not exist in ancient times, then how could ancient people's behaviour be driven by the aim to achieve it? This counter-hypothesis simply makes no sense.

There is perhaps a middle hypothesis: perhaps the concept and therefore the actual emotion of happiness arose sometime after Aristotle. The transformation of the driver of behaviour from instinct to conceptualised emotional objectives occurred during this period, but long before Hume and Rousseau noticed it. I think it is also difficult to argue this middle hypothesis on a practical level because shortly after Aristotle, the Western World was smothered by the rise of Christian orthodoxy and entered the "Dark Ages". Either way, these hypotheses leave completely unanswered the question of how this transformation actually occurred and what caused it.

My belief is that, in the same way that awareness of emotion was dependent upon language in the first instance, this transformation was caused by philosophy. It evolved as a feedback loop between the analysis of philosophers, and how their ideas affected the way that people saw themselves: the evolving concept of what it is to be human. Few people actually read philosophy, and yet the ideas of philosophers somehow seep out into culture. This process is not visible to the casual observer, but Locke has had a permanent influence on America because his theory influenced the US constitution. Rousseau had a permanent influence on France because his ideas were an inspiration for the French revolution. Today, much of the cultural difference between America and France can be traced to the differences between Locke and Rousseau; although that would be to over-simplify. For example, Locke also had an influence in France; mainly through the efforts of Voltaire, who detested Rousseau.[132]

Additionally, the ideas of philosophers can also have dark and unintended consequences. Bertrand Russell noted, for example, that, "Hitler is an outcome of Rousseau; Roosevelt and Churchill, of Locke."[133] If this statement is alarming, then there is a further consequence of this chapter that is more alarming still: if Western philosophers assumed that the point of life is the achievement of some form of higher state, and that the collective conclusion appears to be that this higher state is a positive emotional state; then is it not also possible that the existence of positive emotional states has actually been an invention of Western philosophy? If this is the case, then much of Western philosophy is founded upon a giant circular argument. Perhaps this is the reason that no philosopher in history has ever produced a system of thought that is simultaneously comprehensive, comprehensible, internally consistent and remotely plausible. The problem with Western philosophy possibly being based on misconceptions is that political ideology all derives from it.

In the next chapter, I will address the concept of the unconscious mind. I need to do this because it was once used as an explanation for all human actions that are self-destructive. As will become apparent, this is a detour from the path, but a worthwhile one since it leads to other ideas that are central to my argument.

THE MYTH OF THE GHOST IN A COMA

A couple of centuries ago, a bunch of Ghost in the Machine dogmatists got together and decided to put their ghosts to practical use. They reasoned that the world they lived in was divided into the physical world and the mental world. These two worlds were fundamentally different, and Isaac Newton had tied up the physical world with a set of tidy natural laws: a Theory of Everything. What was needed was a science that would tie up the mental world. That science became known as psychology. We now recognise that Newton's laws weren't quite the tidy tie-up that we thought they were, and psychologists today are generally not Ghost in the Machine dogmatists. The sciences arising from the dogma of the Ghost in the Machine produced one outstanding figure: Sigmund Freud. He is best known for his theories on the unconscious mind.

Throughout much of the twentieth century, there was a tradition of philosophical scepticism regarding psychology. Gilbert Ryle said he didn't understand psychology's programme[134]; Wittgenstein questioned how exactly psychologists could create any theory when the critical data they wanted to study (mental phenomena) was invisible to them. However, Freud had the aura of a juggernaut of genius and even Ryle and Wittgenstein shied from criticising him for fear of being run over. Wittgenstein is known to have questioned the scientific nature of Freud's theories, although never in print. In private conversations, Wittgenstein challenged Freud's idea that anxiety springs from memories of the trauma of birth. He says that such a hypothesis has the appeal of myth in that it is the outcome of something that happened a long time ago.[135] Wittgenstein doubted whether it was possible to design an experiment that would actually establish this as a scientific fact. "Freud is constantly claiming to be scientific. But what he gives is *speculation* – something prior even to the formation of a hypothesis."[136]

Within philosophy, Karl Popper has been about the only fierce critic of Freud willing to commit his opinions to print.[137] Popper claimed that Freud's theories are not scientific because they are not refutable. In the words of Popper: "As for Freud's epic of the Ego, the Super-ego, and the Id, no substantially stronger claim to scientific status can be made for it than for Homer's collective stories from Olympus. These theories describe some facts, but in the manner of myths. They contain most interesting psychological suggestions, but not in a testable form."[138] Popper, like Wittgenstein, uses the myth analogy.

In my opinion, Freud has a more serious problem, and that is the notion that the unconscious mind can generate acts that are "irrational". If we can explain causally why someone acted in such-and-such a way, then by definition the behaviour is rational. This means the class of all "irrational acts" is the same as the class of all actions that we cannot explain causally. Therefore, there is no explanatory content in saying that someone did something "because they were irrational". "Irrationality" is not an explanation of anything, because it is a non-explanation of everything, and this is a misrepresentation. Is it any surprise that such theories are non-testable? I could say "This morning an irrational force made me get out of bed, and then for some irrational reason I ate my breakfast, and finally something deep in my unconscious mind made me floss my teeth." This is complete hokum, but fully compliant with Freudian thinking. It is a non-explanation comparable to creationism – a theory where everything can be non-explained. If someone tried to argue that it was my *conscious* mind that made me floss my teeth, exactly how would they prove it?

Freud, like everyone else, had little idea what the conscious mind was. He was working before Gilbert Ryle busted the myth of the Ghost in the Machine. However, since Ryle, surely any Freudian should have noticed that the conceptual problems of the conscious mind become more severe when we consider a mind that is unconscious. Freud was suffering from a solipsistic bias: because he could see his conscious mind through introspection, he thought it novel that part of the mind was unconscious. But the correct way to look at it is the other way around: what is extraordinary is that part of the brain is conscious. Unconsciousness is what we should expect of it.

Today, scientists have rejected Freud's notion of the Ego, the Super-ego, and the Id. They have also dumped some of his other more outlandish notions, such as his idea of the "Death Instinct". However, many of them still seem to be stuck in the "Unconscious-Mind-Causes-Irrational-Acts" groove. This is utter twaddle.

Freud's notion that primitive irrational forces drive us is clearly diametrically opposed to my own view. I argue that humans are completely rational, but that in pursuing their aim of achieving emotional goals, they rationally self-destruct as a result of corrupt concepts of emotion derived from manipulated behaviour. If the "irrational" has no place in my theory; does this mean that the "unconscious mind" also has no place? It isn't sufficient for me to dismiss Freud's theories solely because they depend upon a myth about the mind, because Freud's theories involved other observations.

Freud saw the unconscious mind as a store of socially unacceptable ideas, of traumatic memories and painful emotions. The repressed thoughts were forced out of the conscious mind by "psychological repression". Neither Freud nor anybody else described this process in simple causal steps. So nobody ever really knew what psychological repression really was. Freud thought that the repressed thoughts and emotions could surface at certain moments as a force to drive irrational acts. At which moments do they surface? What is the causality?

So, without answering the Hard Problem of consciousness, what is the unconscious mind of an entirely rational person? The answer is that the unconscious mind is not a place in a person's brain, but a void in their ability to form concepts of emotion.

Let us assume that F is the set of all emotional feeling qualia for a hypothetical individual person: let's call him Sigmund. I could represent this as follows:

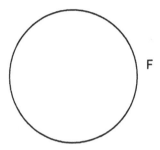

Now let us assume that C is the set of all emotions of which Sigmund has a concept. By this, I mean that he has a belief as to the circumstances that cause the feeling and what behaviour relates to it. I could represent this as follows:

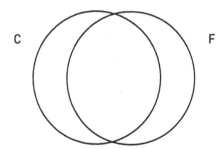

So, what do the three areas represent?

Clearly, normal emotional conception lies in the central area. With idealised normal emotional conception, we experience an emotional quale, and the people in our world experience the same or a similar emotional quale, and nobody fakes or suppresses the behaviour associated with this, so everybody's experience of this emotional state is represented identically to the outside world through behaviour. It is therefore possible for Sigmund to be able to identify and name the emotional quale underlying the emotion, in himself and in others. He will also be able to study the occurrence of the emotional state in himself and others and learn the circumstances that cause this emotional state. He will therefore have a complete (and correct) concept of this particular emotional state: the circumstances that cause it, the internal experience of the feeling, and the behavioural evidence that accompanies the experience of the emotion in himself and other people. He will also likely have a word for it, which will always be correctly applied.

The area on the left is perhaps the area that is conceptually most difficult to understand. I aim to demonstrate that humans can invent their own emotions, and I call these "virtual emotions". I will examine this in the next chapter. For now, I will just say that this area represents concepts of emotion where no feeling is present *ever*, i.e. concepts of emotion that are pure belief.

That leaves the area on the right. For Sigmund, this is the class of all feelings where he has no causal concept of the emotion. This would occur whenever the behaviour is absent. He cannot have an awareness of the feeling in other people, or of what causes the feeling. This is the unconscious mind that Freud and all his followers have misrepresented. Freud is correct that in this space are unacceptable and painful emotions. But "psychological repression" explains nothing without a definition. The feelings for which Sigmund has no concept are in the right-hand section (namely his unconscious mind) because of suppression *of the behaviour* that they would normally cause. When an emotion is unacceptable or painful, is it not entirely to be expected that he (and other people) would suppress the behaviour associated with it?

Examples of this are the abused woman in Scenario A and the angry man of Scenario B. A Freudian might say that the abused woman acted irrationally because of some force from her unconscious mind. This is not the case; she made an error in identifying a feeling because behavioural suppression meant that she could not complete the concept of the emotion to which it related. A Freudian might say that the man had unconscious anger. Actually, this choice of words makes sense, but it is unconscious because he suppresses the behaviour and therefore has no basis for identifying his own emotion. Unconscious anger is not a thought; there is no such thing as an "unconscious thought"; rather, logically incompatible terms are being married together here without explanation. A thought is something in our phenomenal mind, and there is no sense in saying a thought could meaningfully be anywhere else. Unconscious anger is an absence of concept arising from the absence of the behaviour that permits us to complete the concept.

Freud thought that the unconscious mind also contained "suppressed memories". Consider the following: imagine a man has a traumatic experience that is completely beyond his prior experience; say a shell-burst in a trench, or some other near-death experience. Such an experience would trigger a feeling that he has never experienced before; something completely overwhelming. His behavioural reaction to this would almost certainly be something that he has never seen before in another human being. His situation is exactly the same as the abused woman in Scenario A. For the abused woman in Scenario A, there is no difference between her being unable to recognise her feeling because everyone in her world suppresses the behaviour, and her being unable to recognise her feeling because nobody in her world ever experienced it. Severe traumatic experience therefore can have parallel characteristics to emotions that reside in the unconscious mind because the behaviour has been suppressed. The inability to recognise the feeling arises through absence of behaviour with which to identify it. The man who experiences the shell-burst has never seen the relationship between the cause of the feeling and its expression in behavioural form in another person. He has an absence of concept.

When biologists discover a weird appendage on a fish, they ask two questions: firstly, what does the weird appendage do; and secondly, how does it boost the chances of survival of the fish? If the biologists can answer these two questions, then they can explain the purpose of the weird appendage in terms of evolution by natural selection. The unconscious mind as conceived by Freud is a weird appendage on a human, and we have to ask the same two questions. Freud thought he had answered the first question. [I disagree!] But nobody asked the second question. We cannot argue that the unconscious mind improves the chances of survival of humans. In fact, it is connected with our tendency to self-destruct. I suspect that Freud would agree with this. How then, does a Freudian justify the existence of the unconscious mind as they construe it?

The unconscious mind did not evolve because it boosted our survival chances; so it must exist for another reason. It is a product of suppressed behaviour – a non-evolutionary explanation. Since we live in a world where words exist for many of these feelings, despite the behaviour having been removed from our perception of it, we have language without concept. When we experience any feeling in this space, any hypothesis as to what caused the feeling is irrefutable because we lack the conceptual framework that would permit refutation. This is not irrational.

What about cognitive neuroscience? Well, it doesn't really account for the phenomenal mind, so is hardly likely to fair better with a bit of the phenomenal mind that is even stranger. Virtually everything that cognitive neuroscientists know about the functioning of the brain was discovered by looking at unfortunate people who have had parts of their brains destroyed. Neuroscientists then study what normal functions such people have lost and draw their conclusions about which parts of the brain do what function. This process cannot teach us anything about the unconscious mind.

"Oh gosh, Professor Smythers! The patient has become completely rational. The shrapnel must have completely destroyed his unconscious mind."

"Egad, Doctor Jenkins! I believe you have concluded correctly. We will have to normalise him with misinformation therapy."

"By Jove, I think you are right, but it's risky. Misinformation *therapy has only ever been tried on people who are partially rational."*

Does this mean that I am replacing Freud's theory of the unconscious mind with my own theory? No! I don't have a theory of the unconscious mind; but I am not disputing that the concept has meaning. The difference between Freud's theory and my non-theory is that Freud saw the unconscious mind as a cause, and I see it as an effect. For Freud, self-destructive actions are *caused* by the unconscious mind. For me, the unconscious mind is the *effect* of being unable to perceive the causes of feelings because there is no visible behaviour with which to identify them. Since I see the unconscious mind as an effect, it has little more than a walk-on part in this book. The unconscious mind is not a thing; it is a non-thing – a collection of missing concepts of emotion. It has no physical form, only a logical form.

Freud's conception of the unconscious mind is identical to the concept of the soul redefined with pseudo-scientific jargon. We were almost rid of the idea of the soul, and Freud took us right back to Square One.

THE INVENTION OF EMOTION

In the previous chapter, I looked at the unconscious mind. Now I want to explore the parallel to this: the concept of virtual emotion. I have raised the possibility that we could have a concept of emotion where there was no feeling attached – represented by the left hand section of this diagram:

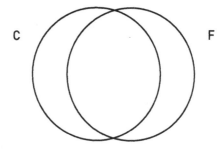

We need to describe the mechanism whereby this can occur. Where the behaviour relating to an *actual* emotional state is systematically affected, it gives rise to a belief in an emotion. But if this affectation of behaviour relates to actual emotional states, this concept would reside in the central area. Virtual emotion is something beyond this: the affectation of behaviour that is invented or which relates to something other than an emotion gives rise to a belief in an emotion for which there is no associated feeling at all. This belief is in an emotion that is pure invention.[139]

The systematic affectation of the behaviour associated with an emotion blurs the determination of what causes the emotion (see for example Scenarios C or D). It makes us unable to distinguish between the true emotion – that is, one where a true feeling is involved – and one that is merely a belief in an emotion. Virtual emotion is a hypothetical extrapolation: something that a mathematician should have no problem understanding, but something that is problematic in science except as a way of generating hypotheses. Is this possible in a real human context? Albert Einstein said "The concept does not exist for the physicist until he has the possibility of discovering whether or not it is fulfilled in an actual case."[140] I have explored how some emotions (e.g. happiness) did not exist at one time, but seem to exist now. We have a specific example of an emotion that does not seem to have come into existence through evolution by natural selection. Is happiness an actual case of an invented emotion? Might there be others?

More examples of virtual emotion will arise in Part II. [Wow, it's tough to build suspense in a philosophy book!] But let us look at mystical religion. Mystics are a diverse bunch, but once you strip off the veneer they are all essentially saying the same thing: that by following specific rituals and practices you can achieve a "Higher State of Being". What is this Higher State of Being, and how do the rituals and practices cause this state? I speculate that the Higher State of Being is an invented emotional state, and this arises because the rituals have the appearance of emotional behaviour, and eventually their habitual repetition creates a belief in an emotion (along the lines of Scenario D), except that this belief does not relate to any innate emotional state. We cannot be sure of this because there is no solid metric to distinguish between innate human behaviour and invented human behaviour, but behaviour that only relates to people from strange religious minorities does not seem likely to be innate. All of this is *not* to say that someone that practices a mystical religion is not *experiencing* something that is real. An experience of an invented emotion is a real experience, but (as I will explain in Part II) I am sceptical that benefits accrue, either to the individual or to society as a whole.

Another possible area for us to explore is the field of aesthetics: what does it mean to be beautiful? If I say that I like something, then I am expressing a personal opinion; however, if I say it is beautiful then I am ascribing a property to the thing described. I am implying that others should see it the same way. What is this property? There are numerous theories about aesthetics; none of them, in my opinion, particularly convincing.

Evolutionary psychology has much to say about aesthetics. For example, men find women beautiful when they have shiny hair and bright eyes because this is evidence that they have never had serious disease and therefore have a strong gene set. Men like women with a particular waist-to-hip ratio because this makes them better child bearers. Also, we are more likely to buy cookies in red packaging than blue packaging, because colour vision likely evolved in our tree-dwelling ancestors to assist them in selecting fruit that was ripe and non-poisonous. Red is the most common colour for ripe fruit, and blue is quite rare. Police cars have blue lights and not red as a form of warning that works because of our evolutionary make-up [otherwise bank robbers would want to lick them]. But what implications does any of this have for abstract art?

I think that aesthetics may be an example of virtual emotion in action.

Imagine that you are teaching a child the words for colours. All you have to do is point at blue and say "blue", and then you point at red and say "red", and the child picks it up with astonishing speed. Now imagine you are trying to teach a child the words 'beautiful' and 'ugly'. You cannot simply point and say the word because the child would not understand the intended meaning of the words, so we point, and say the word along with some form of pretended emotional behaviour: we open our eyes wide and uplift our voice when we say "beyoootiful", and then we frown and scowl when we say "urrrgly". We can speculate about how a child's aesthetic judgement could be completely messed up by our doing this with the pretended emotional behaviour inverted. Actually, we can consider this in real life by looking at the aesthetic judgement of the children of abstract and conceptual artists. So how does behaviour impact upon the aesthetic judgement of adults?

A couple of years ago, I visited a jazz club in New York City. It must have been unknown to the city health inspectors because it existed in a completely inappropriate space with too low a ceiling and almost no ventilation. As the waitress brought my beer, I surveyed the rest of the audience. Mostly, they were older men who sported freestyle facial hair and inorganic knitwear. This was the all-too-obvious clue. Unfortunately, I missed it. The music sounded like a donkey being put through a paper shredder. I had visions of New York City's famously resilient rats scurrying in panic to a soundproof sewer. Had this music started to play on my radio, I would have hit the station tuning button with the speed of a cobra strike. But I was in a crowded room (and I hadn't finished my beer); bearded cheeks twitched in concentration; breasts sighed in brown acrylic. Not only did I stay to the end of the first piece; I actually made it to the end of the set. When I stepped outside into the night, I was really quite at peace.

How can it be that music that is painful to listen to alone is enjoyable when listened to with aficionados? Is it that their behaviour is a glorified collective example of Scenario D? And if they are collectively adopting the behaviour associated with an emotional state, what is the feeling associated with that emotion? I have music that I enjoy when I am alone, but trying to single out the feeling that I experience while listening to it is very difficult. I am actually not sure there is one. When I listen to music alone, I don't have any behaviour. So is the behaviour of the jazz aficionados something that they only do when they are all meet for their tribal gathering?

Sometimes, I have a feeling when I listen to the National Anthem of certain nations, but is this due to the music or the words? Perhaps we should call them "Nationalistic" Anthems, since their purpose is to stoke nationalistic sentiment, but sometimes I have the feeling when I listen to the Nationalistic Anthem of a nation other than my own and, anyway, I'm not patriotic. Alternatively, is it due to the behaviour of the other people listening? I'm not sure they affect me when I am alone. [But why on earth would I listen to them alone?] When the National Anthem is sung with a sob between every note, as is fashionable in one particular nation that springs to mind, my only visible behaviour is a dry-retch. But then again, we are all required to stand up, which I suppose is a form of behaviour, though not one that would normally be associated with an emotion. When the National Anthem is played, we all put our right hand on our left breast and go all misty-eyed. Do we do this spontaneously, or because we think we have to? At what point does thinking we have to do this morph into us believing that it is spontaneous? If you are sure it is spontaneous, consider this interesting comparison: when Josef Stalin finished one of his interminably long and boring speeches, the standing ovation would last for up to an hour. There is nobody left that still thinks that Stalin was a mensch, so we all tend to assume this was because no good Soviet comrade wanted to be seen to be the first to stop clapping. But it is possible that, at the time, they did think that the old boy's speeches were really that great.

Now, I am not going to deny that listening to music or looking at art sometimes causes a real feeling in me. Curiously, if I look at performances of dance, I am much more likely to experience a genuine feeling than if I listen to music. But I think of myself as enjoying music more than dance; so what is the feeling that I experience when I see dance? Perhaps an explanation is that dance is much more directly representative of the behaviour that non-dancing people display when they experience emotions, and that music is more abstract.

I am also not going to deny that listening to music or looking at art might cause a genuine feeling in other people. In 1896, the young Wassily Kandinsky noticed that the music of Wagner could elicit an emotional response without a connection to a recognisable subject, and this led him to believe that painting should be as abstract as music. Now, I admire the paintings of Kandinsky. [Sorry! Can't stand Wagner!] I recognise them as beautiful; I think they produce an emotional response but I cannot be sure that I have ever experienced a feeling as part of this experience. However, I think I can experience a feeling when I listen to music (other than Wagner), but not when I play it in the background while reading. So what occurs when I look at a Kandinsky painting? Is it that I believe that it is *capable* of inducing a feeling, despite the fact that it may never have done so in me? Is this not perhaps a pure belief; a belief in an emotion for which I actually have no evidence of a feeling?

Have you ever had the experience that you are in an art gallery looking at a painting that is just plain weird; when somebody next to you goes into an extravagant wordgasm about the painting? I just love the way that art people talk. I am suspicious that they pretend that they couldn't care less that I haven't got a clue what they are on about; while all along really hoping that I am listening. Otherwise, why would they speak so loudly in hushed galleries?

What I find is that I listen to the art critic's wordgasm; look him or her up and down a couple of times; and then I look back at the painting and think about it again. Hmmm! When I do this, I look at the painting and I look within for a feeling. What if there is no feeling? Never mind! You don't have to let a little detail like that get in the way of believing it.

The interesting thing about the art critic's wordgasm is that the less understandable it is, the more it morphs from being language into behaviour. Here is an example of a critic's wordgasm. For the full effect, read it out loud and only breathe at the end of each sentence:

A pleasure which sometimes goes so deep as to make us suppose we have a direct understanding of the object that causes it; a pleasure which arouses the intelligence, defies it, and makes it love its defeat; still more, a pleasure that can stimulate the strange need to produce or reproduce the thing, event, object, or state to which it seems attached, and which thus becomes a source of activity without any definite end, capable of imposing a discipline, a zeal, a torment on a whole lifetime, and of filling it, sometimes to overflowing – such a pleasure presents a singularly specious enigma, which could scarcely escape the attention or clutches of the metaphysical hydra. What could have been more worthy of our philosopher's will to power than this order of phenomena in which to feel, to possess, to will, and to make seemed to be joined in an essential and highly remarkable interaction that defined his Scholastic, not to say Cartesian, efforts to split up the difficulty. The alliance of a form, a material, an idea an action, and a passion; the absence of any clearly determined aim or of any result that might be expressed in finite terms; a desire and its recompense, each regenerating the other; a desire that creates and hence causes itself; sometimes breaking away from all particular creation and ultimate satisfaction, thus revealing itself to be a desire to create for the sake of creating – all this aroused the metaphysical mind: to this problem it devoted the same attention as to all the other problems it habitually invents in exercising its function of reconstructing knowledge in a universal form.[141]

I hope you are now in full possession of the "knowledge in a universal form" that Paul Valéry is getting at. This little gem of nourishment for the credulous consists of 276 words but only three sentences; that is an average of 92 words per sentence. However, I can translate Valéry's wordgasm into seven words: "We make stuff because we like it. Duh!" [Note: that "Duh!" isn't a word when actually spoken; it is behaviour.] That leaves 269 words of arm-waving and furrowing of the brow. I tried counting the metaphors in his three sentences but my efforts fell into the clutches of the metaphysical hydra.

Restaurant critics describe taste with metaphors. They make comparisons between taste and other sensory experience that have nothing to do with taste, e.g. texture.[142] Well, art critics do the same thing, and a metaphor can make a connection between something that doesn't involve a feeling and something that does. We can create a belief in a feeling where an actual feeling could never occur. For example: "The feeling that I have when I look at this painting evokes the scent of a forest after rainfall." George Orwell's famous essay

Politics and the English Language gives two much simpler examples: "The outstanding feature of Mr. X's work is its living quality", which contrasts with "The immediately striking thing about Mr. X's work is its peculiar deadness."[143] These are simple metaphors, but they don't make a metaphorical connection between something that involves feelings and something that doesn't, such as the Valéry quote above: "a pleasure which ... goes so deep ... and makes it love its defeat", which is a multi-dimensional example of such a metaphor. We constantly use emotional metaphors when talking about art: "The serenity of a landscape"; or "the sombre colours of a portrait". Some of these have become so overused that they have almost lost their emotional overtone. For example, "sombre" in this latter context would often just mean dark and dull. Another example of exhausted emotional metaphor is in music, where the sadness of minor keys and happiness of major keys has become a clichéd emotional connection.

Now I happen to think that the paintings of Willem de Kooning are beautiful; so I am going to propose a hypothetical time-travel journey back to the studio of Michelangelo with a de Kooning painting tucked under my arm. I am absolutely convinced that Michelangelo would vomit on my favourite de Kooning painting. He would tell me it is badly drawn, not lifelike, childish, in all the wrong colours, with no sense of perspective; in fact it is just a thoroughly bad painting. I could argue that I have a more refined artistic sensibility than Michelangelo, but I don't think you are going to buy that. However, if my belief that de Kooning's paintings are beautiful means that I believe that I am capable of responding to them emotionally; and if Michelangelo cannot [present tense correctly used due to the deployment of time travel], then my emotional response must in some way be learned. However, can I learn to feel something, or do I just adopt a belief? To me, the idea of "learning to feel" simply doesn't make sense. If feeling is something you can learn, then surely it must be something you can teach. But how would you teach this? And in any case, I don't know what this emotion feels like; so isn't this an emotion that doesn't have a feeling? Isn't it a belief in an emotion that maybe, just maybe, never had a feeling in the first place? I can see no way of teaching someone to feel, but it is easy to teach them to believe in a feeling: you do it with behaviour – for example, an expression of deep concentration with much sighing; or you do it with metaphor, which for maximum effect will come in the form of a predominately incomprehensible wordgasm. Neither of these forms of behaviour could be said to be derivable from a process of evolution by natural selection. They are post-linguistic; non-instinctive, and therefore not innate.

The transference of aesthetic judgements occurs through behaviour. Don't be fooled by the fact that this behaviour sometimes looks suspiciously like language. It isn't language because there is no way to describe aesthetic judgement, and so the words used in the attempt collectively have no meaning.[144] The ability to transfer aesthetic judgement is what makes that judgement collective. And that is what makes beauty appear to be an absolute.

You can test this theory by putting it into reverse. About thirty years ago, Pierre-Auguste Renoir was considered to be one of the greatest of impressionist painters. But as far as I can tell, most contemporary art critics secretly think Renoir is bourgeois suburban schlock.[145] If you go up to an eminent art critic and say "Aww, y'know, I jus luv Renoir. I fink he like totally rocks! Y'know wot I mean?" And he will drawl "Yeeeesss!" with a small flicker of his upper lip, and a twitch skywards of his left eyebrow. It is the same reaction that I would have if someone told me that they thought Hitler was a real sweet guy, and I just realised that the argument would be a waste of breath. Sometimes, it simply isn't worth it.

So then, if aesthetic judgement is transferred through behaviour, can I be certain that a virtual emotion is involved? Well, I have argued that when the behaviour associated with an emotion is faked, it makes it difficult to distinguish between an emotion and a belief in an emotion; so if I tell you that I know whether art produces a true emotion (i.e. one where a feeling is involved) or a belief in an emotion then I am contradicting myself. I am not going to rationally self-destruct in so simple a fashion. Beliefs in emotion are created through behaviour [Scenario D] and maybe also through metaphor. But there is another possibility: it could be that the true emotion is there, but that I systematically suppress the behaviour because bursting into tears in art galleries is embarrassing, and moaning with pleasure at chamber music concerts is strongly discouraged. I therefore lose the ability to know whether the true feeling is there or not. Or when a feeling is there, I lose the ability to know what caused it [Scenario B].

Not only do I not know the answer, but I actually think the answer is unknowable. It will remain unknowable until the Hard Problem is solved and science can tell me when I have feelings that I am denying to myself. At that point, neuroscientists will be able to distinguish between good art and bad art by tracing the feeling back to the sensation (aural or visual) that caused it. I actually rather hope that this doesn't occur, but perhaps I am being a Luddite.

There is, however, one clue that the truth might be that I conceal the feeling by behavioural suppression, and that is what happens when the element of surprise comes in. We don't expect to be lectured on the joys of seventeenth-century English composers by people better known for smashing up electric guitars on stage; so when, in a BBC radio interview, Pete Townsend of The Who explained how Henry Purcell was his earliest musical influence, I simply didn't see it coming. The first sound clip of Purcell used in the program was probably no more than five seconds long, but I immediately broke down. Did this occur because, not being ready for it, I forgot to suppress the behaviour associated with the emotional feeling; or was it the poignancy of recalling performing Purcell as a choral scholar in my childhood? One other example: nothing that I have said in this chapter applies to Elgar's cello concerto. But is this because of the music? I remember as a cellist in my childhood seeing Jacqueline du Pré performing this live, and I recall her tragic decline as she succumbed to multiple sclerosis. I always have the problem of knowing whether my response is a response to the music or to something I associate with the music. How could I possibly know?

*

So, can we be sure that happiness is a virtual emotion?

Well, hopefully I have persuaded you that happiness has not always been an emotion, and therefore it was at some time acquired by humanity (rather like our appreciation of Willem de Kooning). What was the process of acquisition? Is this an invented emotion or a learned emotion, and if so is there a feeling attached? Tricky one!

We can think of happiness as a hypothetical concept of human worth that is represented behaviourally, and where that behaviour can be affected. However, we can find hypothetical concepts of human worth from other eras or cultures that work exactly the same way: for example, "nobility" or "honour". Once you realise that there is no theoretical limit on the number of such hypothetical concepts, you should be able to think about them purely in the abstract. However, you likely face the difficulty that you are mesmerised by the concept of happiness and think each of the other two a risible farce. But consider that people were mesmerised by the concept of nobility in the eighteenth century, and they are mesmerised by the concept of honour in certain parts of Southern Europe and the Middle East. So, do we need to care about any difference?

When we talk of love, most people understand the distinction between 'loving' and 'being in love'. I think that this distinction can be explained as follows: 'loving' is a belief state, and 'being in love' is a feeling state. Why does this verbal distinction not exist for happiness? Why can't we speak of 'happiness' and 'being in happiness' to make the distinction between belief and feeling? I rather doubt that any piece of language could be missing without reason. However, we do have one verbal distinction connected to happiness: we make the distinction between being 'happy' and being 'overjoyed'. Overjoyed seems to be a feeling state. [But would you just listen to that word! It implies too much of something – like 'oversexed'. The structure of the word seems to imply that it is undesirable or derogatory.] Does the fact that we make the verbal distinction between 'overjoyed' (which is a feeling state) and 'happiness' imply that happiness is a belief state? It seems to me that it is possible that we could be happy without ever being overjoyed, and this would imply that happiness could be purely a belief state. Is it merely an aesthetic, rather than an emotion?

There is behaviour associated with happiness: a smile. But, wait a minute! Haven't I argued that originally that was the behaviour associated with a form of bonding or greeting (like the tail wagging of dogs)? Now to create a virtual emotion, we need to invent a form of behaviour that looks like it is the behaviour caused by a feeling. Is it just possible that most of humanity has made a rather foolish error?

"This is Captain James T. Kirk calling all crew! We absolutely must find the feeling, so that we can save human existence from complete and utter pointlessness."

Everything we do is driven by the desire to be happy, and if we can't find the feeling then the emotion is a feelingless belief. We are driven by the desire to achieve a feeling, but maybe the feeling doesn't exist and we are really driven by the desire to achieve a belief. This is a belief that we will achieve a belief. We are trying to lift ourselves up by our bootstraps. If human purpose is merely an aesthetic ideal, then suddenly we all need art critics to tell us that human existence is worth the bother.

At one point, I thought that I was going to be able to demonstrate that there was a point to human life.

Oh well! I guess that isn't going to happen.

Pity, really!

EMOTIONAL WHITE NOISE

> The invention of deliberately simplified theories is one of the
> major techniques of science, particularly the 'exact' sciences,
> which make extensive use of mathematical analysis. If a
> biophysicist can usefully employ simplified models of the cell
> and the cosmologist simplified models of the universe then
> we can reasonably expect that simplified games may prove to
> be useful models for more complicated conflicts.
> (John Williams, The Compleat strategyst)[146]

I have written each of the four core Scenarios like a short story to
provide a lever for your imagination because I am trying to induce
in you a concept of non-understanding, and we all have problems
imagining *not* knowing what we *do* know. They are a deliberate
oversimplification. I have constructed hypothetical worlds in which
only one emotional state exists. This has enabled me to examine the
consequences of the tactical affecting or suppressing of behaviour
associated with that emotion to determine how the subject's ability
to understand a single emotion is affected. I have therefore broken
down the causality of human actions to an atomic level. It is not
possible to do this scientifically because when working with normal
people (as opposed to hypothetical ones) it is impossible to filter out
the emotional and behavioural white noise in a controlled experimental environment.

The Scenarios not only describe a hypothetical world where only one emotion exists, they also describe a situation where that behaviour is being consistently manipulated. In the real world, it is rare for behavioural manipulation to be absolutely consistent, but common for it to have a strong correlation one way or another. For example, if you lived in a world where *everybody* drank caipirinha and danced the samba, from your perspective it would be *certain* that this caused human wellbeing. But if you lived in a world where *most* people did this then you would consider it merely *highly probable* that this caused human wellbeing. The shift from the binary to the probabilistic does not stop humanity being a maths problem. A woman in Buenos Aires told me that she thought tango was a cliché, and all my preconceptions of Argentinians burst into flames. However, this does not stop there being a genuine thing called Argentinian culture, where *most* people think that human wellbeing is *probably* caused by eating steak, dancing tango and commuting to the office on horseback. We are simply shifting from binary to probabilistic.

However, in real life we also have to consider that real people don't have just one emotion; they have several, or more realistically a spectrum where the boundaries between one emotion and another aren't clear. And then we have the problem that sometimes we suppress or affect the behaviour of one emotion in one particular circumstance, but not another. Still, this does not stop it being a maths problem, but we have moved from the binary to a huge multi-dimensional computational challenge. In real life, the emotional and behavioural white noise reasserts itself. The result is that each of us is stumbling through a maze where various people in our world (including ourselves) are constantly affecting and suppressing the behaviour associated with multiple different emotions, including the shades of grey. Sometimes we do this on a one-off basis, generally as part of a tactical deception; and sometimes we do it systematically once that deception becomes a habit. Each of us is trying to solve a multi-dimensional problem, and even the smartest of us struggle with this. This is what makes humans so diverse and so complex. It is also why, for most of us, determining what brings us contentment is a never-ending project.

I want to close this part of the book dealing with individuals with a final Scenario that illustrates the multi-dimensional nature of behaviour manipulation. What happens when we do a mashup of the four Scenarios and make all four modes of behaviour manipulation occur together?

SCENARIO: BEAUTIFUL PERSON DISEASE

As she entered the room, everyone was aware of her arrival. Men looked furtively, and then pretended they hadn't noticed. Women were made uneasy.

She stepped confidently forward, and then she saw the Not-So-Secret Admirer. It wasn't that she didn't like him; she did. But he was unable to conceal his adoration, and this made him someone she could never regard as an equal. His innocence was charming and a comfort to her, but this could be looked at another way: his naivety was an annoyance. It created a barrier between them that made a romance inconceivable.

She assumed that he was infatuated with her because of her beauty. In fact, this was not the case. What had prompted his belief that he loved her truly was that he alone had perceived her loneliness. This thought was irrefutable to him, since her efforts to suppress her loneliness meant that she portrayed it uniquely, and his feeling of sympathy that he thought was love was a feeling he didn't experience with any other person. His belief that this feeling was love was an assumption that lacked a means of refutation. She held her head high, and talked animatedly to everyone as she passed, but the Not-So-Secret Admirer knew this was a façade. He had glimpsed her in her off-moments; when she was tired, or when she had been upset, and he had seen the look that lay beneath. He knew that she was lost. His feelings towards her were not driven by lust or the desire to possess her as a trophy. He yearned to nurture her, to comfort her so that she might never be lonely again. What made her unable to consider the Not-So-Secret Admirer as an equal also applied to other men. In her world were many who would have loved to treat her with kindness.

The Not-So-Secret Admirer moved to speak to her, but she moved distractedly aside. She had cultivated a flighty absent-minded manner. It was a technique she had learned that allowed her to brush off men without ever being offensive to them. In fact, the effect was often the reverse: many men, particularly older men, were charmed by the casual way she dismissed them. She did this with a smile, as if to say that that she acknowledged their approach, but was oblivious to its motivation. She thought that her obliviousness was pretence but, as will become clear, she had an obliviousness that was real.

She engaged in casual conversations with people in passing, drifting from one acquaintance to another. Everyone acted like they were in a perpetual state of calm rapture. In this world there were no friends; only exploiters. But the pretence of mutual admiration created a denial of this and built a myth of bonding among competitors. And then she caught sight of the Cool One. She was looking at him when he turned towards her, but unlike the others he didn't react. He made eye contact, but his face revealed no emotion, and then he turned away. She was intrigued.

The contrast between the Not-So-Secret Admirer and the Cool One couldn't be greater. The Not-So-Secret Admirer's inability to conceal his feelings excluded him as a romantic partner, but the Cool One betrayed no sign of what he felt. To her, it was almost an affront. She had become so accustomed to the impact she had on men that the absence of it left her feeling strangely powerless. She didn't know what to do; and this was where her obliviousness was real.

She had, without realising it, always chosen lovers who concealed their feelings. Such were the only men she could consider her equal. Men who did not conceal their feelings betrayed the fact that they were overwhelmed by her beauty, and she was unable to deny the power that she had over them. Only men who concealed their feelings could she consider equal. But since all her lovers concealed their feelings, she had no idea what those feelings really were. This was the root of her obliviousness. It was also the cause of her loneliness.

Relationships with men who conceal their feelings always result in emptiness. But the longer this pattern of romantic liaisons continued, the more entrenched it became. She had reached the point where, though very sensitive with respect to her own feelings, she had no ability to understand the feelings of men, and this made relationships with normal men impossible. Whenever a man who did not conceal his feelings broke through her romantic filter, she did not know what to do. A man who does not conceal his feelings, would expect her to respond to these feelings. Her inability to know how to do this initially appeared to be innocent. In fact, it was a genuine innocence, but the innocence of a girl is misplaced in a woman. Soon, such men would back off from her; baffled by their inability to reach her on an emotional level. Some thought that the contrast between her sensitivity regarding her own feelings and her insensitivity to the feelings of men was borne of selfishness. But, as should now be clear, this was not the case, and she yearned for closeness with a man.

Her problems were further deepened by the fact that her emotional blindness extended to the physical. She was a "bad kisser", but she had no way of knowing this. It seems incredible that a woman can reach adulthood, and not know how to kiss, but a lesser woman would somewhere along her journey be rebuked by a man: "Lips and tongue honey! Not teeth!" Lesser women therefore learned. No man would rebuke this woman; to do so would humiliate her, and any man that does this wrecks his chance to sleep with her. The older she gets, the more stinging the humiliation of the rebuke would be, and so the problem deepens with age. A man who gets as far as kissing her is focussed on a destination. Bad kissing is just a pothole on the route.

The Cool One ignored her for a while, and then he made his move. He approached her expressionlessly and introduced himself with a cold politeness. They made small talk for a while. Her normal easy, flighty manner had no impact on him, and her sense of power-lessness grew. He knew the watching eyes of the people in her circle inhibited his designs, so he suggested they move to another venue. The Not-So-Secret Admirer felt the hollow ache under his solar plexus as he watched the Cool One place his hand on the small of her back to guide her towards the exit.

Once alone, the Cool One talked to her in images and metaphors.

She didn't understand what he was saying. Her lack of under-standing fed her sense of weakness, and this gave rise to a feeling. She couldn't put this feeling into a context, and so any attempt she made to name this feeling would result in a belief. Whatever name she gave the feeling could not be refuted because there was no conceptual framework – no means of analysing the thought. When the Cool One suggested they go, she agreed without knowing to where they were going. She stepped into the taxi in a trance. The Cool One told the driver the destination, but she didn't take it in.

Alone in his apartment, she had no power to resist. It wasn't that she didn't know, at some level, that what was happening was going to hurt her. But she didn't have the strength to say "no". He was gentle with her, but still he displayed no feeling. The certainty with which he proceeded made her resistance unthinkable. She submitted to him gradually in stages until he possessed her fully. Afterwards, she lay on her side and looked at him, and he sat on the side of the bed with his back to her. He only glanced over his shoulder at her face after he had lit a cigarette. Before she had left the next morning, she already knew he would not call.

Some days later, she was again breezing into a bustling room with her hair swinging behind her. She held her head high and talked con-fidently to business contacts and acquaintances. She worked her way through the crowd. Then she saw the Cool One. She was looking at him when he turned to look at her. Again he looked away without betraying any emotion. It was, she thought, just like the first time, but the implications could not have been more different. Last time, it had been an invitation, but this time it was a rejection.

Concealing her loneliness had become something she was used to, but now it was a struggle that she could not ignore. She felt distressed. She picked up a glass of champagne to try to regain her composure. At that moment, the voice of the Not-So-Secret Admirer came from behind her. She was overjoyed to find him there. She turned to talk to him. She knew she could rely on him for companionship. But the Not-So-Secret Admirer was the one person who could see her

loneliness. As she spoke to him, she could see the concern in his face.
Talking to him, she could not pretend that her feeling did not exist.
The one person she could rely on at that moment, was the one person
who could see the emotion that she was trying to conceal.

She exchanged pleasantries with him; asked after his family. And
then she put down her barely touched glass of champagne and left.
She hailed a taxi, and sank into the seat in the back. As the taxi sped
her home, she stared upwards and let the lights of the city flicker
across her field of view. They washed her thoughts clean, and let her
bury her feelings. She forced her loneliness down inside, so that when
she arrived home she had regained her outward calm.

This Scenario can be broken down into its components as follows:

- Suppression of loneliness is Scenario B. (She doesn't know she is lonely.)
- Affecting flightiness is Scenario C. (She is disrupting her ability to relate to men normally.)
- Suppression of emotions by the Cool One is a modification of Scenario A. (The suppression makes her unable to understand the emotions of men, but these may include emotions that a woman could not experience herself.) However, the seduction is also a modified version of Scenario A. (Metaphors create beliefs in feelings, and she has the same inability to understand these feelings as the woman in Scenario A, and hence she is unable to identify her feeling.) The love of the Not-So-Secret Admirer is also Scenario A.
- Affecting contentment by the people in the woman's world is Scenario D (Collectively they are constructing a micro-world where everybody belongs – a fashionista tribe. Affecting contentment denies the people in the woman's world the understanding of what causes their own wellbeing. It confuses her that the world in which she lives is somehow real.)

I could have gone on, but the clock struck midnight and the Creative Writing Fairy vanished.

So let me sum up the whole of Part I in a single sentence: the evolutionary origin of emotions is that they drive actions that promote biological fitness; but humans with language can speculate future emotions and so they goal-seek emotional outcomes, reversing the causality; but tactical deception of the behaviour associated with emotions corrupts the data that each of us needs to goal-seek, and so we deduce suboptimal actions. [I can explain anything in one sentence if I am allowed to breathe at the semicolons.]

I would like to say that *all* self-destructive actions are derived from falsified behaviour. But can I really say "all"? Perhaps not! However, we have to start somewhere, and I am starting with the simplest idea that produces the maximum amount of explanation. This is *good* reductionism – reduction to simple axioms from which we can work causally and logically. Bad reductionism is the building of intellectual edifices with words that nobody can define to create the false impression that something is understood. This would include terms such as: souls, unconscious minds (which are the same thing), intentions (towards what?), objectives (to what end?), morality, God, free will, etc. Each of these unexplainable concept words has generated a library of explanatory literature, and part of the foundation for this industry is that some people don't *want* these things explained.

Part I explains the cause of an individual human action. What happens when we all start tactically manipulating our behaviour and deriving strange courses of action from this together? In Part II, I want to elevate this theory to collective mass phenomenon. I want to show that by distorting collective perceptions of emotion; it serves as the origin of beliefs – political, cultural and religious.

PART II:
IRREFUTABLE THOUGHTS

History makes one aware that there is no finality in
human affairs; there is not a static perfection and an
unimprovable wisdom to be achieved.

(Bertrand Russell, History As An Art, 1954)

THE LOGIC OF BELIEVING

HYPOCRISY FOR BEGINNERS

AUTHOR'S NOTE: *If you are already an advanced hypocrite, you could save time by skipping to the next section.*

The verb "to believe" has two forms. The first is "I believe that...". If you start a sentence using these words, you tend to complete it with a statement of fact – something that either can or cannot be backed up with evidence.

The other form is "I believe in . . .". Start a sentence with these words, and you end it with a concept or something that cannot be empirically supported. For example, "I believe *in* freedom of speech."

What is noteworthy about the "I believe *that*" form is its clarity. Two people will almost never have an argument that starts with one of them saying, "I believe *that*" because the matter can usually be settled with a demonstration of fact. They conduct an investigation or experiment, and one is forced to accept that they were misinformed. Sometimes, the empirical demonstration presents practical difficulties; for example "I believe *that* there is an afterlife" is theoretically demonstrable but no one has yet managed it. Practical difficulties also exist in science. For example, physicists are limited because although they can measure the precise location or speed of a sub-atomic particle, they cannot measure both at the same time – a problem known as the Uncertainty Principal.

Start a conversation with "I believe *in* the American Way" and there will ensue a screaming argument where the only conclusion is that each person thought "the American Way" meant something completely different. The funny thing is that the end result is that the understanding of "the American Way" is left entirely unshaken by an hour of shouting. In fact, it is likely that each position might become more entrenched after the debate.

This is the problem with concepts. We can never be sure that two people understand it in the same way because concept words are intended to summarise very complex sets of beliefs.

Ronald Reagan, "The Man Who Beat Communism",[147] persuaded Gorbachev to believe *in* capitalism and free-market ideology. However, Reagan (not exactly a detail man) forgot to mention to Gorbachev that capitalism and free markets did not function without the control of contract law or company law. Not only that, but they also needed a regulated securities market, a stock exchange, properly capitalised and regulated banks and insurance companies, a progressive tax system, educated consumers, and trade associations; not to mention the need for laws to prevent monopolies, money-laundering, price fixing, pollution and deceiving consumers.

The old Soviet world had none of these things. Whoops!

Sadly for Russia, the old communist system was abandoned in 1991 before the essential capitalist infrastructure could be put into place. The result was perhaps the greatest asset-stripping exercise in the history of mankind. Russia's new magnates bought everything from factories to oil reserves at prices fixed by the remnants of the Soviet government, and sold them at market prices. A few men became spectacularly wealthy overnight. Russia was not a wealthy country at the time, but over the next two decades it sprouted sixty-two billionaires.[148] The ideological vacuum between Soviet communism and Western capitalism that created these opportunities for enrichment also made holding on to your wealth a bit tricky. Result: most of Russia's wealth was stripped and relocated overseas – to England, Switzerland and other piggybank countries.

The point to take from this tragic story of Russia's journey from communism to Reagan's capitalism is simple: if you say you believe *in* capitalism you don't actually need to say what it is that you believe at all. What you believe in is a word – a simple little word. The fact that that word encompasses a whole system of interrelated beliefs and complex thoughts gets swept under the carpet.

This avoidance of the complexity that underlies the word is often a deliberate form of denial. Perhaps this was the case with Reagan. The American cold warriors might say that Reagan caused the total collapse of the Soviet Union *because* he skipped the details. A more recent example is Barrack Obama, who ran for President of the United States under the slogan "Change We Can Believe In". He swept up a whole generation of voters, and the very vagueness of the slogan meant that he had already captured these voters before he had to bother with actual policies.

This avoidance of detail, this assumption that everybody knows what a concept word means, goes on generation after generation. After a time, the original meaning creeps imperceptibly from something once clear and precise to something completely different. We can call this "belief creep" and it happens all around us.

Take "I believe in Christianity" as an example. One man's teaching is written into a book 2,000 years ago, and today the followers of his teaching are as diverse as the Amish of America's mid-west and the Pope in Rome. A Tibetan Buddhist and an Afghan Muslim may practice different religions but end up living their lives in very similar ways, but Christians like the Amish and the Pope who practice the same religion live very differently. The teachings of Christianity include humility, so surely nobody who claims to follow these teachings could credibly go to a Christian service in anything more elaborate than an Amish horse-drawn buggy. So what justifies the pomp of the Vatican? Christianity also preaches pacifism. Why then has so much war been waged in its name? The Bible is full of contradictions – in some parts preaching peace and in others recommending smashing children against rocks.[149]

Not to be outdone, Islam has been an equally rich source of belief drift. It started before the body of the Prophet Mohammed was cold in its grave with the split into Sunnis and Shias, and to this day Islam continues to sprout new sects.

What of political ideology? Thirty years or so ago, it was not so unusual to find people in Europe who called themselves communists while wearing Armani suits. This seems completely incongruous now, but is it any more incongruous than the Cadillac Christians of America?

So, concept words are necessary because they encapsulate compound beliefs. But is belief drift unavoidable?

The only way to be sure that you are avoiding belief drift is to translate your "I believe *in*" statements into "I believe *that*" statements. However, the more belief drift that your understanding of a concept has accumulated, the harder it is. For example "I believe in capitalism" could be translated into "I believe that if the owners of capital are allowed to deploy it in ways that suit their own interest and to retain the returns for themselves, that the broad wealth of society will ultimately be enhanced." And immediately you will say, "Yes, but . . ." Like Reagan's vision, this "belief *that*" statement still skips necessary detail – we return to the problem of de-summarising a concept word.

Religious concepts tend to be particularly prone to belief drift. This is mainly because many of the concepts are very old and first appeared when people lived in a very different way. So, for example, I could translate "I believe in God", into "I believe that there is a moral metabeing who blesses America whenever I ask him to." At which point, all Canadians wonder if God is racist.

Clearly, another contentious point is that the phrase "I believe *in* God" means that God is a concept and not a thing or person. If I say that I believe *in* Osama bin Laden, I am not saying that I believe that the man physically existed. George W. Bush believed that Osama B. Laden existed (sadly for both of them). Saying that you believe *in* him means that you subscribe to a system of beliefs that the name represents – and this is conceptual. George W. Bush certainly did not believe this.

The translation process is not all one way. Sometimes we can translate a "believe *that*" statement into a "believe *in*" statement. By playing with words, we can conceptify a fact or can factify a concept; for example, "I believe *that* the Earth is round" can be conceptified into "I believe *in* the idea of a round Earth". However, we have to be careful when we are dealing with facts about concepts; for example "I believe that there is hope for mankind" refers to a fact about a concept that is literally true if someone is merely doing some hoping. However, this is not what the statement is generally taken to mean, but rather that the believer thinks that mankind's future will work out OK and it isn't entirely clear whether this is a fact or a concept. The more commonly accepted meaning of the expression would perhaps be better expressed "I believe *in* the future of mankind." This, of course, is a conceptual statement.

So, believing *in* is intended to encapsulate whole complex conceptual thoughts, but ends up just being something that happens in your head. Believing *in* is thought-fluff. Nobody gets to look in your head to see what is going on. What is happening in your head is what we're aiming to explain.

"To believe" is not the only word that has two forms; one that rests on solid foundation and another that rests on thought-fluff. How about "to wage war *against* . . ." and "to wage war *on* . . ."? When you wage war *against*, you actually know what you are doing, and what would constitute victory. When you wage war *on*, you never know whether you have won or lost. The objective is a concept, generally which nobody bothers to define.

The term "War on Terror" was coined by a man for whom thought-fluff was something to be proud of. Nobody asked what it meant because we were in shock following the 9/11 attacks. With the benefit of hindsight, it now clear that the "War *on* Terror" is a war *against* a belief system. Whichever way you look at it, there is an undefined concept in there. And nobody understands how the belief propagates. Put this way, it is doubtful that anyone in the Pentagon would think it winnable by military means; hence all the crude fumbling about "hearts and minds" – that demonstrably never changed anybody's beliefs. Part II of this book demonstrates how beliefs *in* propagate. You can't change someone's beliefs by bombing them, and being nice to them won't work either. All belief *in* is something other than what the believer thinks it is.

Consider the term "War *on* Iraq", and ask yourself why World War II wasn't a war *on* Germany or *on* Japan. In the latter case, we knew what the objective was, so it was a War *against*. When it ended there was a treaty and a victory parade and all the soldiers went home. With Iraq, we never knew who we were supposed to shoot so we called them terrorists after we shot them, and the conceptual aim was crudely reinvented as we went along (weapons of mass destruction / regime change / establishment of democracy / etc).

Wars *against* have definite end points, whereas wars *on* never end, they just fade out with an embarrassed cough, when it gradually dawns on everyone that the objective was conceptual, and nobody understood the concept.

Consider the War *on* Drugs, which could be a momentous instantaneous victory if we simply made a clear decision to stop fighting it. If we legalised drugs, we could tax them heavily and use the proceeds to fight the War *on* Poverty.

And for our final example of thought-fluff in action, consider the verb "to care"! The two forms are "to care *for* . . ." and "to care *about* . . .". Caring *for* is real, but caring *about* is just thought-fluff. If you care *for* your elderly mother, this is demonstrable in fact: every day you go around to her house and make sure she is eating properly and has remembered to take her pills. If you care *about* your mother, she is not likely to show you much gratitude. For that reason, you might actually tend to avoid her. So caring *about* somebody might actually make it less likely that you will care *for* them. But the wonderful thing with caring *about* is that it feels so good.

Try this at your earliest convenience: Settle down in your favourite armchair and pour yourself some 1990 Château Pétrus into your finest crystal glass. After you have spent a moment or two considering its bouquet, you will be ready to commence caring about the poor. Savour the moment! While letting the mellow richness of the Château Pétrus roll over your tongue, feel the warmth that flows from all that caring.

Of course, there may be some miserable killjoys who say "yes, but you don't *really* care about the poor." How do they know? Caring *about* is thought-fluff: It only happens in your head, and nobody else gets to look in there.

Having experienced the hum of good karma that comes from caring about the poor, you will no doubt want to share your moment of rapture. Get one of those coiled ribbons – a plastic one (in red naturally) that says on it "God bless poor people" and stick it on the back of your SUV. (Don't do this on your Bentley because that would be tacky.)

Now that you are giddy with the feeling that comes from caring about, you will no doubt want to get another plastic ribbon (in green of course) that says "Save the planet!" You could put this on the back of the SUV too. Put it just above the exhaust pipe! Then you could take the empty Château Pétrus bottle to the recycling depot. Wait a minute! You have been drinking and you *really* care about road safety, so send the butler. While he is gone, you can spend more time caring about the poor.

When you are sober again, you can drive around your neighbourhood and people will see the ribbon stickers on the back of the SUV, and they look at you admiringly: "There is a man who *really* cares", they will think. And the wonderful thing; the thing that just completes how fabulous caring *about* makes you feel, is that you won't actually have to do anything that could vaguely be called work.

BELIEF AND THE PROBLEM OF PERSPECTIVE

Edward Said's book *Orientalism*[150] is a defining work in cultural studies. An Orientalist, he explains, is a Westerner who believes in the inferiority of Oriental people. Much of the detail of his argument centres on the creation of the orientalist beliefs about Arabs. These beliefs were self-servingly created by European colonial powers seeking to conceal their selfish interests under a cloak of morality. However, what is shocking is that it originated in scholarly research that was considered to be objective and was often exhaustingly thorough. Such beliefs, Said claims, were reinforced by people who were considered to be champions of the downtrodden.[151]

Perhaps the simplest evidence that Said's argument is correct is to consider the expression "Anti-Semitic". It is accepted that a Semite is a person who speaks a Semitic language and this includes Jews and Arabs. But the expression "Anti-Semitic" means "hostility to or prejudice against Jews". Arabs are not included. Go on – check your dictionary! It would appear that hostility to or prejudice against Arabs is so culturally accepted, that it has shifted the meanings of the words.

Orientalism is a hugely influential book, but Said is not without his critics. So fixated is Said on the negative beliefs of Westerners regarding Orientals, that he fails to acknowledge that many sub-groups of Orientals have negative beliefs about each other that cannot be attributed to Western influence. I have a concern that a Westerner cannot criticise Said without being accused of being an Orientalist himself. To attack him and avoid this criticism, it is necessary to be an Oriental.

V.S. Naipaul is an acclaimed novelist and winner of the Nobel Prize for Literature. He expressed his counter-argument to Said in his non-fiction writing. Naipaul wrote a trilogy of books on India that documented his travels there between 1962 and 1990.[152] He also wrote two similar books on the Islamic World.[153] These books are brutal in their honesty.

Naipaul's argument is that Indian inferiority is not a Western myth, but is a fact that results from Indian religious belief. He does not soften his language; for example referring to "India's intellectual secondratedness".[154] His argument is that the caste system of Hindu belief traps Indians and prevents their development. The caste system designates a man's occupation at birth, and has resisted all attempts at reform. It is at least as old as the Bhagavad Gita – the Hindu "manual for mankind" that was written between the fifth and second centuries BC. Many of India's newer religions split from Hinduism as an attempt to escape the caste system (e.g. Jainism and Sikhism). It demarcates in ways that are hardly perceptible to a foreigner but are obvious to an Indian. For example, the "husbands wanted" and "wives wanted" ads in Indian newspapers always include the poster's family name, because this enables readers to determine the poster's caste. Marriage, even today, almost always occurs between people of the same caste. Caste marks can include the way a beard is cut or a turban is worn; and caste denotes occupation that could be priest or latrine cleaner. For example, the Dhor is a sub-caste group that has the role of disposing of dead cattle and running tanneries, and it is almost inconceivable that a Hindu from another caste would consider performing this function. Naipaul quotes from the Bhagavad Gita " 'And do thy duty, even if it be humble, rather than another's, even if it be great. To die in one's duty is life: To live in another's is death.' "[155] So caste locks a Hindu man into an occupation for life. Self-improvement is therefore forbidden by religion: the talented latrine cleaner remains a latrine cleaner, and the inept priest remains a priest.

The effect of the caste system on the execution of necessary work is interesting: Naipaul describes four men sweeping the steps of a Bombay hotel. After they finished, the steps were still filthy.

> You cannot complain that the hotel is dirty. No Indian will agree with you. Four sweepers are in daily attendance, and it is enough in India that the sweepers attend. They are not required to *clean*, that is a subsidiary part of their function which is to *be* sweepers.[156]

Since they cannot escape sweeping except in the next life, they sweep floors in the ritually correct way, and the objective of the function is irrelevant.

Class is a system of rewards. Caste imprisons a man in his function. From this it follows, since there are no rewards, that duties and responsibilities become irrelevant to position. A man is proclaimed his function.[157]

Said and Naipaul have beliefs that are almost exact opposites. This is inevitable because they have perspectives that are also uncannily exact opposites: Said (a Christian Palestinian Arab) was raised in the culture he defends and then moved to a society that considers that culture irrelevant (the USA); Naipaul (an atheist of Brahmin Hindu Indian origin) was raised in a society that considers his culture irrelevant (Colonial Trinidad) and then travelled extensively in the culture he attacks.

Said accused Naipaul of being a neo-colonial apologist. However, this is unjust because little in Naipaul's work even concerns the colonial period. Said might accuse Naipaul of being an Orientalist himself, but Naipaul's origins make him as close to culturally stateless as it is possible to be. Would Said similarly accuse Mahatma Gandhi of being an Orientalist? Gandhi could see what was wrong with India because he was (like Naipaul) an outsider. He could see that there was something wrong with members of one caste eating alone to avoid being polluted by the sight of other castes. Similarly, he understood that it was wrong to use the veranda as a latrine, not thinking about whether someone of the caste designated to clean up excrement was present.[158]

Whatever the merits of each position, Said must be considered the victor in this debate in the West. We have arrived at the point where everyone is so terrified of being accused of racism that all we can say of other cultures are a few insipid remarks with a vapid positive spin. No Western academic would dare say that the people of another culture were intellectually second-rate in any scholarly journal. Even Naipaul's own publisher sides with Said: The blurb on the back of my copy of *India: A Wounded Civilization* says Naipaul had "a conviction that India, wounded by centuries of foreign rule, has not yet found an ideology of regeneration" – in other words it is the fault of foreigners that India is a mess, which is *not* what Naipaul is saying. He is saying that India cannot fix itself because Indians have self-destructive beliefs that predate foreign rule. Naipaul's own publisher seems to think it has to "de-Orientalise" its own author on the back of his own book. However, there is little doubt that Naipaul has won the debate in the East. Indians are paranoid about China's regional ambitions. China took Indian territory by force in 1962, and appears to be biding its time before further subjugating its neighbour to the South. Surprisingly, Naipaul also has considerable acceptance in India, despite his devastating criticism. You can buy his India trilogy in almost every English language bookshop in the country.

So what can be added to this debate?

There is little point trying to arbitrate between Said and Naipaul. Since their opposite views arise from opposite perspectives, what needs to be done is to eliminate the problem of perspective. In the real world this is not possible because we think our own beliefs are true – that is what belief means. When someone studies the beliefs of another culture, they are bound to misunderstand certain critical elements. All global conflict is driven by incompatible beliefs that derive from differing perspectives. To eliminate the problem of perspective, it is necessary to consider beliefs as an entirely abstract concept. In this way, one can explore how a self-destructive belief can arise without getting into the messy business of considering whether it is true or not. By ignoring the rightness or wrongness of beliefs their structures can be examined and explanations deduced as to why they are believed.

In Part I, I constructed atomic-level models of how emotional behaviour determines human action, by creating hypothetical people, each of whom had only one emotion, and each of whom was exposed to a systematically distorted behaviour pattern relating to that emotion. Using a series of interrelated thought experiments, I demonstrated that humans derive their self-destructive actions by a rational process. In Part II, I will place these idealised hypothetical people into a hypothetical society – one that (unlike the world of Said and Naipaul) has no culture and no history. I will construct a complete set of beliefs for these hypothetical people. But it isn't enough to simply invent beliefs; I must be able to demonstrate that they *would be believed*. This is an exercise in logic. I will do this by constructing a hypothetical system of perception, where the individual is trapped and unable to see that he is in a trap.

SCENARIO: THE GENERIC C/D IDEOLOGY

The Man lived in a world where everybody believed in the Way. Many centuries ago, the Sage had explained that the Way would create human wellbeing. Initially, people followed the Way because they understood the reasoning of the Sage and thought it made sense, but gradually people stopped bothering to read the writings of the Sage, and so they started to forget them. They continued to think that they believed in the Way, but, through belief drift, the ideology changed and with it their way of living. They convinced themselves that they believed the Way by gradually starting to act out their wellbeing to demonstrate compliance.

The Man wondered – how was it that the Way made the people happy? The people in the Man's world would admonish him, and say "you cannot be happy because you do not believe in the Way"; so the man was left doubting himself. He wanted to be happy. Not believing the Way meant that he was in danger of being an outsider in his own world, and he wanted to belong; so he decided to believe. But how could this be done?

He consulted one of the elders – someone whose belief in the Way could not be doubted. The elder told him that if he accepted the Way in his heart, that happiness would come to him. The man went away. He wasn't sure what "accepting in his heart" meant, so he acted out the belief: he affected the happiness that he was taught came from the Way, and gradually he became comfortable with this, and then it became a habit. Once it became habit, he believed in his happiness and he assumed that his happiness came from believing the Way. It had to be true that believing in the Way caused happiness. This had become irrefutable to him.

In a normal world, circumstances cause feelings, and they are expressed to others through behaviour. We observe the behaviour of others, but cannot see the feelings themselves. Normally, we can study the causal relationship between the body language of others and the circumstances that cause it. We can replicate these circumstances in our own lives and thereby create the feeling in ourselves. The body language of others is therefore essential for us to be able to find a path to our own happiness. For this to be a reliable path to happiness, it is necessary that everyone's path is similar. It is also necessary that everyone's behaviour is an accurate reflection of what they feel.

In the Man's world, everybody who believes in the Way affects happiness habitually. They act happy because belief drift has gradually transformed the Way into a belief system where people act out their happiness to demonstrate ideological compliance. Once this occurs, it no longer matters what it is that they are complying with. They also do this to ensure other people's acceptance. There is no connection between a true inner feeling and the outer expression of happiness. The habitual affectation of the outward signs of happiness has the effect of changing the actual meaning of the word "happiness": the word refers to whatever causes the outer expression of happiness, and now what causes this is the belief system that the people call the Way.

Happiness isn't a feeling in the Man's world, it is a belief in a feeling: a self-belief that is both individual and collective. However, there is circularity here: believers in the Way habitually act happy, but happiness is not a feeling, it is a belief – a value. But happiness *must* be good; this is emotionally axiomatic. And the happiness is caused by the Way. How then is it possible to question the goodness of the Way? The Way is therefore True, and in the Man's world this is irrefutable. So the Man believes in the Way, despite the fact that he (like the writer and readers of this Scenario) doesn't know what the Way actually is. He believes in an ideology without needing to understand its content.

IRREFUTABLE UNTRUTHS

In arithmetic, the double negative is equal to the positive; so the negative of minus one is plus one [$--1 = +1$]. In formal logic, the double negative is also equal to the positive: something that is not true is false, and something that is not false is true, so it is clearly the case that something that is not not true [$\sim\sim T$] is true.

Irrefutability is a special case of the double negative: a refutation is a demonstration that something is false; and if something is irrefutable, it is impossible to demonstrate that it is false – so it is presumed true. If a thought is irrefutable, then *to the person who has that thought*, it must be true. It is therefore a belief because the believer cannot refute it. The only way it can cease to be a belief is for it to be forgotten, but then it isn't a thought anymore. So, an irrefutable thought is always a belief.

Irrefutability in this context is not simply a concept of logic. To understand this you need to understand that the Scenarios in this book are not simply stories. They are an unusual type of thought experiment that use dramatic irony to set up a hypothetical individual or group of individuals who are obviously operating under a misconception of which they have no awareness. They permit the exploration of rationality in hypothetical minds where words and concepts have become misunderstood. This book is an attempt to put together a set of such Scenarios that accounts for all the strangeness of humanity.

Understanding the phenomenon of belief is important because it is what motivates people to put children into gas chambers and fly jet aircraft into skyscrapers. It would be nice if we could ignore all the good beliefs (which you no doubt think are yours) and only look at the bad beliefs (i.e. everybody else's) but nobody can separate good beliefs from bad ones until we can look back at their devastating aftermath. If you think you don't need to care about your carbon footprint, it is possible that your beliefs are more destructive than Hitler's or bin Laden's. By ignoring the distinction between good and bad, we can look at belief as a totally abstract concept. This involves suspending the idea of truth, which would seem appropriate since general observation of humanity makes it pretty clear that humans can believe in anything and can do it on a global scale.

Truth is for wimps, and we have to look at belief as a truth-independent human phenomenon.

I am seeking to demonstrate that there is a logical mechanism to beliefs that makes them irrefutable to the believer. I also intend to demonstrate why different people believe completely different things: if a word for an emotion is derived from the behaviour associated with that emotion, and each of us lives in a slightly different behavioural environment, then emotion words have subtly different meanings for each of us. Therefore, a thought may be irrefutable to one individual, but not others who may express the thought in exactly the same words. Hence a belief can be unique to a single person.

I am specifically seeking to explain why a person has a belief *in*. Belief *that* derives from information that is empirically observable, and incorrect belief *that* derives from misinformation or misinterpretation of empirical evidence. It would be misguided to say that a belief *in* that is simply a behavioural construct is false. In fact it doesn't really make much sense to say that a belief *in* anything is actually correct or incorrect. What I hope to demonstrate is that such a belief is almost inevitably going to be something entirely different to what the believer thinks it is.

Let us consider an example: George W. Bush talked of "good and evil". But his antagonist Osama B. Laden talked of exactly the same thing. War between them was inevitable because their definitions of good and evil were opposites of one another: they each thought the other evil. To consider this, we first need to suspend our judgement of which was right and look objectively at the causality of belief. (This is easier if you think neither of them was right.) Each of them had irrefutable thoughts that were irreconcilable with the other. We cannot understand this while our own beliefs stand in the way.

Likewise, capitalism and communism are both believed by their proponents. This too needs to be explored objectively. (Again, this is easier if you think they are both busted ideologies.)

Let us assume for now that *your* religion is The-One-True-Religion. Is it not reasonable to ask why most of the rest of our species practices a false one? Wars almost always occur between people of different religions (although they usually pretend another cause). If someone with a false religion is going to declare war on you, don't you think that you ought to attempt to understand why? You cannot do this objectively if your own religious belief stands in the way. It might actually be some other belief of yours that is the problem, or it may simply be that your beliefs are incompatible with someone else's.

For you, the reader, this is difficult because if I am to look at the causality of belief *in*, then it raises questions about your own beliefs, including the possibility that they are all merely behavioural constructs. If you are not ready to question some of your own beliefs in a harsh light (whatever they might be) then perhaps you might at this point choose not to read on.

While the thesis of Part I is that self-destructive actions are rationally derived from manipulated behaviour associated with emotional states, the thesis of Part II is that belief *in* is derived from exactly the same thing. Therefore, all belief is likely some sort of misconception. In Part I we encountered false beliefs. For example, the abused woman in Scenario A believed that the feeling she felt when the man grabbed her arm was love, when in fact the feeling was fear. This of course is an incorrect belief *that* although one that is rather uniquely difficult to empirically demonstrate, which as it turns out is the key to the problem of belief *in*. It is crucial that we keep in mind the distinction between believing *that* and believing *in* because, if I am to demonstrate that believing *in* derives from a circularity of causality, we have to be sure that the entire theory in this book does not derive from a similar logical dysfunction. Believing *in* this book would be a rather grand tautology, so I want you to believe *that* this is really how beliefs *in* actually work. For this to become science, we would then need to demonstrate that empirically. This is technically possible if we can demonstrate over time that behaviour changes over time as ideology shifts, and we can see this when opposing ideologies are forced to confront one another at moments of history like the Berlin Wall coming down.

To understand why believing *in* derives from behaviour let us analyse the previous Scenario *Generic C/D ideology*: This Scenario is a combination of Scenario C and Scenario D reconfigured as a belief system. Scenario C explains that if someone affects the behaviour of an emotional state it makes that person unable to correctly identify the presence of the feeling in themself. Scenario D explains that when other people affect such behaviour, it creates false beliefs in the causality of feelings, i.e. beliefs in feelings where the feeling is not actually present. An ideology requires collective belief, so the distinction between the first person and the second/third person disappears because everybody is acting together. *The Generic C/D ideology* is a logical tautology – it derives from circular causality as follows:

- To be believed, a belief *in* (e.g. an ideology or moral code) needs to persuade people that it promotes human wellbeing;
- The only evidence of human wellbeing is behaviour emanating from emotional states;
- Beliefs cause us to change our behaviour, in particular in *The Generic C/D ideology* the believers affect happiness, and eventually this becomes habitual and unconscious;
- Believers tend to affect emotional states to demonstrate their compliance with a belief;
- This interplay creates a causal loop, whereby the belief manufactures the evidence of its own truth, creating a pseudo-empirical irrefutability.

Following this causality, we create an irrefutable thought that is a trap resulting from a feedback loop involving a misconception of an emotion. Clearly, nobody thinks that this is how their beliefs work, but belief is like a magic trick – once you have been shown how it works, it isn't magic anymore. That a belief constructed this way is self-destructive is not immediately obvious. But most human emotions evolved by natural selection as drivers of survival-enhancing actions. So, if belief causes systematic alteration of emotional behaviour, it leads to collective suboptimal actions, and hence ultimately both self-destruction and an impediment to our species' survival as a whole. To explore this, I will invent political ideologies devoid of any politics (for example the *Generic C/D ideology*), and then I will invent religions devoid of any theology.

The *Generic C/D ideology* is believed because its believers think it causes happiness – i.e. positive emotional states. But human well-being can also be defined by the absence of undesirable emotional states, and so we can also construct a generic ideology derived from Scenarios A and B.

SCENARIO: THE GENERIC A/B IDEOLOGY

AUTHORS NOTE: *apologies to Lao-Tzu, and all practitioners of Taoism.*

The Way is not the only way, but it is the way of the Sage.
So the Sage teaches that the Way brings contentment.
[There is no crime greater than being desirable;
There is no disaster greater than not being content;
There is no misfortune more painful than being covetous:
Hence in knowing the sufficiency of being content, one will
*   constantly have sufficient.]*
Contentment follows from having no desire.
One who practices the Way will be subordinate to all men, but
*   will not know humiliation.*
Hence in [knowing contentment

You will suffer no humiliation]
The true disciple of the Way will know no anxiety, because the
   wisdom of the Way means accepting the world.

The Disciple listened to the words of the Sage, with rapt concen-
tration. She wanted to learn from the Sage and live by the Way. She
yearned for the contentment that would come from the Way. The
Sage counselled the Disciple that if she meditated on the Way, she
would find her own path to the practice of the Way.

The Disciple did as the Sage bid her. She sat motionless and let all
feeling drift away from her body. She allowed herself to relax and to
forget. She concentrated on all the worries and ills of her life, and as
she visualised them in her mind, she relaxed and felt them melt away.

The Disciple practised daily. Every day, she found that her
meditation became more natural. Gradually it became a part of her
life, until eventually she found that her worries dissolved even when
she wasn't meditating. Practising the Way slowly bought her the
contentment that she sought. And therefore the Way must be true.
The Disciple's belief in the Way was complete, even though she didn't
know what the Way was.

The Way causes the outward suppression of negative emotional
states. In the world of the Disciple, no practitioner of the Way
displays any negative emotional states, and therefore there is no
evidence of any lack of contentment in a practitioner. The Way
promises contentment, but also causes its practitioners to suppress
all physical manifestation of negative emotional states; so the Way
manufactures the evidence of its own truth, and is irrefutable to its
believers.

This Scenario is a combination of Scenario A and Scenario B
reconfigured as a belief system. Scenario A shows that if someone
lives in a world where other people suppress the behaviour of an
emotional state, it makes that individual unable to correctly identify
that emotion in themselves. Scenario B shows that when someone
suppresses such behaviour in themselves, they are unable to know that

they experience that emotion, despite the fact that they may recognise it in other people. As with *The Generic C/D ideology*, an ideology is collective, so the distinction between the first person and the second/third person disappears. People believe that the Way releases them from all negative emotional states, but together they gradually begin to habitually suppress all the behavioural manifestations of such emotions, so they manufacture the evidence that their belief is true. The parts of this Scenario that are enclosed in square brackets are direct quotes from the *Tao Te Ching*.[159] I interpret the *Tao Te Ching* as an A/B belief system in that it promises the avoidance of negative emotional states to its believers. However, it is not (we hope) a *generic* A/B belief system.

THE CAUSE AND CONTENT OF BELIEF

Let us consider the lifecycle of a belief.

Originally, someone comes up with an idea that they argue enhances human wellbeing. In the Generic Ideologies, I called this person "the Sage" but history provides plenty of real examples. In Part I, we encountered Confucius and Jean-Jacques Rousseau, to name but two. Shortly, we will look at Karl Marx, Chairman Mao and Adam Smith. Initially, people believe these theories because they rectify whatever chaos immediately preceded them. Generally, new ideologies promote freedom from whatever was the scourge of humanity beforehand. If you had just survived a famine, you would believe a theory that abolished famines irrespective of what its other consequences might be. This is convenient because it makes the essential step of defining human wellbeing something that is easy to overlook. So a theory is adopted, and the squeaky wheels of political power put it into practice. Immediately, it becomes clear that this is tricky. Problems arise that the Sage didn't visualise and these problems are solved with political fudge and sticking tape.

Soon, people stop reading the great works of the Sage. This occurs because the political fudge and sticking tape quite quickly makes them obsolete. When we return to read these works, we find they are surprisingly difficult to read anyway. Adam Smith is mind-numbingly dull, and reading Marx is like having lead weights attached to your eyelids. Mao, by contrast, is hysterically funny, but only because he is so incomprehensible. I rather fancy calling myself a "Splitist Anti-Rightist Reactionary Capitalist Roader", just because it would look so good on the tee shirt. Maoist slogans all used simplistic principals which sound like the "Four No's" or the "Three Yes's" and it was all tickety-boo, because nobody dared to ask how they were actually supposed to put this into practice.

When people stop reading the words of the particular Sage of their belief, the process of belief drift begins. People still think they believe the belief, but it starts to change, and gradually the *process* of believing takes over from the *purpose* of believing. The purpose of the belief was to enhance human wellbeing, but the process morphs into the behavioural enactment of that wellbeing. People want to believe, even though they are gradually forgetting what they are supposed to believe. They believe that the belief causes human wellbeing; so, to prove that they are loyal to the belief, they start to enact that wellbeing and slowly this becomes habitual. Without realising it, the believers manufacture the evidence that their belief truly does promote human wellbeing, even though they forget what the belief actually is.

Taking this process to its logical conclusion, we can completely separate the *cause* of a belief from its *content*; and once the cause of the belief has been independently established as a behavioural and perceptive feedback loop, we can replace its content with any tooth fairy nonsense that happens to be close at hand. This is the very simple reason why belief drift is inevitable, and humans can believe anything.

Let us compare North Korean Communism with American Republicanism [which I can do without blinking]. We find that these two belief systems have something surprising in common: they both would be unrecognisable to their spiritual founders. With both belief systems, the *process* of the belief has replaced the *purpose* of the belief. Were Karl Marx or Vladimir Lenin alive today, they simply wouldn't recognise North Korean Communism, despite the fact that most North Koreans (and everybody else) think that they are Marxist–Leninists. North Korean Communism is a sort of personality cult where nobody can gain access to the "Dear Leader" (or is it "Great Successor" these days?) unless they enact a perpetual fake ecstasy. Along these lines, I will shortly demonstrate that a tyrant's belief of faithfully serving their people can be a sincere belief.

Similarly, Adam Smith wouldn't recognise American Republicanism, despite the fact that he practically invented free-market capitalism and members of the Republican Party think they are free-market capitalists. What makes Republicanism madder than a python on a bicycle is that the revulsion that Republicans feel towards "Socialism" has become a behavioural reflex. They all try to outdo each other's revulsion to prove their ideological commitment. Over time, they have learned to enact this reflex automatically, so they don't have to ask themselves what the word means anymore. Now they are unable to say what is wrong with it without resorting to a slogan that could have been invented by Chairman Mao. Gradually as the process of their belief takes over from its purpose, a surprising inversion occurs. Whereas European Socialism was all about benefiting the poor, Republicanism has turned into Socialism to benefit the rich. Few seem to have noticed this but it really isn't so surprising since many of them drive Cadillacs to a place of worship that preaches humility. The result is the growing tendency in America where poor people vote for the party of the wealthy and wealthy people vote for the party of the poor; and the risk is that when nobody votes for their own self-interest, that democracy becomes self-destructive to the people it represents.

Let us return to serious politics! What is the greatest belief drift in history? To find this, you need to consider that we can not only separate the cause of a belief from its content, but also the origin of a belief can be something that is completely different from what we think it is. To demonstrate this, we need to plunge into history.

THE HISTORY OF A BELIEF:
IT'S NOT ABOUT MARX!

HOW TO BE POWERFUL

Ying Zheng was born in 259BC and although the name might not ring a bell, he has had a huge impact on your life because he invented modern government.

Ying Zheng was the son of the king of Qin (pronounced Chin) in central China. Like many great figures of history, he started improbably young and killed a lot of people along the way. At the age of thirteen he succeeded his father, and by thirty-eight he had conquered most of what we now think of as China, marking the first time that all of China had been united. Ying Zheng celebrated his great achievement by renaming himself Qinshi Huangdi (pronounced Chin Shur Hwang Dee), the first Emperor of China.

Qinshi Huangdi's achievements were based on his phenomenal powers of organisation. Before we can examine that, we need to go back a bit further to explore Chinese thinking at the time. I want to demonstrate that although there have been apparent dramatic shifts in Chinese thought, it has ultimately been a stable A/B ideology since ancient times. At the beginning of this story, there were two conflicting schools of thought in Chinese Philosophy: Confucianism and the Legalist Tradition.

I have already introduced the philosophy of Confucius and his follower Mencius. Confucius' influence spread throughout East Asia. He lived at a time when China was torn apart by civil war, and sought to teach that morality led to correct government and that this would be to the benefit of all. He taught that personal and government morality could be developed through education. Correct behaviour, honesty and justice could be maintained by meditation and study. His teachings on morality emphasised self-development and emulation of role models. One should develop judgement rather than knowledge. His famous "Golden Rule" was "never do to others what you would not like them to do to you."[160]

Legalism was a contrasting philosophy that had more to do with the exercise of power than the concept of law. The underlying conception of humanity upon which Legalism rests is that all people seek to avoid punishment while seeking to achieve gains. Effectively, it ignores the possibility of morality by assuming that everybody acts selfishly. The Legalist philosopher Guan Zong (died 645BC) summed it up as follows: "The Ruler is the creator of the law. The Ministers are the keeper of the law. The people are the object of the law." A principle of Legalism is that the ruler can create a stable society by exploiting his superior vantage point to ensure domination.

Legalism resembles the European thought of Thomas Hobbes – we need government because people are bad – while Confucianism more reflects Jean-Jacques Rousseau in assuming that people are good. Clearly, Confucianism was all about the individual and Legalism was all about totalitarian rule or the suppression of the individual. So Qinshi Huangdi did the obvious thing: he ordered all Confucian texts to be burned and Confucian scholars to be buried alive.[161]

The whole concept of Legalist thinking was that the people should be close to automata (i.e. should suppress all emotional behaviour) and should be ruled by fear. The people's ability to rebel should be restricted by ensuring that they were kept ignorant. Essentially it is a vision of human society that is approximately modelled upon a bee colony.

The Legalist philosopher Han Fei Tzu (died 233BC) recommended that government departments should not be permitted to communicate laterally and all communication should flow along the spokes of the wheel to the Ruler at the centre. Qinshi Huangdi no doubt really liked this idea. Han Fei Tzu taught that the Ruler should conceal his own motivations to prevent people exploiting them for their own advantage – an explicit recommendation to suppress behaviour. The Confucian belief that people should develop their own moral judgement endangered the edicts of the Ruler. If the people could question those edicts, the power would not be absolute.

Qinshi Huangdi's greatest accomplishment was to establish the first true civil service bureaucracy and therefore the first modern state. He abolished the hereditary right of noblemen to hold government office and established a civil service drawn from the brightest scholars in the land. These were promoted on merit – as defined by Qinshi Huangdi. There was no place for nepotism or personal relationships in his government.

Qinshi Huangdi was a totalitarian dictator who ruled entirely by fear. Any merit-based hierarchy ruled by a despot comes to mark loyalty as the highest form of merit. All imperial commands were concluded with the words "Tremble and Obey", and this continued almost until the end of imperial rule in China.

The imperial system established by Qinshi Huangdi survived for two millennia. Although dynasties rose and fell (usually with civil war in between), each new dynasty adopted the same system of government control. Even when Genghis Khan, a nomadic tribesman from Mongolia, conquered China, he saw the superiority of the Chinese system of government and adopted it to form his own imperial dynasty.

POWER OF THE PEOPLE VS POWER OVER THE PEOPLE

Despite the incredible efficiency of the Chinese imperial system of government, eventually it collapsed. Qing was the last Chinese imperial dynasty. The Qing imperial government refused to adopt the superior technological methods of the Western powers. Ultimately it was doomed when faced with their superior military and trading know-how.

In 1912, Sun Yat-sen, a reformer turned republican revolutionary, founded the Nationalist government known as the Kuomintang or KMT. They sought to build a Chinese republic based largely on Western concepts of democracy, free markets and capitalism. A free press briefly flourished along with diverse political parties. The KMT officially abandoned most of the imperial system along with most of its bureaucracy. This was their downfall. In doing this, they destroyed the only mechanism of government that the country possessed. The KMT failed to impose Western ideas of government upon China because Chinese people did not understand such ideas, and they could not be learned overnight.

The Chinese Communist Party (CCP) was formed in 1921 by a group of intellectuals. They had a different vision of China's future and were encouraged by the success of the Soviets in establishing rule in Russia after the fall of the Russian imperial system. The CCP waged civil war with the KMT (not to mention remnants of the imperialist forces and the unwelcome intervention of the Japanese). Early CCP defeats caused a retreat that became known as the Long March, where the Red Army fled to China's south-west province of Yunnan before heading North and regrouping in the province of Shanxi. This was a key event in Chinese history, as Mao Zedong emerged as the CCP's leader. The Japanese threat was removed in 1945 by their defeat in World War II and the CCP conquered the whole country by 1949, when the KMT leadership fled to Taiwan.

Mao Zedong finally declared the People's Republic of China.

IDEOLOGY: WHAT'S IN A NAME?

This has been a fairly long preamble, but it brings us to the point of this chapter, which is an examination of belief drift. China is a truly unique case of ideology-warp.

Communism, as Karl Marx saw it, would arise from class struggle, but he based this theory on his Western perspective of class. China had a very different class structure under imperialism. In particular, there was no industrial working class, and there were no huge agricultural estates owned by an aristocracy. So naturally,

Marxist theory applied literally to China produced some bizarre results. For example, Marx talked of rich landowners, but since these did not exist in China, people who owned a single acre of land were persecuted and brutally murdered. Marx also saw communism taking hold in industrial societies, and it is one of the curious facts of twentieth-century history that communism only ever took root in agrarian societies, as China was at the time.

But the most interesting thing about communism in China is that it pretty much bypassed Marx from the beginning.

Mao's rise to power was pure Josef Stalin, complete with the terror and brutal purging of opposing forces. However, his studies at the time were split between reading Marxist ideology, and the study of imperialist theory of government based in Legalism. Mao's political genius was recognising that the two were essentially the same thing. He made it very clear that he was a great admirer of Qinshi Huangdi. (Mao revered all of China's most brutal emperors.) So although his consolidation of power was Stalinist, his exercise of it was pure Legalist. He had an almost mystical faith in the role of the leader. Although he took pains to present a humble image to the masses, he essentially continued to live an imperial life and even compared himself to the Emperor.[162]

Mao acted early to re-establish all the instruments of power that had existed in imperial China. The structure of his government was near identical to that of the imperialist era. He set about establishing over a hundred ministries to micro-manage all aspects of government and the economy. They all reported to Mao and his immediate associates at the head of the CCP (with very limited cross-communication) – another bee colony under a different name – pure Legalism. The civil service was very hierarchical with approximately twenty grades from senior Politburo members in Beijing to local clerks, each trained in ideology – again, Legalism. Legalist jargon was replaced by communist jargon but with no change of meaning. Imperial magistrates became local party secretaries – same job; different title. Imperial officials became 'ganbu' or cadres – same function; different name.

The relationship between the peasant and the state also hardly changed. Mao gave orders that everyone had to carry a residence permit called a 'hukou'. These booklets are issued on a family basis. They list the names of all family members, their birth dates, their relationship with each other, marriage status, class (e.g. peasant), racial origin and the address of their employer. All *hukou* state the district where you are required to live. This system is also an imperial power mechanism. In imperial times the family registration document was known as a 'baojia' – same document; new name. Records of *baojia* go back to the fourteenth century, but there is evidence of systematic family registration going back two millennia.

The power of the *hukou* as a method of social control is immense. Chinese police can check your *hukou* at any time, and if you are found in a place where you are not a registered resident you can be arrested. Periodically, the police conduct sweeps in cities and round up all people who are not registered to be there.[163] The effect is striking: a Chinese city has an atmosphere of Western affluence because the *hukou* laws ban rural peasants. For comparison, India has no restriction on movement, so Indian cities are swarming with beggars, casual labourers and street sellers. This *hukou* system is often called the "Chinese apartheid". It segregates between city dwellers who benefit from economic development, and rural dwellers who are denied the benefits of economic development because they have no freedom of movement.

Mao enhanced the rigidity of the old imperial system by requiring people to buy food with coupons known as 'liangpiao'. People could only buy food with *liangpiao* in the place where their *hukou* was registered. Leave this district, and you can't eat![164] You were therefore a prisoner without bars. Outside the place of your *hukou* registration, you couldn't get education, medical services, employment, or any sort of government service.

Mao retained another element of imperial government structure concerning the peasants: the system of taxation. In the West, we think of taxation as the payment of money to the government.

However, Chinese peasants have little money and mostly operate in a non-cash economy. Again, Qinshi Huangdi displayed his genius as the creator of modern government. He devised a system whereby peasants were taxed in grain and labour – a sort of barter taxation. It was through the mechanism of grain taxation that China was able to support a thriving urban population, military and government bureaucracy a thousand years before this was common elsewhere in the world. It was due to the mechanism of taxation with labour that China's infrastructure and great monuments were built. In imperial times the extent of these taxations varied according to the needs of the state. Most of the time, peasants were required to give the state 15 – 20% of their grain crop and about a month a year of labour. However, there were periods during the imperial era where these taxes were much higher – for example when the Great Wall was built. Some Chinese dynasties fell as a direct result of peasant rebellion following periods when these taxes were raised beyond the peasants' pain threshold.

Mao retained these methods of taxing the peasants. However, Mao became obsessed with peasant productivity because he needed to prove the validity of his political theory. Mao set ludicrous targets for peasant grain productivity, while also setting targets to overtake Britain in steel production in just fifteen years.[165] Anybody who dared to point out that this was unrealistic was purged and exiled to hard labour in the countryside. To meet their steel quotas, Chinese peasants melted down their tools into worthless raw metal. These policies, known as "The Great Leap Forward", triggered famine among the peasants that killed thirty million Chinese.[166] Mao thereby became the leader who killed more people than any other in history.

PASSING THE IDEOLOGICAL BATON

In 1976, Mao died and by 1978, Deng Xiaoping established control of the Party. Deng had long been ideologically opposed to Mao, but held power within Mao's circle by biting his lip and biding his time.

Deng's most famous saying was, "It does not matter whether the cat is black or white as long as it catches mice."[167] The significance of this quotation is that the Chinese word for "cat" is derived from the sound it makes: "mao". In my trips to China, I repeatedly ask Chinese people whether they see the irony in this saying, and everyone seems mystified by my question. Deng's words were carefully chosen. He thrust the knife into Mao's ideology.

Despite Deng's subtle disavowal of Maoism, he did what all successful successor dictators do: he retained the cult of personality of his predecessor. (Compare Stalin's cult of Lenin, Castro's cult of Che Guevara, the Vietnamese cult of Ho Chi Minh, etc.) This was necessary, because successor dictators have no other means of establishing legitimacy of their rule. Deng's stated protection of the legacy of Mao concealed the fact that he moved great parts of the Chinese economy from communism to capitalism. "To get rich is glorious" was another famous Deng slogan. He unleashed the reforms that permitted the spectacular industrialisation of China. He permitted selective entrepreneurship and capitalism to thrive within the communist framework. But Deng did not abandon the old imperialist infrastructure that Mao had preserved. In fact, such was its effectiveness as a means of social control, that Deng's reforms only needed a slight tweaking of the old ways.

He needed to find a way to transform the peasants into industrial workers. As previously explained, the peasants were imprisoned by the *hukou* and *liangpiao* system. Deng modified this system to transform peasants from prisoners on the land to prisoners in factories.

After 1980, he abolished the *liangpiao* food coupon system. This made it possible to relocate and eat at the same time. He then permitted people to become factory workers in development zones without needing a local *hukou*. However, all highly paid, government or professional jobs still require a local *hukou*. The *hukou* system retains total social control. A peasant is permitted to become a migrant factory worker. From there, they can go nowhere. They are still a prisoner without bars. Because they are trapped in this factory sub-class, they are easy to exploit by factory managers and this keeps the cost of their labour artificially low. The *hukou* is therefore the instrument that preserves a system of industrial slavery on a colossal scale.

Understanding this requires only a brief visit to a Chinese factory. It doesn't take long to register the dead-eyed numbness of the people who work there.[168] All emotional expression is self-suppressed as a survival strategy. This fact is a closely guarded secret, but the sheer numbers of people involved mean that this information cannot be hushed up. Western consumers were recently alerted to the possibility that the person who assembled their new iPad might have committed suicide before they took it out of the box.[169]

A peasant *hukou* may permit them to work in a factory outside their district, but it still won't permit them to obtain education or other public services. But if you are a migrant factory worker, you are so easy to exploit that you can't afford much more than your food and your bed anyway, particularly if your family in your home village relies upon your money to help them survive.

Outside these economic zones where non-local *hukou* workers are permitted, people are still arrested if they are found with the wrong *hukou*. In 2003, there was a widely reported case of a man called Sun Zhigang who died in custody after being arrested for a *hukou* offence. This case was a watershed moment in China's embryonic human rights movement. But don't expect the *hukou* system to be abolished. It is too effective a method of social control.

THE BELIEF THAT KEEPS ON CREEPING

So, back to the original topic: belief creep. China moved from imperialism to communism without much actually changing. Chinese communism is merely Legalism spoken in Marxist jargon. It has now evolved into an amazing split system of industrial capitalism working alongside agrarian communism, but still fundamentally based in ancient Chinese philosophical views of government. Looking at the economic expansion and blatant capitalism that represents China's industrial growth, it seems astonishing that this country is still ruled by a party that calls itself the "Chinese *Communist* Party". The problem is that China cannot reform politically because Party and bureaucracy are one. The CCP bureaucracy is the largest bureaucracy that the world has ever seen – thirty-six million people in 2000.[170] Every one of these civil servants is a CCP member, and in true Legalist tradition, their highest ideal of service is total obedience and loyalty to the Party.

Chinese society is still based on the bee colony model of human society: anyone with a rural or agricultural *hukou* is a worker bee, anyone with an urban *hukou* or some education is a drone, and the queen bees meet in secret and command total loyalty to "the Party" that is effectively the Emperor disembodied. The Politburo has therefore replaced the Emperor, and the sixth-century BC Legalist maxim barely needs updating: "The Ruler is the creator of the law. The Ministers are the keeper of the law. The people are the object of the law." We could simply say "The Party is the creator of the law. The Cadres are the keeper of the law. The people are the object of the law." Imperial jargon effortlessly translates to communist jargon, and the people remain slaves of a system.

This is the reason that Chinese communism has outlasted communism in virtually every other country – the causality of the belief has nothing to do with the German with the bushy beard, but is an A/B ideology that is thousands of years old: it is preserved by suppressing all emotion other than fear of destitution and chaos. This is why the CCP leadership detests the Dalai Lama and the Falun Gong, despite both being about as harmless as an old lady's Pilates class. Neither rejects the CCP's rule, but talk of compassion is an attack on Chinese ideology as serious as flying planes into their skyscrapers. Freedom in this ideology requires suppression of all negative emotions. If one atom of compassion is permitted to enter a Chinese factory, the entire edifice collapses because the workers would refuse to put up with the conditions. The Dalai Lama is therefore as dangerous to the Chinese as bin Laden was to the Americans. The CCP makes pictures of the Dalai Lama and the practice of Falun Gong illegal for exactly the same reason that Qinshi Huangdi banned Confucianism.

So, what has changed in two and a half thousand years of Chinese history?

In Imperial times, the role of Emperor passed to the Emperor's son. Now the role of General Secretary of the Communist Party passes by anointment by a secret process. Abolition of the Imperial patrimony has made Imperial paternity no longer paramount. It is no longer necessary for all government officials with access to the Imperial presence to be eunuchs. Basically, high-ranking government officials are now permitted to keep their testicles. That is a very important development. I really care about my testicles. In fact, you could say that I believe in them.

SCENARIO: THE MORAL LOGIC OF TYRANNY

They cowered before him in adoration. He had the power to order them killed, and so he also had the power of mercy. They did not look at his face. To do so would be insolence towards his divinity, but they kept their eyes fixed on him. The whole of his court gazed fixedly at his feet.

He did not look back at them. He needed to keep his thoughts on higher matters, so his gaze was over their heads. His look was fixed on the back wall of the Chamber to the portraits of his forebears. They were the inspiration for his greatness. They were proof of his majesty.

He did not choose to be the people's leader, but it was his fate. The peoples' lives were a bestial struggle for survival. Every day that they went to sleep still living was a victory against the odds. They lived with a gnawing desperation; a dread that their worthlessness would end with random annihilation. But in his presence, they did not show these feelings. In his presence they felt fear, but they did not show this either. They gazed meekly at his feet, their faces blank in total submission.

A supplicant came forward and lay face down on the Petition Stone. "Great Lord, the people are hungry."

He wondered: What is this "hungry" that they speak of?

His thoughts drifted off. He was thinking about the night before when his favourite concubine came to his chamber. He had lain back in his bed, and the concubine followed the usual procedure to bring about his release.

What troubled him was that, at the moment of his release, he suspended all power. Here was his favourite concubine: he could demand her presence whenever he wanted, and could send her away afterwards. But at that moment; at the precise moment of his release he was an infant in her care. She did not show him the love of a mother. Like all the people at Court, she expressed silent submission. It had never occurred to him to talk to her or ask her what she thought. It did not occur to him that she might have feelings. Why would it? Like everybody else, in his presence she kept her feelings concealed. He was oblivious to the one thing that mattered most to the people: they had feelings, and most of these were negative feelings of despair.

Sometimes his own feelings raged within, but he was divine and this could not be displayed. His walk was a glide. His robe covered his feet so that he seemed to float on air. His face was a constant state of passive calm. He had no idea what his feelings meant. He had no ability to see that these feelings occurred in the people. How could he have any such idea? His role was to project majesty, and they affected numbness in his presence.

He awoke from his daydream, and realised that the supplicant was still face down on the Petition Stone. The chamber was silent.

"Minister, what is to be done?" he asked. As he spoke, he continued to gaze forward, but his right hand gestured towards a minister seated cross-legged in the front row.

"Great Lord, the dykes have broken and the fields have flooded", said the Minister.

"The people will repair the dykes."

"Great Lord, the people are working in the fields trying to save what is left of the crop", said the Minister.

"The people will stop working in the fields and repair the dykes."

He gazed at the ancestor portraits, and there was silence in the Chamber. Gradually, the silence was broken by the scuffing of the supplicant dragging himself backwards off the Petition Stone.

A feeling welled up inside him. He struggled with this feeling. What was it, he thought? Could it be that this is what greatness feels like? To him, greatness had always been a belief. He lived in a world in which it was constantly spoken of. There was no alternative theory to this belief. But now, something different had occurred: greatness had become an emotion. His greatness gave rise to a feeling, and now this thought was irrefutable.

He arose slowly from his throne, and glided forwards as the people in the Chamber parted before him.

The will of the people had been served.

This is a more extreme version of Scenario A. A person who lives in an environment where people suppress emotional behaviour is unable to correctly identify their own emotions. Powerful people often find themselves in such an environment, which is the root cause of the old cliché of power corrupting and absolute power corrupting absolutely. What I have tried to do in this Scenario is demonstrate that a cruel tyrant's belief of faithfully serving their people can be a sincerely held belief that is a consequence of being in an environment of almost total emotional suppression. The mechanism for identifying an emotion is missing, and in that state such a person would be almost infinitely suggestible. A feeling arising in such a tyrant could be identified by him or her as simply anything – it doesn't even have to be an emotion; anything conceptual could do. And this thought would be irrefutable because of the absence of any means of empirical refutation. Had I analysed the impact on the subjects in this story, it would also have become a version of Scenario B, but caring about the subjects of tyrants is oxymoronic when viewed from the perspective of power.

THE HISTORY OF A BELIEF:
TRICKLE-UP ECONOMICS

Let us explore belief creep closer to home. If Chinese communism was really Legalism, and now superficially looks like capitalism, what of the Western version of capitalism? First, let us look at the content of the belief, and we can consider the causal mechanism later. (You are probably guessing that it is a C/D ideology, but it's a little more complicated than that.)

Capitalism is an economic system whereby the means of production is privately owned, and the operation of business is determined by a market economy without interference by government. The content of the belief can be broken down into two main elements. Firstly, if owners of capital and providers of labour all operate with a view of maximising their return, it will maximise the aggregate wealth of all people; and secondly, society and the individuals within it always benefit from greater wealth. The second element appears self-evident in a society where poverty is widespread, but I will explore this in detail later. In this chapter, I want to focus on the first element.

THE HISTORY OF GREED

Aspects of free markets and merchant capitalism can be traced to ancient Rome and medieval Europe. However, most historians see capitalism as evolving in England and its origins can be traced to the sixteenth century. Prior to this, the dominant social and economic system was feudalism (which is basically the same as Chinese Legalism).

Feudalism gradually came undone with the rise of mercantilism, which arose from the expansion of European colonial power. Mercantilism is the theory that trade alone produces wealth, i.e. it does not address the means of production. Traders from England (and other European powers) returned home from their new colonies with previously unknown goods that they sold for profit. Mercantilism replaced feudalism simply because the merchants quickly became richer than the landowning aristocracy. Because these goods were new, there were no laws regulating their supply thus ushering in free trade. However, mercantilism was not true capitalism because these new goods were produced far away under conditions that were not capitalist. In fact, they were produced under conditions somewhat approximating feudalism or legalism.

The wealth that resulted from mercantilism was reinvested in industrial machinery, and this gave birth to industrial capitalism. The focus of this was England in the late eighteenth and early nineteenth centuries – a period usually referred to as the Industrial Revolution. Complex systems of production and labour organisation were developed. None of this was regulated, and this gave rise to rapid economic development.

Capitalism was born of shifting historical forces, but it was Adam Smith who gave it a theoretical structure that replaced mercantilism as an ideology. Many regard Smith as being the founder of modern political economic thought. In *The Wealth of Nations*[171] he argued that individual self-interest of capital owners has the unintended consequence of the greater benefit of society. He argued against monopolies, duties and tariffs and government regulation of business. Smith was a close friend of the philosopher David Hume, and was certainly influenced by Rousseau and his views on how primitive societies evolved into advanced civilisations. It is no surprise that Smith's day-job was professor of moral philosophy at The University of Glasgow. His masterwork is, as much as it is the first true work of economics, a treatise on social justice. Readers of the ideologically redacted sound bites never get to the bit where he explores the exploitative consequences of laissez-faire capitalism – driving down wages to worker's pain threshold.

David Ricardo, a sometime critic of Smith, was much more in favour of laissez-faire capitalism. His "Law of Comparative Advantage"[172] demonstrated that, even if trading party A could produce all goods more efficiently that trading party B, there were still benefits to both parties in trading with each other. Essentially, the overall production of both parties, and therefore their aggregate wealth, would be increased if B focusses on producing the goods in which their relative inefficiency is the least. The Law of Comparative Advantage became the theoretical basis for free trade. This idea gained rapid acceptance and had political consequences. Prior to the Law of Comparative Advantage, England had numerous laws designed to prevent free trade and protect domestic producers and business owners. The Corn Laws were a system of tariffs on grain designed to protect English landowners from being undercut by cheaper overseas producers. The Navigation Acts similarly restricted operations in English ports to English ships. The Corn Laws were repealed in 1846 and the Navigation Acts in 1849. This is the beginning of free trade, and perhaps marks the true origin of globalisation.

The late nineteenth century saw other important developments in capitalism: most notably, the rise of finance capitalism. Under industrial capitalism, owners of the means of production were also the operators. Finance capitalism was the gradual separation of owners and managers of business. Control of production and the financing of industry became distinct specialties. These developments led to the expansion of stock markets, company law and complex banking systems. The downside of finance capitalism quickly became apparent. Once it became possible to syndicate the ownership of business, there ceased to be a limit on how large a business could be. This led to monopolies, and today, most governments of industrialised countries have laws limiting market concentrations.

Finance capitalism also led to the rapid development of financial speculation and this led to cycles of boom and bust. These emerged in the late nineteenth century and reached their peak with the stock market crash of October 1929 that caused the Great Depression of the 1930s. At this time, many Marxists predicted the collapse of capitalism. During the Great Depression, it appeared that the Soviet Union could avoid these cycles, and the Soviet practice of central planning briefly appeared to be the future of economic thought. But capitalism had a new trick: Franklin Delano Roosevelt announced the "New Deal". This was the dramatic increase in government spending that ultimately dug the US and the world out of their slump.

The New Deal was a political strategy largely based on the economic theories of the economist John Maynard Keynes. He argued that government could increase economic activity by direct spending or "pump-priming". Keynes was the dominant economist for a period, and his theories led to the emergence of what is known as the "mixed economy" – one where private and public spending and investment combine to maintain economic growth and stability.[173] The theories of Keynes and the evolution of mixed economies caused the Great Depression to become a distant memory. It led to the post World War II boom. This period saw the evolution of the welfare state, most notably in Europe, where government captured excess economic output through taxation and redirected it to provide safety nets to the people. This period also saw economic trends away from industrial production towards service industry – the so-called "Post Industrial Society".

The post-war boom was already over by the 1970s, which saw the emergence of "stagflation" – a period of both high inflation and low economic growth. This led us to dump Keynes, and replace him with Milton Friedman, whose big idea became known as "Monetarism". This is a return to laissez-faire capitalism, but with a twist: the government can move the level of economic activity up and down by controlling the supply of money. Central banks emerged as the principal tool by which governments controlled their economies.

The incredible thing about capitalism today is just how dominant an ideology it has become. It transcends every known culture and creed. Even the Chinese Communist Party is capitalist now. Capitalism is the dominant economic model in almost all countries, irrespective of what religion is dominant. The only exception to this is that there is no capitalist country that is Buddhist – the reason for which I will explain later.

GREED VS GOVERNMENT

The previous section, a deliberately rapid history of capitalism, is included because I am trying to stress that it is belief creep on steroids. We should call the capitalism of Adam Smith **CAPITALISM**™ to separate it from all the stuff inspired by it. Compared to the almost static ideology of China, capitalism is an ideological jumping bean. The frequency with which new theories of capitalism arise is driven by the increasing speed at which old theories lead to economic disequilibrium and become discredited. Governments rely on economists to explain to them why the last collapse occurred, so that they can adjust policy to prevent a recurrence. In fact, the history of capitalism could be said to be the history of how new theories of economics were developed purely to correct the unfortunate consequences of the old one.

This process will never end.

At the time of writing, we are still recovering from the last economic collapse – the Great Credit Crunch of 2007. Economists on the political Left blame this on bankers and those on the Right blame it on regulators, and the regulators are desperately trying to prove that someone did something criminal. The central problem is that all of them believe *in* capitalism, and therefore are logically unable to see there is a problem with the ideology itself. Belief creep in Western capitalism has bought us to a point where it simply stops functioning. Like Chinese communism, it has evolved into something totally different to what it says it is.

Almost all capitalist theories have underlying them the "Trickle-down Theory". This is that if the owners of capital are permitted to pursue profit without restriction, that wealth trickles down to all members of society. The idea is that the wealthy will spend their money on goods and services and this will lead to a flow of money right down to the lowest levels of society – maids and shoe-shine boys.

The strange thing about trickle-down economics is that you will never hear an economist use the term. "Trickle-down economics" is the height of economist uncool because they need to keep their science pure, and this means addressing the overall level of economic activity. The distribution of wealth is solely a political matter. While economists might be a bit touchy about the expression, the fact remains that if wealth isn't trickling down, then capitalism is failing to serve humanity. Has something happened in the evolution of capitalism that means that this could actually be the case?

Yes it has!

What I want to demonstrate is that when capitalism is properly organised by financial elites, the wealth does not trickle down; it trickles up.

HEADS I WIN, TAILS YOU LOSE

The central principle of capitalism is that capitalists should make economic decisions based on their self-interest. But who is a capitalist? In Adam Smith's day, a capitalist was an owner-operator of the means of production. Their fortunes both rose and fell with the success of the enterprise. The successful ones retired and delegated the running of the enterprise to managers, who were paid servants who did the owners' bidding. The identity of the capitalist is already getting murky because the separation of ownership and management has started to create conflicts of interest – a problem area generically referred to as "corporate governance". The balance of power gradually shifted from owners to managers, with owners gradually becoming passive. Today, we should think of a capitalist, not as the owner of the capital, but as the person who makes the decisions concerning its allocation. If the ideology works because the capitalist acts in his self-interest, we need to look to the interests of today's capitalist: the decision maker, who likely isn't the owner.

The conventional mechanism for ensuring aligned interests between managers and owners is to give managers share options in the company they manage. But this is a problem. If the managers have share options, then they get the upside of the enterprise, but not the downside. The owners of the enterprise get both the upside and the downside. This does *not* make their interests aligned because the manager does not care about downside risk. The managers' share option is the option to buy shares at a fixed price on or before a fixed date. This is called a "call option". The manager has an incentive to maximise the value of a call option, but the owners want him to maximise the value of the shares.

What is the difference?

The value of a call option can be calculated using a formula known as the Black-Scholes formula, devised by two economist / mathematicians, Fischer Black and Myron Scholes. The formula computes the value of an option based on the following variables:

1. The stock price;
2. Interest rates;
3. The strike price (which is the price at which the option permits the manager to buy the shares);
4. The time to expiry (which is the period before which the manager must cash-in or "exercise" his option); and
5. Volatility of the share price.

The manager has the incentive to maximise the value of the option, not the stock price. The value of his option is dependent on other things than just the stock price. Clearly, the strike price and the time to expiry are not within the control of the manager because these are contractual terms. However, the manager has the incentive to maximise the stock price at the time of expiry. He can do this (for example) by delaying the payment of dividends until after expiry of the option. The manager cannot influence interest rates, but he can lower the cost of the enterprise's debt by skilful treasury management. However, it is difficult to argue that the manager's and the owner's interest diverges much over this.

That leaves volatility.

Volatility is the variability of the share price. This can be defined mathematically, but essentially it is a measure of how much share price changes in either direction. Volatility, in other words, is a measure of the likelihood that the share price will make a very large move in either direction. If volatility increases, the value of the option increases. If this happens, then the manager will (on average) get rich disproportionately more than the owner.

Can the manager act to increase the volatility of the enterprise's share price? You bet he can!

- Leverage up;
- Launch a hostile takeover;
- Announce a new marketing strategy (a radical one, of course);
- Leverage up;
- Reconstruct the divisional structure;
- Streamline reporting lines and cut out a layer of clerical workers;
- Retain dividends because investment opportunities are just *so* good;
- Did I mention leveraging up?
- Then he could make some bold new product launches, and
- Just to top it off, he could leverage up.

It is important to distinguish between the volatility of the share price (which is the variable in the Black-Scholes model) and volatility in the operation of the enterprise. However, if the manager shakes up the operation as hard as he can, then he is increasing the likelihood that the share price will make a big move – either up or down. If you aren't a natural mathematician, the simplest way to visualise this is to imagine that I take you to a casino and tell you that you can keep 10% of the winnings, but you bear none of the losses. Assuming that you act in your own self-interest, you would find the table that played the biggest stakes and would place the biggest bets. In other words, you would max-out the risk that I permitted you to take.

If the manager follows my simple advice, then he has a 50% chance of making $10 million on his share options and a 50% chance of wrecking the company. Nothing in Las Vegas offers better odds than this because he gets the upside but not the downside. What is fabulous about this strategy is that it requires very little business acumen. Obviously, the employees and shareholders must not realise that the manager is pursuing this strategy, but that is easy. To conceal it, he needs some really good business jargon that can be bought from any business school. If a single manager pursued this strategy it would be obvious, but the invisibility of the strategy is that almost all managers are doing it and so the strategy has become accepted business practice. Family businesses (where the family owns shares and not options) are invariably carefully and prudently run, and this is the way a business should be run in the **CAPITALISM**™ of Adam Smith – it benefits the owners *and* society. Share-option-owning executives dismiss this family business approach as archaic. But the swashbuckling strategy is rational when the decision-makers get upside, but not downside. In this case, the capitalist benefits, but society does not.

Let's get back to trickle-down economics. If the above is going on throughout the economy, then in which direction is the trickling going? Certainly, the manager is going to have to spend his $10 million (assuming the outcome is the lucky 50%). This could be to the benefit of some fortunate pool-boys, nannies and all the nice people who work at the Mercedes factory. But what if the outcome is the unlucky 50%? The manager has the incentive to max-out risk, and this increases the chances that the company will fail. The unlucky 50% means that lots of workers (who cannot fall back on savings) will lose their jobs. If the manager runs the business in a prudent fashion, then it will be safe and boring and will pay healthy dividends to its shareholders and nobody will lose their job. However, the value of the share option is not optimised. Managers might counter my argument by saying that they are professional or that they have an incentive to protect their reputation. I disagree. What is more, I think that this has shifted over the past two decades.

Twenty years ago, even the most high-flying of corporate executives rarely made enough money to retire in a year. Most of them needed at least ten good years to finance retirement. In these circumstances, reputation did matter because if things went wrong, they needed to be able work somewhere else. Today, a half-decent executive can earn enough money to retire in a single good year. Currently, the pay of US CEOs is 262 times the average worker. This ratio was 24 in the 1960s.[174] Their pay jumped 27% in 2010, while everybody else's was stagnant[175] and the stock market barely moved. In fact, many CEOs get a pay rise when their company goes bankrupt.[176] Why care about your reputation?

The corporate governance problem is simply that managers and shareholders do *not* have alignment of interests. However, the ideology of capitalism makes clear that a capitalist should act in his own interest. But the flow of trickle-down has reversed – the capitalist gains upside from maximising risk, while the little guy takes all the downside. Capitalists will all argue that they are honest hard-working people. But incentives are thought-fluff – they only happen in your head and nobody else gets to look in there. This is often summarised as "socialism for the rich and capitalism for the poor" – a classic political argument. This contrast is interesting because what I want to demonstrate is that capitalism is a form of hybrid that is a C/D ideology from the perspective of the masses, and an A/B ideology from the perspective of financial elites.

Adam Smith's **CAPITALISM**™ was that the self-interest of capitalists maximised society's wealth. But belief drift has resulted in ideological failure, and the result is the maximisation of society's risk.

HEDGE TO REDUCE YOUR RISK

All this might sound like a problem, but corporate CEOs are mere amateurs at this game. One hedge fund trader summed this up nicely: "You ask a big CEO what he makes, and it's a huge number, but it's all tied up in stock and options. Traders get paid in cash. It's liquid. It's real. You can go 'Here, look', and slap someone across the face with it."[177]

It is unclear exactly when the hedge fund made its first entry in the history of capitalism, partly because their initial growth was slow. However, once the concept gained acceptance, they went exponential. The invention of the concept is generally attributed to Alfred Winslow Jones who was originally a financial journalist. He sought to find a way that would enable investors to make money whether markets were going up or down. If capitalists profit from the failure of enterprises, then this is antithetical to CAPITALISM™.

Hedge funds adopt numerous strategies, but the general idea is that they should be profitable whichever direction the economy or the market is heading. They achieve this by utilising every type of financial instrument ever invented. In fact, banks invent financial instruments purely because they permit hedge funds to pursue their intended strategies. The term "hedge" fund is a misnomer. A "hedge" is a financial contract that you enter into purely to protect yourself from market movements. The "hedge fund" name originates from the vision of Alfred Winslow Jones that you could hedge against downward market moves, and it was a small step from here to the realisation that you could use hedging instruments to profit outright from downward movements. However, everyone in the industry wants to keep the term because it gives a cosy impression of prudence and considered risk-management.

This impression is false.

Corporate executives get upside but not downside, and so it is with hedge funds. It is the fee structure that is perhaps their defining feature. Hedge fund managers charge their investors a flat management fee based on the net asset value, say 2%, and a performance fee which is a percentage of the upside achieved by the fund, say 25%, as measured against a benchmark index. In hedge fund jargon, this is often summarised as "2 and 25". Generally, the amount of fees that a hedge fund manager can charge is based on the manager's reputation, which basically means past performance. Note that the losses all go to the investors. The prize for outrageous fee structures probably goes to the Medallion Fund, managed by Renaissance Technologies Corp, which charged 5 and 44.[178] That means that even if the fund makes a gross investment return of zero, the investors will be charged 5% for the privilege of putting up their capital. On top of this the manager will take 44% of any upside over a bench-mark performance measure.[179]

What then is the incentive of the manager? It is the same as the incentive of a corporate executive but magnified. This fact is not lost on hedge fund managers, who talk opaquely about the "trader's option". At least, this is opaque to anyone who does not understand option theory. In simple terms, what it means is that the trader has the incentive to take as much risk as he is permitted. By following this simple strategy, the trader has the possibility of making $1 billion for himself, or losing $100 billion of other people's money. Pretty good odds you might think, and I'm not kidding about the numbers.

In 2005 there were two hedge fund managers whose personal income exceeded $1 billion, and in 2006 the number rose to five.[180] That is their income for a single year. The five one-year billionaires from 2006 included the head of the aforementioned Renaissance Technologies Corp. 2007 also produced five one-year billionaires, topped out by John Paulson of Paulson & Co. (I think there is a connection.) He earned $3.7 billion in 2007 and another $2 billion in 2008.[181] He made most of this money betting that the US mortgage market would collapse. He was right. His personal $3.7 billion represents $26 for every US household[182], and his profit came from the fact that so many people lost their homes to foreclosure. Mr. Paulson celebrated his payday by making a donation of $15 million to the Center for Responsible Lending, a Washington-based non-profit organisation[183] Oh! The irony! On my calculation, this donation is about a day's work assuming that Mr. Paulson doesn't work weekends. I would like to hope that this donation was tax-deductible, but due to a loophole in tax law most hedge fund managers only paid tax on their fees at 15%. But why, Mr Paulson? Why? Was not this token act compunctious?

In terms of the potential for losses, we need to explore the history of hedge fund wipe-outs and look at the growth of the industry. The first wipe-out of international infamy was Long-Term Capital Management. Hedge funds like to boast about how many maths PhDs they have on the staff. Of course they do! They need them to work out the arbitrage in their fee structures. Sadly, the maths PhDs just weren't clever enough to prevent the collapse of this hedge fund. LTCM collapsed in 1998 with a loss estimated at $4.6 billion. The US Government was concerned that LTCM could bring down the entire financial system, so the Federal Reserve orchestrated a $3.5 billion bailout. A syndicate of banks to took over LTCM's positions and unwound them in an orderly fashion.

In 1998, this was a near disaster for the entire financial system. At the time of writing, $4.6 billion would be considered quite a small hedge fund. The period 1998 to 2013 saw total hedge fund assets under management (not including leverage) increase from $210 billion to $2.4 trillion.[184] In September 2006, Amaranth Advisors LLC collapsed with losses of $6.5 billion.[185] According to some reports, they lost $6 billion in a single week.

So is it possible that the system could incur the $100 billion wipe-out that could herald the start of the economic ice age? There is not yet a single hedge fund that is that large. At the time of writing, the five largest fall in the range of $20 to $50 billion (with some of the managers also running several other funds). However, this is not the limit of the losses that could arise from a hedge fund's trading strategy going awry because we have to add their debt (provided by banks) to their equity (provided by their investors). There have certainly been hedge fund wipe-outs that have annihilated their investors' capital and some of their banker's debt as well. AIG was an insurance company, not a hedge fund. However, their total loss for 2008 was $99 billion[186]; tantalisingly close to my nice round number, and almost all of this loss occurred from a unit of AIG that operated much like a hedge fund. The executives in this unit exploited the "trader's option": maxing-out of the risk they were permitted to take.

An added aspect of the potential for hedge fund losses is that their fortunes are not independent, and many of them will be following similar strategies at the same time. Although it is not just a hedge fund loss (despite many of them being involved), the International Monetary Fund estimated that total losses from the Great Credit Crunch of 2007 will total $1 trillion.[187] The US mortgage giants Freddie Mac and Fannie Mae alone are estimated to account for $154 billion.[188] Much of this problem arose because different firms were simultaneously following similar strategies, but the executives didn't care because it wasn't their money at risk. In these circumstances, there is safety in numbers because if everybody is doing it, it can't be your fault.

So, looking at this from the point of view of the hedge fund manager, if their upside is so huge, what is their downside?

Practically nothing!

OK, so if your hedge fund blows up and you lose all your investors' money, you won't be a member of the billion-dollar club that year.

Never mind!

Brian Hunter, the natural gas trader who gets the blame for bringing down Ameranth in 2006 was reported to have had personal earnings of $75–100 million in the previous year.[189] Not only that, but the destruction of Ameranth didn't seem to blot Hunter's career. Memories fade rapidly in this business. Even with the pedantic bores at the Federal Energy Regulatory Commission charging him with market manipulation, he still managed to get back to trading with an outfit called Peak Ridge. Rumours started to circulate that he was involved with a giant hole in their profit and loss account too.[190] Even Ameranth wasn't his first little slip-up. He was suspended from trading by Deutsche Bank in February 2004.[191]

Brian Hunter is not the only phoenix to rise from the ashes of other people's losses. Eric Rosenfelt, a co-founder of the collapsed

LTCM was briefly back in business with Quantitative Alternatives[192] – a name that suggests that, like LTCM, it employed mathematical algorithms in its trading strategies – and then he settled at Crescendo Partners. Myron Scholes (of Black-Scholes model fame), another co-founder of LTCM and a Nobel laureate, was also back in business with Platinum Grove Asset Management. It would seem that a Nobel Prize trumps a hedge fund collapse when weighing up one's past.

Where does all this leave trickle-down economics?

Totally forgotten!

Arbitrage is the creation of value by buying in one market and selling higher in another. Early mercantilism was about arbitrage between goods produced in the colonies and sold in Europe. Industrial capitalism was about the arbitrage between raw materials and labour, and manufactured goods.

The benefit of **CAPITALISM**™ is that when capitalists pursue arbitrage they generate net wealth and individual self-interest benefits society as a whole. Capitalism does not do this any more. It no longer serves mankind and has ceased to generate wealth for the whole of society. A group of powerful individuals have figured out how to circumvent the ideology. By taking the upside and none of the downside they have created the ability to enrich themselves irrespective of whether society benefits. Arbitrage can now lead to reallocations of wealth simultaneously with a diminution of wealth.

Self-interest has led capitalists to figure out a way to arbitrage the very ideology of capitalism itself, and consequently the ideology has failed.

NON-LINEAR ECONOMICS

The first principle of economics is that every agent
is actuated only by self-interest.
(Francis Ysidro Edgeworth)

conomics is a dry discipline about graphs and statistics. But it is solely concerned with a fascinating question: what drives human action? Economists ask this implicitly because every movement of money, whether a purchase or an investment, is a consequence of human action. This book is also solely about what drives human action, but I am not going to produce another theory of economics. I am going to explain why economics fails to deliver on its promise, and why listening to economists is self-destructive. There is almost nothing on which all economists agree, and the predictive ability of economics is barely better than random guesswork.

Economists assume that all humans are rational. I *like* that assumption. But I am concerned with how people can misunderstand their self-interest. Self-destructive actions are rationally derived from the tactical deception of behaviour, and the history of economic cycles demonstrates that humans can self-destruct on a national or even global scale. So what would it do to the theories of economics if I could prove that a circumstance exists when a rational individual would prefer to have one dollar rather than two? What if such a circumstance arose systematically throughout an entire society? In this chapter, I will explain the first of two critiques of economics: economic theories make implicit assumptions about human nature that bear no resemblance to how a human actually functions. In a subsequent chapter I will explain that economic theories very rapidly turn into ideologies, and all ideologies eventually become destructive to the people that believe them – so economic theories only every produce benefits during a honeymoon period.

The history of economics is quite unlike any other academic discipline because its nature has shifted so many times during its development. During Adam Smith's day, it was a branch of political philosophy; then Karl Marx tried to make it into a science. Eventually, it started to seem that it could be translated into a branch of mathematics. I will now explain why economics needs to become a branch of psychology (whatever *that* is).

Edgeworth was one of the first to think of economics as a mathematical discipline, and Keynes lamented the inadequacy of economic mathematics while actually indulging in some quite complicated mathematics of his own. However, economics did not really start to seem like a rigorous mathematical science until the solving of non-cooperative game theory by John Nash.[193] This was one of history's obscure little ideas that caused a ripple that spread wide through human thought. I have already mentioned it as the theoretical basis for the biological concept of the "evolutionarily stable strategy". Non-cooperative game theory seemed to be the Holy Grail that economics had been seeking, but even that idea is looking pretty thin these days.

The idea that game theory is a driver of human decision-making had been around in mathematics before Nash. John von Neumann and Oskar Morgenstern were the first to apply game theory to economics. Their book *The Theory of Games and Economic Behaviour* (written in 1944) was the economists' bible for a decade. However, it was eventually realised that zero-sum games (that assume that one person's loss is another person's gain) have little application in the real world. Nash expanded the theory and generalised it to include non-zero-sum games and non-cooperative games (that don't assume people are bound by their promises or are allowed to communicate). Nash appeared to have created a powerful model of how humans make economic decisions. It can be summarised thus: each player in a non-cooperative game can optimise their individual position if each adopts the best response to the other players' best strategy. A "Nash equilibrium point" is defined as a position where no player can improve his position in the game by altering his strategy.[194] What Nash was able to prove mathematically – and for this he won a Nobel Prize – is that for a certain broad class of games, there will always be a Nash equilibrium point.

Economists took this to mean that they could mathematically calculate the outcome of economic bargaining situations using Nash's game theory; and bargaining situations aren't just two people at a street stall, they include nations in a global market. Sadly, it turned out that this dream of economists wasn't fulfilled, because when economists assume that humans are rational, they are using the word 'rational' in a completely unrealistic way. They interpret it to mean that humans compute their best economic interest without the intervention of emotion. If economics is concerned with people making decisions in this way, then it is of no relevance to the species that I belong to. Emotion is the driver of human action. Without it we would slump on the floor like a rag-doll and wouldn't do anything until we died. The scriptwriters of *Star Trek* failed to notice that if Spock made decisions without emotion, he would have been nothing more than a highly computational vegetable.

What I want to do is to take an example of game theory from the real world, and describe how two groups of people coming to completely opposite strategies are both acting rationally. In mathspeak, we construct the same game with different equilibrium points depending upon who the players are. The point of this is to demonstrate the falsity of the economist assumption that emotional bias in decision-making will average out; so the idea that we can statistically predict decision-making without regard to emotion is rubbish. Since economists use the word 'rational' in the wrong way, I will translate this into language that they will understand: they are *irrational* to make this assumption.

*

Prisoner's Dilemma is an example of a game that demonstrates that two people might not cooperate even when it is in their collective interest to do so. The story is as follows:

Two criminals have been arrested by the police and are being interrogated in separate cells without being able to communicate. Each criminal can either betray the other criminal, or can remain silent. The outcomes in the classical form of the game are as follows:

- If both prisoners stay silent, they both get six months in prison;
- If they both betray each other, they both get five years; and
- If only one betrays the other, then the betrayer gets off scot-free and the betrayed gets ten years.

The problem is that neither knows what the other will do, and whatever the other does, each criminal's own position is best if they betray, so both will betray and each gets five years. This is rational, despite it producing a worse outcome than cooperation where each gets just six months.[195] Most people reading this go "Yes, but . . ." and cannot get their sorry little heads around the fact that betrayal is rational. That is because they have emotions, and the emotion of guilt prevents us betraying, while the emotion of anger is a reaction to the betrayal of others. Emotions prevent us seeing the outcome purely in terms of limiting our own prison sentence – a human making a rational decision would not leave out the emotions of guilt and anger unless they were actively suppressing it. These emotions are a product of evolution by natural selection and they exist as an evolutionarily stable strategy precisely to prevent problems of prisoners' dilemma that exist in the natural world.

I want to raise two problems with this classical formulation, and then I want to reformulate it. The first problem is assuming that the punishment value of a prison term is linear. The fallacy of this can be immediately realised if one considers Bernie Madoff, who was sentenced to 150 years in prison at the age of 71 – the punishment value of the 149th year of Bernie's term is *zero*. The true punishment value of a prison term is what it means to the prisoner – an emotional value that clearly cannot be measured.[196] The judicial system assumes that the punishment value of a prison term is linear, purely as an assumption of convenience because the alternative isn't quantifiable.

The second problem is that if we make the economist's assumption that emotional averaging-out means that we can treat people as determining self-interest without the intervention of emotion, then they are assuming that the "currency" of outcome (in this case prison terms) doesn't have an emotional value, when clearly it does. An economist assumes that the currency (whether money or prison terms) is linear – in other words: two of it is "worth" twice one of it: This is a mathematical certainty if we are valuing it in terms of itself, but a mathematical fallacy if we are valuing it in terms of something else (like an emotional value) to which it does not have a linear relationship.

Here is my reformulation of the Prisoner's Dilemma. I solve the first problem, and demonstrate that the second problem is inescapable. (Excuse the pun!)

- Forty English motorists approach a gated railway crossing as a train is approaching; twenty from each side. Each of them lines up behind the car in front of them, and waits for the train to pass. (The English drive on the left.) Waiting for the train to pass is a prison sentence that is measured in minutes. The prison sentence is immaterial relative to the life expectancy of the motorists; so we can reasonably assume that punishment value is linear with respect to time. When the barrier is raised, the English motorists drive off in the order in which they arrived. The one at the front of the queue waits two minutes, and the one at the back waits four.

- At the same time, forty Indian drivers approach a railway crossing. All the facts of the case are the same. However, the twentieth driver on one side realises that if he crosses the road and drives up to the barrier on the wrong side, he will be able to make a quick getaway, and he will only have to wait three minutes instead of four. However, this plan backfires because the tenth driver sees him doing this and dives in front of him; and the same happens on the road on the other side of the railway. As soon as the other drivers see what is happening they all drive forward as far as they can. When the barrier is raised, on each side of the railway crossing is a block of vehicles spread the entire width of the road. The resultant traffic jam means that drivers at the front take ten minutes to drive away and drivers at the back take twenty. In fact, before the traffic jam clears another train arrives.

Now we can see that this is a case of prisoner's dilemma. Cooperation means staying on the left side of the road and betrayal means trying to get as far forward as possible by driving on the opposite side. The pay-off matrix (seen from the perspective of the twentieth driver on each side) is as follows:

"Prison term"	They cooperate	They betray
I cooperate	4 minutes	20 minutes
I betray	3 minutes	10 minutes

I used Indian and English motorists in my example because they both drive on the same side of the road, so nobody can throw any right eye/left brain stuff at me. I also used these two examples because I have actually witnessed this situation in both countries. Nobody should doubt that this really is what happens at English and Indian railway crossings. They are free to go and check for themselves. A few chapters ago, I deftly sidestepped the argument between Edward Said, who claims that ideas of Oriental incompetence are a Western myth, and V.S. Naipaul who claims that such incompetence is a fact. If I am to sidestep this argument again, it is going to involve some fancy footwork. Firstly, I avoid the argument by making it clear that *both* Indians and Englishmen are rational. If I were to say that Englishmen are rational and Indians are not, that would be racist. Secondly, I will later describe a circumstance where this result is the other way around.

In the case of the classical formulation of prisoner's dilemma, whatever the other side chooses, you would personally be better off betraying. Therefore, if we were to use the word 'rational' as an economist would (i.e. assuming that no emotion is involved), it is the English who are irrational, not the Indians. Let me explain why *both* sets of motorists are rational. The clue is to consider the *currency* in which they both evaluate the outcome. The classical formulation of prisoner's dilemma only considers the currency of time.

I know quite a lot about Indian traffic. I rode a bicycle over 3,000km through India, but amidst all the chaos of motorbikes, bullock carts and motor rickshaws the only road traffic accidents that I witnessed were the ones that I caused myself. You probably think that I wasn't paying attention, but I think that the problem was subtler than that. I caused accidents because I couldn't achieve the right *sort* of oblivion – the ability to filter out all the information that wasn't relevant. It might seem strange to say that a nation has a particular sort of oblivion, but Indians have a form of oblivion that is tailor-made for the circumstances they have to deal with. Watch an Indian walk down a Varanasi backstreet, and they will act as if oblivious to the excrement (dog, cow and human) that is everywhere. But they are demonstrably *not* oblivious because they never step in it.

Living in a poor country requires people to manage their emotions in a particular way. When stepping through shit, Indians suppress their revulsion because they realise that if they didn't they wouldn't be able to walk down the street. Likewise, if you repeatedly have to navigate a chaotic road situation, you eventually learn that anger isn't going to improve the outcome, so you suppress it. Naipaul comments that, "It is well that Indians are unable to look at their country directly, for the distress they would see would drive them mad."[197] Indian conditions produce in people a particular portfolio of emotional manipulation that is highly correlated among all Indian people. This is because they all face the same conditions. As a comparison, British conditions during the colonial period required them to treat their colonial subjects like cattle, and the

British could only manage this if they suppressed their moral emotions. This contributed to the peculiar portfolio of emotional manipulation that we know as "the stiff upper lip".

If Indians need to achieve a form of oblivion that is actually a portfolio of emotional suppression, then getting responses out of Indians can in certain circumstances require vigorous stimulation. If you are in a hurry in India and you toot your horn, the oblivion of others means that they don't react, so you have to *blare* your horn. It is not uncommon in a busy Indian street for someone to come through on a motorbike with the horn more on than off. Nobody is going to achieve anything by getting angry with such a motorcyclist, so this creates the need for greater oblivion. We can now see that we are in a spiral of increasing oblivion and increasing horn-blowing. Many of the problems of India are unsolvable because of this spiral: coping with them on a daily basis requires suppressing your emotional response to them, and this creates a systematic problem-blindness.

It might be difficult for you to understand that suppressing your emotional reaction to shit might eventually make you unable to know that there is anything wrong with it. But ask yourself how you know that shit is revolting – you know because you have an emotional reaction to it, and that reaction is known as revulsion. Revulsion is an emotion that arose through evolution by natural selection: animals that recoil from noxious substances are more likely to survive and pass on their genes. We can see a striking example of this in Varanasi. In Europe, water is considered unsafe for swimming if it contains more than 5,000 faecal coliform bacteria per litre, but the River Ganges contain 600,000 per litre.[198] However, Indians consider the River Ganges holy and so they bathe in it. Small children are fully immersed! Varanasi also contains a large population of stray dogs that are some of the sorriest creatures you could ever see. These dogs will not touch the Ganges – they will not drink it, and they will not put a paw into it; so they know something that Indian humans don't. On the banks of the River Ganges, we can see the evolutionary origin of the human emotion of revulsion, but we see it in the dog, not the human. A human (unlike a dog) has a concept of its own behaviour, and by suppressing this behaviour systematically until the act of suppression is forgotten, they eventually lose the ability to know that shit is revolting. You probably cannot imagine such a circumstance occurring in yourself, but this is because it isn't possible to imagine *not* knowing something that you *do* know.

Consider this example: ask yourself how you know what your name is. [Answer: you know because your parents told you.] And now try to imagine not knowing your name. I'll bet you cannot do that. So consider that when Auschwitz was liberated, it contained some little Romani children who had been kept there for medical experiments. Many of them did not know what their name was because the means for them to know (i.e. their parents) had been eliminated. If the means for you to know has been erased, then logically you won't know; and if the only way you know that shit is revolting is an emotional reaction, then habitual suppression makes you unable to know that it is revolting. Remove the means to know, and *obvious* simply evaporates.

Let us get back to our prisoner's dilemma at the railway crossing. Economists assume that we should ignore emotion in human decision-making, and I am now going to demonstrate why they can't do this. The classical example of prisoner's dilemma assumes that the only currency in which the outcome should be measured is time. But our railway crossing experiment produces the seemingly contradictory outcome where the famously unemotional English behave irrationally (using the economist form of the word). The English (if they are leaving emotion out of the equation) should all betray. Now let us see what happens when we put emotion back in. What I am now doing is converting the one-currency model of prisoner's dilemma into a two-currency model.

When an Englishman betrays, i.e. drives to the barrier on the wrong side, all the other motorists roll down their windows and loudly proclaim their disapproval. This is the emotion of anger that evolved as a mechanism for punishing cheaters. This triggers the moral emotion of guilt. Since this is a chapter about economics, we could say that the disapprobation of other motorists has a "cost", and since we started using the currency of time, we have to translate the cost of guilt into time (assuming for now that the relationship is linear). Let us assume that when someone says to an Englishman "Eww, ah say ewld tchap, thet's just nawwt cricket!" is worth one 'guilt point'. How many minutes does this equate to? In other words, how many minutes would an Englishman have to save to consider one guilt point *worth it*. Let us say, for the sake of argument, that it is worth ten minutes.

We can now reformulate our prisoner's dilemma pay-off matrix. But first we have to consider the Indians under the two-currency model. It would be easy to assume that Indians just don't care about disapprobation, but that would be grossly unfair. In fact, disapprobation makes Indians very upset, perhaps because they don't see it very often – and *that* is the point. When the Indian motorist betrays at the railway crossing, the other motorists are all operating within their selective oblivion – they all do a motionless shrug and let out a breathless sigh. Nobody complains. It isn't that Indians are immune to the disapprobation of others so much as it is that they suppress it in themselves. An Indian knows that showing anger produces no result, and so the Indian pay-off matrix under the two-currency model doesn't change. This shouldn't be a surprise, since we knew that Indians were rational to betray in the first place. From this we can deduce an interesting result: in the same way that the suppression of revulsion eventually removes your ability to know that shit is revolting, the only reason you know that there is something wrong with cheating is because you have an emotional reaction to it – anger. And this is also the product of evolution by natural selection. Suppressing the emotion of anger eventually removes your ability to know that there is anything wrong with cheating. In other words: cheating ceases to be immoral!

So what does the English pay-off matrix now look like?

We can now see why it is that Englishmen are rational to cooperate. If others cooperate, then I am better off cooperating, but if

English two-currency pay-off	They cooperate	They betray
I cooperate	4 minutes	20 minutes
I betray	13 minutes (3 minutes plus 1 guilt point)	20 minutes (10 minutes plus 1 guilt point)

others betray I am indifferent; so if I don't know what others are going to do, on average it is better to cooperate. This is rational in the sense that I use the word, and now that we have translated everything into one currency of evaluation, it is also rational as an economist would understand it.

So what does this mean for economics? A central assumption of economics is simply false. Emotional variables in decision-making do *not* average out and so cannot be disregarded. Now that we can see that economists are using the word 'rational' in the wrong way, we can translate Alan Greenspan's famous remark about people behaving with "irrational exuberance" into its proper meaning. What he should have said was that people are rational but demonstrating a correlated emotional bias towards exuberance, and the way this affects their economic decision-making makes economic models utterly worthless. The pomposity of economics: if our model doesn't work, it *must* mean that humans are irrational. No! It means that your model doesn't work.

Emotional variables in economic decision-making have correlated biases that impact one cultural group one way and another quite differently. One solution might be for economists to team up with psychologists in examining the way that each nation systematically suppresses various emotions. They could then come up with a different economic model for each country, but this would make studying global trends a mathematical nightmare. Economists cannot consider the emotional biases to average out globally because some of these operate on a global scale (e.g. anxiety about population growth, food shortages, climate change, etc.)

Is it possible to put emotional variables back into economics? Economists assume that money is linear – in other words your first dollar is worth the same as your millionth. But recall what I pointed out in the case of prison terms, i.e. that we should see their punishment value as the emotional response of the criminal. The alternative linear punishment value is merely an assumption of convenience. Let us assume that money is non-linear: The value of a dollar should be measured in terms of the emotional response of its owner. It would be reasonable to assume that the value of a dollar to a poor man is higher than it is to a rich man. We can now ask ourselves the question: was Robin Hood an economist? It has always been understood that he stole from the rich and gave to the poor for moral reasons, but we can now speculate that he did it for economic reasons because transferring money from rich people to poor people has the effect of increasing aggregate wealth (which is no longer measured in dollars) – something that economists see as the only goal of life.

We could construct a mathematical curve of the value of money, based on the idea that the first dollar you own is worth ten times as much as the millionth dollar you own. Actually, this assumption is plausible – the curve might even be steeper than that. From this, it would be mathematically feasible to construct an entirely new non-linear economics. There is no technical reason why we couldn't do this, but there are three practical problems that we cannot ignore. Firstly, the mathematics would be somewhat daunting. This, however, should not put us off if the result is a theory of economics that actually works (unlike existing theories). The second problem is that, as previously mentioned, there is no way to measure emotional variables. Our curve of the value of money could not be scientifically rigorous. The only measure of its correctness is that it "feels" right, but clearly this feeling will be different for different humans, and we could never agree upon it. This "feeling of curve correctness" would have correlated biases among rich people and poor people. Poor people have no way of knowing what the millionth dollar feels like, and rich people have forgotten their first. However, we should not forget that this correlated bias will occur in the real world because most economists are quite rich.[199] Also, they almost exclusively have their salaries paid by economic elites, and have a strong incentive to say what their employers want to hear. Thirdly, the ideological implications of each non-linear economic model would be immense. For example, the money curve I just assumed would logically imply socialism since we would increase the aggregate wealth of society by transferring money from rich people to poor people.

So our problem is now becoming quite focussed. We can construct a whole range of non-linear economic models, despite the frightening mathematics, but each would be arbitrary and each would have wildly different ideological implications. If assuming that the punishment value of prison terms is linear is merely an assumption of convenience, is it not also an assumption of convenience to assume that money is linear? It isn't excusable to make this assumption purely because it makes the mathematics a lot easier. But if the *only* reason for making this assumption is that all other assumptions are arbitrary, isn't this assumption equally arbitrary other than its rather aesthetic mathematical appeal?

"What went wrong with economics?" asked The Economist[200] magazine. The answer is simple. The outright bankruptcy of economics as a discipline stems from its dependence upon an assumption that is simultaneously false *and* irreplaceable.

What ideological outcome is the logical consequence of the linear-money assumption? Is it not capitalism? The false assumption of linear money logically implies the false conclusion that individual wellbeing is linear with respect to wealth. Could it be that the almost global belief in capitalism is the logical consequence of a simple little assumption of mathematical convenience?

What I will explore in the next chapter is the belief that human wellbeing is proportional to wealth, and that emotional wellbeing is proportional to consumption. I will show that these beliefs are merely a feedback loop in which most of humanity is trapped. However, before I do that, I have a small job to complete.

RACISM VS SPECIESISM

Some of you may still think that I am a racist for comparing Indians to Englishmen. And to you I say: I think you are ignorant Antarcticans. How are we supposed to explain why South Korea works but Pakistan does not if we are forbidden to perform this type of analysis? If I could choose my nationality, I would choose *Stateless*, but then I couldn't get a passport. Patriotism is just a form of racism that governments promote for the purposes of social control, and so I dispense with it. But just to ensure that any lingering doubt is properly stamped into the dust, let me take the example of the railway crossing and invert it. And because taking the example of another pair of national groupings just isn't going far enough, I will prove to you that a bunch of white dudes are less evolved than a non-human. I am going to compare investment bankers (who are mostly white dudes) to chimpanzees. Firstly, I have to take the emotions of anger and guilt and convert them into mathematical functions. It no doubt caught your attention that in prisoners' dilemma leaving out emotion makes betrayal rational, and it is the emotion that makes cooperation rational.

When I explained in Part I that most emotions are the product of evolution by natural selection, I explained that guilt drives social animals to repay altruism, and anger punishes cheaters who do not repay. This is quite difficult to see in humans because layers of behavioural tactical deception blur the picture. Therefore to understand how it works in evolutionary terms, we need to look at a human without language (i.e. a chimpanzee) because they can't do the deception. And this is how it works:

- I groom your fleas;
- You don't groom my fleas;
- I bounce up and down and scream at you – just like a two year-old human;
- My anger makes you feel guilty, so grudgingly you perform your grooming duty.

There is clear evidence that the emotion of anger is present in chimpanzees, but there is another important deduction that we can make from chimpanzee behaviour. Anger *works* in chimpanzees without the need to hit or bite. When one chimpanzee gets angry with another, it is punishment without injury and so we can conclude that the emotion of guilt is also present.[201] The evolution of anger must come first because guilt is triggered by anger. An animal without language cannot have a concept of its own behaviour, and so (unlike a human) cannot feel guilty by being conscious that it is doing wrong. In other words, animals don't have a concept of morality, despite the fact that they have moral emotions. Clearly, there must have been an intermediate stage in evolution where the only means to punish was to inflict pain, and we can see this in a number of social animals that punish by biting and kicking. Guilt evolved because it is beneficial to have a punishment mechanism that avoids physical injury. Perhaps it evolved from the fear of being bitten.

Flea grooming in chimpanzees is a form of prisoners' dilemma that is only resolved when we put the emotional variables in. Without them, cheating would always be the rational result. Let us reiterate some game theory: flea grooming is an example of a non-zero-sum game because the cost of grooming is less than the benefit of being groomed. Let us say, for the sake of argument that the cost of grooming is 2 because of the effort involved, but the benefit of being groomed is 5 because of the health benefit of having one's fleas removed. However, flea grooming is also a non-cooperative game because the chimpanzees (like the prisoners in the classical dilemma) cannot make a secret deal. This is because lacking language is like being in separate prison cells. A chimpanzee's facial expressions constitute a complex system of communication, but it is a safe bet that this system of communication does not permit the subtleties of negotiation (beyond the interplay of guilt and anger). So let us state the pay-off matrix of chimpanzee flea grooming without the emotional variables:

From my perspective	You cooperate	You cheat
I cooperate	3 points (5 – 2 deduct the cost of grooming)	- 2 points being the cost of grooming
I cheat	5 points	Zero points

As in the classical form of prisoners' dilemma, whatever you do, I am better off cheating, so I would cheat – unless we put in the emotional variables. When we looked at the railway crossing, we used a two variable model of prisoners' dilemma, but that is a tad simplistic because really we need a three variable model. Previously, I just assumed that the cost of anger was zero, but actually it consumes energy. I got away with this before because Englishmen have perfected the art of expressing anger without exerting themselves.

But we can be sure that the cost of guilt must be higher than the cost of anger because otherwise guilt would not be an evolutionarily stable strategy and would not exist. However, we can also deduce that the cost of guilt must be higher than the cost of grooming because otherwise, a chimpanzee would prefer to feel guilty than to bother to groom its mate. It is therefore reasonable to assume that the effort involved in anger costs 1 and the punishment value of guilt costs 3. We can restate our matrix as follows:

From my perspective	You cooperate	You cheat
I cooperate	3 points (5 – 2)	- 3 points (- 2 – 1 cost of both grooming and anger)
I cheat	2 points (5 – 3 deduct the cost of guilt)	- 4 points (-3 – 1 cost of both guilt and anger)

Now we can see that cooperation will always be the best result. The interplay of anger and guilt in chimpanzees resolves the prisoners' dilemma: grooming like a good little chimpanzee is the evolutionarily stable strategy.

Now let us compare chimpanzees with investment bankers. The mortgage crisis was simply a case of Indians at a railway crossing.

Investment bankers have adopted the economist concept of what it is to be rational. They assume that this means that economic decisions must be made without the intervention of emotion. Emotion is suppressed in investment banks because this is considered to be *professional*. This is systematic and pervasive and over time it leads to what I call the "Wall Street Disease" – the belief that you can do anything that is legal because cheating is no longer immoral.

People are angry with investment bankers in the proper evolutionary sense of anger – we are punishing them for cheating. But bankers are genuinely oblivious of their immorality [Scenario B]. I recall a time when I was slowing down a deal by trying to structure it in the *right* way, and the salesman on the deal pulled me into an empty office and shouted in my face "this bank is *not* run for the benefit of shareholders." To him, cheating was not immoral. For people who are not investment bankers this is hard to fathom, but think of the Romani children in Auschwitz or the Hindus bathing in the Ganges – remove the means to know, and the obviousness evaporates. The reason you know that cheating is immoral (assuming that you ignore economists) is because you have emotional reactions to it. When others cheat you experience anger, and when you cheat you experience guilt; and the suppression of these reactions ultimately removes your ability to know.[202] An investment bank is like prisoners' dilemma where cheating is rational because there are no emotional variables.

The study of chimpanzees is essential to our understanding of ourselves because they enable us to understand how we behaved before we had language and the ability to perform tactical deception with our emotional behaviour. The charm of a chimpanzee is that you can almost sense them reaching for the concept of their own behaviour but they are unable to grasp it fully. And this is also the charm of John Paulson. When he donated $15 million to the Center for Responsible Lending after making billions shorting the mortgage market, he was reaching for the concept of his own morality but struggled to grasp it. Most investment professionals would do well to be like chimpanzees, but they only make it as far as the

Indian at the railway crossing. They don't know that their actions are immoral because the means for them to know has been erased.

If listening to economists has caused the 1% (in Occupy Wall Street parlance) to believe that financial decisions should be made without emotion, and if this causes them to suppress their emotions, then this has a far-reaching consequence. Economics isn't a science at all, not even a "social" science. It is an A/B ideology. Wealth is the only measure of human wellbeing, and this is irrefutable to the believers of this ideology because all other evidence of human wellbeing has been erased. People who act according to another incentive are, in this ideology, *irrational*. The consequence is that corporate theft feeds wealth, the only measure of human wellbeing that counts; so, therefore, it is moral.

This is the logical consequence of the assumption that economic decisions should be made with the emotion left out. It needs to be put back in. Rather than getting angry at investment bankers, we need to let them know that tears of joy and hugging are OK at deal closing ceremonies; it is not unprofessional for economists to weep when announcing that unemployment and foreclosure rates are up; and hedge fund managers should feel guilty when profiting from the misery of other people.

SCENARIO: PERFECTLY OPPOSITE IDEOLOGIES

The woman lived in a society where most people were right wing and nationalistic. People in the woman's world suppressed the emotion of pity with reference to the unemployed but not with reference to military veterans. In the woman's world, it was empirically demonstrable that the unemployed were not pitiable because nobody pitied them. This was, of course, a tautology. But it was a tautology that resulted from the selective alteration of the meaning of "pity" that was caused by the behavioural tactical deception of the people in the woman's world. Since she was herself part of the mechanism of the tautology, how could she possibly find her way out of it? To her, the thought was irrefutable.

*

The man lived among people who were left wing and pacifist. The man and all his associates suppressed the emotion of pity with reference to military veterans, but not with reference to the unemployed. In the man's world it was empirically certain that . . . [etc. etc.]

The man and the woman believe simplistic ideologies that are perfect mirror images of one another. I did this to demonstrate that I am not on some ideological gig of my own. Why would I take a side in an argument when I can step over it? Why can't we let the emotion of pity just do its thing without having to meddle with it? Everybody in this life has their difficulties, including the rich kid whose daddy didn't love him, and the beautiful woman whose boyfriends always cheat on her. Even the rich kids with loving daddies and faithful partners have their difficulties because, having never witnessed or experienced human suffering, they have no hope of understanding human nature.

HAPPITRONOMICS

In the chapter *History of a Belief: Trickle-up Economics*, I mentioned that there were really two premises on which capitalism was based: firstly, that it makes people richer; and secondly that wealth enhances human wellbeing. Unless we can demonstrate this second premise, then there is no point to getting richer. The exploration of the relationship between money and happiness is a tricky one. People who are both professors of psychology and economics are a bit thin on the ground, so there are two ways to approach the problem. Firstly, we are going to explore what happens when economists try to be psychologists, and then we will look at it the other way around.

The bridge is beautifully constructed from both riverbanks.

Sadly, it does not meet in the middle.

ECONOMISTS PLAY AT PSYCHOLOGY

It makes sense to start the debate from the point of view of economists. They are the more motivated players in the debate because if they fail to demonstrate that wealth causes happiness, then their entire discipline is as much use as a chocolate teapot.

So how good are economists at psychology?

The first economist who achieved fame by playing psychology was Richard Easterlin.[203] His research gave rise to what became known as the "Easterlin Paradox". This states that once people have obtained the basics of nutrition and shelter, then increasing their wealth does not make them any happier. The Easterlin Paradox is a very important conclusion, because if it is true, then capitalism has ceased to benefit mankind.

Easterlin's research is valuable up to a point, but relies on one rather significant flaw: his measurement of happiness. To measure happiness, first we need a unit of measurement. Let's call it a 'happitron'. We also need a device to count happitrons. Let's call it a 'happitronometer'. Easterlin's happitronometer consisted of, uh . . . asking people! Unfortunately, this means that he was not measuring happitrons; he was measuring beliefs, and these will be subject to correlated bias according to cultural emotional behavioural manipulations. To his credit, Easterlin recognised this shortcoming. He distinguished between "avowed" or "reported" happiness, and more sophisticated measures that asked respondents to describe what happiness means to them, and then place themselves on a scale of 1 to 10. For the most part, Easterlin relied on a technique developed by an earlier researcher called Cantril, who developed the "self-anchoring striving scale". However, even this more sophisticated measure relies on the questionnaire respondent calibrating their own happitronometer.

In any case, the only outputs of Easterlin's respondent-calibrated happitronometers were "very happy", "fairly happy" or "not very happy". His happitronometer scale does not go all the way to the bottom. This of course creates an interesting problem in happitronometer calibration: does "completely depressed" count as zero happitrons, or can the scale go negative? This is not a trivial question because it is difficult to know if 'unhappy' means simply the absence of happiness, or a completely distinct emotion. In other words, is its apparent oppositeness just a quirk of language?

There are other problems with this research. For example, when you perform these happiness surveys internationally you have to translate the survey questions into other languages. Cantril (whose data Easterlin used) claimed that great care was taken in this translation. But when the research data is self-calibrated by respondents, there is considerable scope for cultural bias.

Despite all these problems, Easterlin was able to draw some

persuasive conclusions. One conclusion is that he found that at any point of time *within* a country that wealth made a significant difference to people's reported happiness. Pretty much all research seems to come up with this same conclusion. One could conclude that this is a matter of perception, namely that poor people assume that rich people are happier without having a basis for knowing this. Alternatively, seeing people richer than you creates aspirations that you cannot fulfil for economic reasons. This was a phenomenon that Karl Marx recognised about a century earlier.

Another of Easterlin's conclusions was that comparing international levels of happiness produced no evidence that citizens of wealthy countries were happier than those of somewhat poor ones, although it does appear that they are happier than citizens of countries with extreme poverty. For example, in the data used by Easterlin, Cuba was about as happy as the USA, and Egypt (one of the poorest countries in his survey) was the third happiest. However, as noted before, it is difficult to avoid data distortion: Much of this data came from 1960. At this time, Cuba was in a honeymoon period following its revolution, and Egypt had just kicked out their British colonial masters and seized the Suez Canal; so the political climate in each country could have produced a blip in reported happiness that had nothing to do with wealth.

Perhaps his most interesting conclusion relates to time series of happiness within a country. The most consistent data seemed to come from Japan in the period since the 1950s and the USA since the 1940s. There is also emerging data from China. What this seems to indicate is that, over time, people within a country don't get any happier despite significant economic growth over the years. This is particularly shocking in the case of Japan: at the start of this data series, Japan was still crawling out of the rubble of the world's only two nuclear detonations set off in anger; but by the end of the time series, it was one of the richest countries in the world.

Easterlin's conclusions have recently been challenged[204] both with new data and re-examination of the old data. There has been an explosion of international opinion surveys, notably by Gallup.

They talk about "life satisfaction" and researchers are all keen to point out that this is not the same as happiness, but most undermine themselves with a hand-wavy definition of "life satisfaction" that includes a host of emotional factors.

The latest research from Stevenson and Wolfer agrees with Easterlin's conclusion that relative wealth within a country increases happiness. They also agree with Easterlin that the data from the USA shows that happiness has shown no improvement despite considerable economic growth. However, they challenge Easterlin's conclusions on Japan because some of the survey questions changed subtly over time, and this causes problems in comparing the data over the time series. I read all this research and I remain convinced of Easterlin's conclusion regarding the Japanese: their spectacular economic growth has not made them happier. However, Stevenson and Wolfer's biggest divergence from Easterlin is in their data across countries. Clearly their data, shown in the table below, is much more extensive than Easterlin's. I have only identified some of the countries, hopefully the more important ones, to avoid the chart becoming too cluttered.

Satisfaction Ladder (Gallup World Poll, 2008–2012)[205].

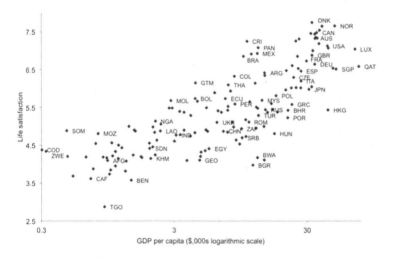

The chart overleaf seems to show a nice relationship between wealth and wellbeing. However, the data scatter is quite wide and the x-axis scale is logarithmic – which is how this data is usually presented. If we remove the logarithmic scale, then an entirely different picture emerges:

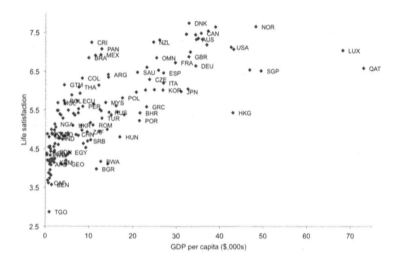

Here it can be seen quite clearly that above a GDP per capita in the high-twenty thousands – the level of New Zealand, Czech Republic and South Korea – increasing GDP per capita has no discernable impact on wellbeing, or at least the impact is completely masked by other factors. Stevenson and Wolfers argue that there is no evidence of a satiation point, but they appear to have only statistically analysed it up to a level of $25,000. However, even if you accept that wellbeing is proportional to the logarithm of GDP without a satiation point, then this still supports wealth redistribution because incremental income has a greater wellbeing impact on poorer people.

My suspicion is that this divergence from Easterlin's conclusion has a simple explanation. It is that the tendency of poorer people *within* a country to be less happy has gone global. Easterlin's research was from 1974, but most of his data was much earlier. At that time, poor people (for example in Asia or Africa) had no clue that rich people in other countries had Digital-Microwave-Programmable-Cappuccino-Makers. Today, this knowledge is inescapable because even the poorest people will see TV (even if they don't own one) and will walk past advertising billboards showing happy people drinking soft-drinks in speedboats. Advertising in less developed countries such as India and China is an incredibly simplistic behavioural deception: a good-looking actor pretending to be happy while consuming a product. It is a relentless and completely unsubtle message. Global media has bought awareness of income disparity to the world's poor in a way that only existed on a local basis before. Easterlin used 1960s data from (among others) poor people who compared their wealth with the richest person in their neighbourhood. Stevenson and Wolfer use data from the twenty-first century based on people who compare their wealth with people living far away that they see through the media. This difference is therefore affected by the development of media over that period.

Stevenson and Wolfer's data could even come from people who compare their wealth with people who don't actually exist – namely actors in American TV shows. It is normal in American TV shows for characters to live a lifestyle that real people with their fictional careers could never afford. For example, the sit-com *Friends* shows viewers in many poor countries a group of people with mostly me-diocre careers who live in New York apartments that would only be affordable to successful professionals. Another example is *Sex and the City*, where the central character survived on a columnist's income, but was depicted living in a house in New York's West Village that recently sold for almost $10 million.[206] This is a case of media distortion negatively impacting people's sense of worth, but it has had almost no media attention. However, it is exactly equivalent to fashion magazines showing thin models and giving all their readers a poor body image. Would poor people be happier if these TV shows depicted the true draughty bedbug squalor that average New Yorkers live with? When I travel in poor countries people react with incredulity when I tell them that there are poor people in America and Europe.

I outlined earlier some of the problems caused by talking to questionnaire respondents who calibrated their own data. There is one other problem that all these researchers share: the scales on their happitronometers only go as low as "Not Very Happy". What is that? "Not very happy" is how I would describe myself on the days I have root-canal surgery. The data for all this research is just not complete.

Andrew Oswald is a cheery economist whose happitronometer scale goes all the way into the danger-zone.[207] His conclusions are closer to Easterlin than to Stevenson and Wolfer. Oswald points out that suicide rates in the USA are the same as they were in 1900, despite six-fold growth in income (although there has been a slight decline in Britain). Oswald also points out that mental health problems, such as depression, are increasing; so is stress at work.

Kate Pickett and Richard Wilkinson picked up this theme in The Spirit Level.[208] They demonstrated statistically by using eleven different measures of health and social problems from drug abuse to teenage pregnancy that countries with greater equality perform better. This provoked a stormy debate that split along predictable left/right lines, and as this became more heated the statistical analysis of the protagonists became dodgier and more cherry-picked.

The problem with all this research is that ideology always trumps empirical evidence, and when the evidence contradicts your ideology you reject the evidence. This is because the ideology is a logical tautology that is irrefutable to its believers, but all evidence is subject to interpretation. As with most sociology, the data is sufficiently dirty that it permits statistical creativity: debaters from the left seek out countries that have high inequality and poor wellbeing, and ones from the right seek out countries that are the other way around. This isn't hard: Japan is a miserable place with extraordinary equality, and in Brazil they never stop partying despite a colossal wealth gap. But there is plenty of evidence that the correlation pointed to by Pickett and Wilkinson is indeed there if you incorporate all the data in a statistically rigorous fashion.

Whether mathematics is politically left- or right-leaning or not leaning at all, all research shows no improvement in happiness in the US over time. Getting richer from one generation to another does *not* improve the happiness of Americans. There is even research that demonstrates that economic growth *negatively* impacts human wellbeing.[209] This is a vital conclusion because if economic growth has to shrink to avoid environmental collapse there is absolutely no reason why this could not be achieved without people's perception of their own wellbeing deteriorating.

The view that these factors need to be considered further appears to be growing. All of these ideas are extensively debated in the World Happiness Report[210] that debates different measures of happiness and how to achieve them sustainably. Another academic to explore these ideas is Ed Diener of the University of Illinois, who authored an online petition calling for a replacement of economic growth as the arbiter of a nation's success with measures of wellbeing and ill-being.[211] The interesting thing about this is that Diener is a psychologist, but many of his signatories are economists.

PSYCHOLOGISTS PLAY AT ECONOMICS

Let's revive discussion of Sigmund Freud, the father of psychoanalysis. His theories of the human mind and the treatment of mental illness and his contribution to the understanding of psychology were controversial in his day and remains so in ours. He is best known for his theory of the unconscious mind. [Wait! Haven't I refuted that already?]

Freud believed that sexual desire was the primary motivator of human beings, and that human personality was formed by childhood experiences. In particular, he believed that we carry into adulthood unconscious desires and fears that have been repressed in childhood.

Freud first published his theories at the beginning of the twentieth century. At this time, his views were in direct opposition to the social views of the time. Contemporary European class structures required respect, and this required the suppression of emotional behaviour. However, it was not long before historical events started to provide new evidence. Freud saw the outbreak of World War I as support for his theories. He argued that this was the release of the primitive unconscious forces that he claimed existed in all humans. World War I demonstrated exactly how he thought we should expect people to behave based on the findings of psychoanalysis.[212]

World War I bought the seriousness of psychiatric illness to the public's attention for the first time. The term "shell-shock" had been in use in the military for some time, but it was only after the early offences of the Great War that the term became generally used, including in the medical profession. There had always been psychiatric illness in warfare, but in earlier wars the problem was buried because sufferers were executed for cowardice. World War I was a new kind of war, where men in fixed trenches bombarded one another with heavy artillery. What quickly emerged was that the psychiatric casualties exceeded the physical ones.

Early in the war, the medical profession had little idea how to deal with these mental illnesses. Psychology barely existed at the time, and it wasn't until the battle of Passchendaele in 1917 that Charles Myers and William Brown started to treat shell-shocked soldiers with hypnosis. Myers' early efforts concentrated on persuading soldiers under hypnosis that they were not afraid, but Brown realised that the right approach was to take them straight back to their fear. His hypnosis treatment involved encouraging soldiers to relive their experience in its full horror, and thereby release suppressed memories of emotional trauma. It is difficult to be sure that these soldiers were "cured" because the only criteria of the time was that they could return to active duty, but Brown was achieving success rates on this measure of up to 70%.[213] These reports of "curing" shell-shock were considered at the time to demonstrate the validity of Freud's theories.

Freud in his practice in Vienna, and the many psychiatrists and psychologists who developed their knowledge treating the psychiatric casualties of World War I, were only interested in applying these new theories for the mentally ill or emotionally disturbed. However, it wasn't long before it was realised that these theories could also be used to manipulate the sane. Some of this was motivated by the desire to create better societies. For others, the reason for doing so was profit.

Edward Bernays was born in Vienna, but moved with his family to New York as an infant. Most significantly, Bernays was the double nephew of Sigmund Freud – his parents were Freud's sister and Freud's wife's brother.

Bernays started his career in journalism and went on to become a press agent. From here he launched the career that caused Life Magazine to name him one of the 100 most influential Americans of the twentieth century. Bernays realised that he could combine his uncle's theories on the unconscious and the newly emerging theories of Gustav LeBon on crowd psychology. The combination of these theories enabled Bernays to develop the business of public relations.[214]

Bernays' earliest success was in promoting Diaghilev's Ballet Russes that toured the USA in 1915. Bernays admitted "I was given a job about which I knew nothing. In fact I was positively uninterested in the dance."[215] At the time, Americans had no interest in ballet. They thought that male dancers were deviants.[216] Bernays prepared editorial letters for all the major magazines and newspapers. Already at this early stage of his public relations career, he was showing his subtle ability to manipulate the perceptions of the public: he countered the prejudice towards male dancers with a questionnaire called "are American men ashamed to be graceful?" This too was placed in certain magazines. Bernays persuaded designers to sell clothing based on the costume design of the dancers, and when they arrived at New York docks, he photographed the onlookers and made sure the pictures appeared in the newspapers. The tour of the Ballet Russes was a spectacular success, and their New York performances were sold out before the first show.

Bernays' knowledge of his uncle's theories quickly persuaded him to directly consult with psychologists in his public relations business. In the 1920s, public prejudice (and some laws) prevented women smoking in public. George Washington Hill, the president of the American Tobacco Company realised that he was losing half his market, and he asked Bernays to break the taboo against women smoking. Bernays consulted a psychoanalyst called Dr. A A Brill.[217] Dr. Brill told Bernays that cigarettes were subconsciously representative of the penis,[218] and that he would need to find a way of countering this image that was exclusively male.

Bernays recruited a group of debutants to smuggle packets of cigarettes to a major parade in New York City. At a given signal, the debutants lit their cigarettes right in front of the assembled newspaper reporters. When amazed observers asked what they were doing, the debutants declared that their cigarettes were "torches of freedom". This was very shortly after women got the vote in America, and this was a gesture of protest for social equality with men. In Freudian psychoanalytic terms, the image gave women their own penises. This publicity stunt appeared in all the papers, and had a lasting effect on the prejudice against women smoking.

Perhaps Bernays' greatest contribution was to teach corporate America that they should create products that appealed to consumers' unconscious desires, rather than their needs. This was an era when the mass-production of consumer goods was in its infancy. The idea that you could make consumers want a Digital-Microwave-Programmable-Cappuccino-Maker that they didn't need was revolutionary.

Bernays set out to create emotional attachment to consumer goods in the minds of consumers. Later, he went further in that he created emotional attachments to the corporations themselves – for example, the Ford Motor Company. Bernays reinvented economic nationalism – he converted it from a matter of government policy and placed it into the hands of consumers.

Paul Mazur, who became a partner of Lehman Brothers in 1927, wrote: "We must shift America from a needs to a desires culture. People must be trained to desire, to want new things, even before the old are entirely consumed. We must shape a new mentality. Man's desires must overshadow his needs."[219] What Mazur is talking about here is the re-engineering of what happiness is, and he was talking about doing this to fulfil a profit motive.

In 1928, President Herbert Hoover addressed a group of advertisers and public relations people: "You have taken over the job of creating desire and have transformed people into constantly moving happiness machines; machines which have become the key to economic progress."[220] Hoover is perhaps the first President to recognise that America had become a consumerist society. However, what he is talking about is the reversal of the causal link that I discussed in the first half of this chapter: It is not that economic progress causes happiness; rather happiness can be re-engineered to cause economic progress.

Vance Packard's *The Hidden Persuaders* describes how the advertising and marketing industry manipulates the masses into obedient shoppers and voters. People become malleable dough, but the objective of this manipulation seems to be lost in the simple maths of who is paying the advertising industry. US children see on average over 40,000 TV commercials per year.[221] This equates to approximately 3,000 hours of TV commercials by the time they have finished high school. This is up from about 1,500 hours in 1980.[222] Children younger than nine-years old are incapable of distinguishing between fact and the intent to influence in a TV commercial. Commercials essentially portray people acting happy in conjunction with consumption of a product, and young children absorb this uncritically. Adults might be more critical, but the relentlessness of it means that eventually your critical faculties become fatigued.

If we have been persuaded that buying the Digital-Microwave-Programmable-Cappuccino-Maker will make us happier, then what exactly does 'happiness' now mean? If it is indeed the case that the human concept of happiness can be re-engineered to suit commercial or political interests, then all the research referred to in the first part of this chapter is meaningless. It relies on questionnaire respondents to report their *belief* in their own happiness, but ignores the fact that this belief has been systematically manipulated to correlate with consumption. The research is based upon systematically corrupt data.

If someone *believes* that they are happy, then does that make their happiness a certainty? Put it another way: Can someone believe that they are happy, but be mistaken? If people are being manipulated to believe that happiness is caused by consumption, and their happiness does *not* increase despite increased consumption, then we should conclude that their true wellbeing has declined.

Vance Packard explores the morality of the persuasive methods used by the advertising and marketing industry. Surprisingly, the people in this industry are very aware of the issue, and have no problem with expressing it openly. Packard notes an article in *Printers Ink* in which an ad executive from Milwaukee expresses the view that "America was growing great by the systematic creation of dissatisfaction." The executive talks about how the cosmetic industry expands by deliberately causing women anxiety about their appearance, and he concludes the article by expressing triumphantly "and everybody is happy".

Packard points out that many people in the industry simply assume that the moral issues can be dealt with simply: manipulating peoples desires increases economic output, and that has to be good. Again, we are dealing with the reversal of the original causal effect: economic growth may cause happiness, but let's work on the assumption that dissatisfaction causes economic growth – a contradictory logic.

We reduce the problem to a simple disconnect: economists focus on wealth creation, and assume that this makes people happy. The psychologists who have been our focus here manipulate our perception of happiness to create economic growth. Each party to this argument is creating the assumption that the other relies upon. Each assumes that their argument demonstrates benefit to mankind. But combined, they have created a circular argument.

Capitalism is founded on a belief in a wealth-happiness relationship. However, the sole extent to which this relationship exists is that the ideology that creates the wealth also changes the perception of the happiness.

The ideology manufactures the evidence of its own truth.

The thought is irrefutable.

SCENARIO: CERTAIN HAPPINESS

The Man lived in a world that valued hard work and prosperity. Hard work enabled the people in the Man's world to build beautiful homes for themselves and live in comfort, and successful people lived in communities with other successful people. They wanted to make friends with people who were happy.

The Man worked in an office. He was good at his job. His boss praised him, and he received regular promotions. Every day, he went to work, opened his mail and delegated tasks to the people who reported to him.

The Man had a Wife. She was pretty and cheerful, and she greeted him when he returned from the office. People in the Man's world valued cheerfulness. They considered it to be polite to be cheerful, so people were cheerful all the time. If you showed any unhappiness, it might upset other people and that would be selfish. Everyone smiled and greeted one another with a wave.

The Man and the Wife were friendly with the neighbours. The Neighbour Husband had a nicer car that the Man, but the Man pretended that it didn't matter. The Neighbour Wife was slim and elegant in her designer dresses. She mixed cocktails for the Man and the Wife, and they all laughed and acted happy together.

On holy days, the Man and the Wife went to church. The priest would address the congregation and encourage them to give thanks for all their good fortune. He never preached to them about morality, or tried to make them feel guilty about anything. He didn't need to. His congregation lived happy, simple, affluent lives and everybody was good to one another.

On the way out of church, the Man noticed that the Wife had a handbag that he hadn't seen before. "That's funny," he thought. "I don't remember her buying that." The Man wondered sometimes what she did when he was at the office. Anyway, she was always happy, so why did he need to worry about it?

It wasn't that the Man had any complaints. He had none. His life was pretty much perfect. It was just that lately he had been wondering what it was that made his world such a good place. He was wondering why everybody couldn't live this way.

That night, the Wife's favourite TV show was on. The studio audience was laughing, and he watched the Wife as her face lit up with laughter. But he wasn't laughing. He was watching her. He was thinking that life was wonderful in an abstract way – thinking it, but not feeling it. He needed to explore these thoughts, but the laughter of the studio audience distracted him; so he went out into the garden. He didn't want to disturb the Wife because that would be inconsiderate, so he slipped out silently. He walked across the grass in his bare feet.

The sun had gone down, and the clouds were fading from blue purple to the slate grey of night. It was beautiful. The Man told himself that it was so beautiful that he did not need to consider again what had driven him out of the house for his nocturnal think. He stood on the lawn and breathed deeply. He stared at the darkening sky in aimless contemplation. He tried to reach for his feelings. He thought that if he relaxed sufficiently, that these feelings would arise naturally.

So still was the night that only one sound caught his ear. It was the sound of muffled sobbing, and it came from the Neighbour's garden. He crept over to the hedge, and as he came closer it became clear: The Neighbour Wife was crying in their garden. He called her name in a whisper, and the crying stopped abruptly. He called again, but there was silence. He tried to peer through the hedge, but it was too dense. In the Man's world, people valued privacy. It was rude to pry.

He went to bed with an uncertain frown, but the Wife was bathed in the warm glow of laughter after her TV show. She fell asleep on his arm with a peaceful smile, and the Man stared at the ceiling *breathing the fresh scent of her hair until he too drifted off to sleep.*

Next morning, as he drove to work, he saw the Neighbour Wife. As she saw him there was a flash of anxiety across her face. She searched his face for any sign that he might have known it was her crying in the garden, but then she suppressed the anxiety. Denial is the best policy; so she smiled and gave him a cheery wave. Better to pretend that I know nothing he thought, so he waved back. "See you at the party tonight" she called. The Man nodded and smiled.

At the office he was irritable. One of his subordinates was suggesting a better way to execute a project than the way he had devised. He felt disconnected from his function. He knew that his productivity was lower than normal. His boss asked him if everything was OK. "I'm fine," he said.

That night at the party he was with the Wife and the Neighbours. Several other friends from the Man's world were also there. Everyone was happy and laughing. Everybody had a drink and the food was as delicious as ever. The conversation was frivolous and people told jokes.

Suddenly, the Man said, "Sometimes I wonder what causes happiness."

"Ha ha!" said the Neighbour Husband. "You think too much." But the Neighbour Wife scurried off to get another drink, or to speak to someone else who had caught her attention. The Man thought she was avoiding him. And then the Man caught sight of the Wife's look. She was staring at him with a look of terror and accusation. Her look was tight. She wanted him to see her look but she wanted her look concealed from everybody else. The look appeared to threaten the Man: "Everything is perfect. Don't mess with it."

In the Man's world, everybody acts happy all the time in accordance with a value system that includes consumerism and a work ethic. They do this because otherwise they will be socially excluded. In the Man's world, the systematic affectation of happiness has caused a belief in a feeling, where the belief is that the feeling is caused by their values.

In the Man's world, 'happiness' means living in a particular way. The causality is reversed: normally living in a particular way would cause happiness, but in this situation, happiness has been redefined to mean the product of living that way.

Like any other belief system, the belief works due to a logic trap. The value system requires people to act happy all the time, so the ability to relate the behaviour to the feeling has disappeared. But if the value system makes people behave happy all the time, then surely it must be working. The rightness of the value system is irrefutable to the people in the Man's world. Happiness must be good, but in fact it is merely a behavioural construct.

In the Man's world, it is of course a problem for the individuals that nobody can identify the feeling of happiness. But it is not a problem for society as a whole because the individuals collectively pressure each other to maintain the denial. The Wife's look of accusation is part of that system of denial. The system of denial works because nobody can see anyone else's feeling, and any problem that nobody can see is ignored.

The Neighbour Husband is completely unaware that he does not know what happiness feels like. It has never occurred to him that he is missing part of the experience.

The Wife ignores the issue, but is dimly conscious that she is ignoring it. She buries the issue in conformity. It is a contract that she has made with herself – it guarantees both acceptance and happiness (whatever that means). When the Man raises the question of what makes people happy, it terrifies her because it threatens to break her numb equilibrium.

But the Man cannot ignore his inability to experience the feeling because he yearns for it. He believes that he is happy while not being able to identify the feeling. He needs the feeling.

The Neighbour Wife could be undergoing a more extreme version of the Man's concern. She is living the perfect life but yearning for a feeling that she cannot isolate – a feeling that she needs without being able to determine what causes it. However, she could be experiencing something more complex: maybe she has, through some great perception, seen though the mask of the people in the Man's world. Maybe she has learned to identify a subtle glitch of human expression that enables her to tell when people are affecting happiness. By this perception she has become aware of true happiness: the feeling; not the belief. Through this observation she has been able to determine that her own happiness is entirely pretended.

The next morning, the Man set his alarm clock especially early. All good resolutions start with getting up early. He had to throw off this doubt. He was worried that if he didn't put a stop to his doubts, his friends would sense it. Then they would not want to spend time with him. It was just one of his moods, nothing more. He knew it.

The thought crossed his mind that he might lose his job. "Oh that's ridiculous," he thought. Maybe he needed to lose some weight, so all he had for breakfast was a single piece of dry toast and a black coffee.

As he set off for work, the Neighbour Husband was in the drive. He wound down the window of the car.

"Wonderful morning!" he called out.

"You bet it is," said the Neighbour Husband.

"How is the missus?"

"Oh, she's great," said the Neighbour Husband. "She is just doing fantastic."

As he drove to work, the Man thought that he would get his hair cut at lunchtime, and he would go to the gym on the way home. As he parked his car and walked to the office, he could already feel the spring come back into his step. He bounced up the stairs and greeted the security guard.

It felt good to be at his desk early. There was nobody else there, and he instantly felt his productivity get back into gear. He had read all his daily mail before anyone else arrived. The first to arrive was his boss.

"How is it going?" asked his boss.

"Oh it's great," he said automatically. "It's just great."

This Scenario is essentially the same as the Generic C/D ideology, but reconfigured to make the ideology centred upon consumerism and a work ethic. I have also expanded upon the basic Generic C/D ideology. The four central characters are stuck in a belief feedback loop, but each of them has achieved a different level of understanding of their situation. A logic trap is only a trap until you have a realisation of what it is. Then it can be escaped.

CTRL-ALT-DELETE

Imagine that you are stuck in your office cubicle at 3am. You are the only person there because you are building a computer model for a client of yours who needs it the next day. After the latest batch of fixes, you run the model again. Previously, it has taken a few seconds to run, but this time it never stops. You realise that by accident you have programmed in a circular argument. The program will run forever in a circle; the memory bank that records the number of iterations will accumulate into the millions, and then into the billions. You have to press Ctrl-Alt-Delete and force the program to quit. Then, you can look at the source code and try to find your mistake.

If we believe a political ideology because it is an irrefutable thought, but the reason for that irrefutability is that it is based on feedback loop, then how can we press Ctrl-Alt-Delete? The source code in this case is a set of beliefs. The belief in capitalism does not exist in a single place, but in the heads of about half the world's population. If the belief system derives from circular causality, is there an equivalent of the infinitely accumulating memory bank? Sure there is! People eat until they are obese; they buy things and get bored of them before they have used them; they pay the GDP of a hungry city in Africa to go on tourist trips into space; and they can't go to the supermarket to buy their daily overdose of calories without three tons of metal to transport them there.

It has all gone completely bonkers!

To escape this lunacy, we could take two separate approaches.

Firstly, each of us can look to what we can do as individuals. This is about true self-interest, which involves escaping our own illusion of self-interest. Secondly, we can work to address the mechanisms that make these illusions become mass-phenomena. Neither approach is sufficient on its own.

CTRL-ALT-DELETE FOR INDIVIDUALS

At this stage, it should be clear that happiness is a lot more complicated than it first appeared. If it is possible that your belief that you are happy is completely manufactured, should you care? The risk is that something will happen that will trigger a "Road to Damascus" moment, when you see through the mist of thought-fluff and your whole world comes crashing down; your life suddenly loses meaning.

The distinction between 'happiness: the emotional state' and 'happiness: the belief' is generally invisible, which is why an emotion can be invented without the believer having any perception of this. It is entirely possible that happiness only exists as a belief state. We can't be completely sure, but we should be suspicious given that we can't find an evolutionary origin for it. However, if we can identify certain causes of our happiness belief, we can start to question whether they really serve our interest.

I can start with a simple observation about happiness. There are only two strategies for achieving it: one is to obtain more of what you want; and the other is to want it less. Western capitalism throws a spanner in the works here, because it is based around making people want more – principally through the advertising industry. But is it possible to achieve happiness by wanting less?

Wanting less is a more secure route to happiness – where both cause and effect exist in your head and have limited dependence on the outside world. The reverse ideology has become dominant in countries that practice every major religion except Buddhism. A central teaching of Buddhism is that suffering comes from the various forms of desire. Capitalism and Buddhism are ideologically incompatible because one promotes needs and the other seeks to minimise them. Capitalism is a form of a C/D ideology and Buddhism is a form of an A/B ideology. So, one way to achieve happiness by wanting less might be to become a Buddhist.

The writer Eric Weiner travelled the world in a subjective search for its happiest places.[223] In his opinion Thailand and Bhutan are somewhere up there – and both are almost entirely Buddhist. The King of Bhutan has even announced that he would consider the Gross National Happiness as the true measure of the country's progress.[224] Weiner's criterion for happiness is biased – though no more than that which economist researchers rely upon – because he asks people themselves whether they are happy. I have travelled in Thailand, but not Bhutan. Thailand certainly registered highly on my smileometer. However, the happiest place that I have visited is Tibet – also Buddhist. My smileometer gives the Buddhists of Tibet the highest score that I have recorded – and this is despite the Chinese invasion of their country in 1949 and their systematic attempts to destroy the culture. This is a book about the effects of tactical deception in human behaviour, and it is possible that the Tibetans are faking their smiles. They might be faking them to piss off the Chinese; in which case it's working! However, when I see smiling of such intensity that it has become permanently creased into someone's face, and that person lives in a remote village where he isn't fooling anybody, I tend to assume that his expression is genuine.

Is it possible to become happier by wanting less without becoming a Buddhist? Of course it is! Seek to live your life such that you minimise the intrusion of societal forces that fuel your desires. The best way to do this is to chuck out your TV. Smoking tobacco is an addictive habit that takes ten years off the end of your life; watching TV is an addictive habit that takes ten years out of the middle of it. Giving up smoking is one of the only ways that people in capitalist countries are encouraged to experience becoming happier by wanting something less. If you give up smoking, your friends will congratulate you, but give up your TV and they will think it odd.

Ignore them!

It is difficult to measure the real cost to oneself of watching TV. For many of us, we can watch it for free, but by doing so we are placing ourselves in harm's way. We are permitting ourselves to be caught up in the forces of advertising that fuel all the wants that we don't need. This is what economists call the 'aspirational treadmill' – the never-ending cycle of want and dissatisfaction. Corporations spend billions of dollars working out exactly how much incremental sales they achieve from an advertising campaign. And that means that when you permit yourself to be subjected to the deception of advertising, you buy things without realising that you have been persuaded to make purchases that otherwise you wouldn't have done. This costs you money, and the entertainment TV gives you in exchange constitutes a very cheap bribe.

Another way to check the validity of your happiness is to travel. When you visit a culture that is completely different from your own, you see people able to live without the things you consider essential. I have travelled quite extensively and it is clear that America and Western Europe have far more intrusive advertising than elsewhere. This escape from your own culture and media enables you to think about what is really necessary. Not only will you reassess material possessions, but also your beliefs; values; ways of doing things. This perspective empowers you to look at your values through the eyes of another, someone who does not have your manufactured beliefs. It gives you a glimpse into the workings of your own values to see what is real and what is not. And when you return home, you look at your fellow countrymen and realise that some of the things they do and want are ridiculous.

CTRL-ALT-DELETE FOR SOCIETY

Our belief in capitalism results from a dodgy maths assumption by economists and a blatantly deliberate behavioural tactical deception by the advertising industry – good-looking people pretending to be happy while consuming products. And gradually, we are all sucked into a creeping process where we all start acting out happiness at certain promptings. We do this to demonstrate our ideological compliance and, thereby, we manufacture the evidence of the truth of our belief.

I am not attacking capitalism as an ideology *in comparison to* some other ideology. I picked on capitalism for my ideology demolition because it is the world's biggest ideology. I did it, as George Mallory said when asked why he wanted to conquer Mount Everest, "Because it's there!" I am merely using it as an example to attack the idea (which again most of us believe) that a political process must be driven by an ideology of human wellbeing. The problem is not with capitalism per se, it is with the underlying assumption that we can define human wellbeing in terms of *emotional* wellbeing. In other words, we should not dump capitalism and replace it with another ideology. Instead, we need to look for a new way of driving politics.

The central problem is this: if it is indeed possible to re-engineer what people perceive as central to their happiness, then it must be theoretically possible to persuade people to adopt *any* political ideology. If happiness is a belief and not a feeling, is there not a risk that we can be engineered to believe that happiness can be caused by any social environment? Political leaders who acted on this hypothesis produced some of the worst aberrations in history, for example Nazism, or the bizarre ideology of North Korea that involves more smiley flag-waving than Americans at the Olympics.

It could be argued that the sole objective of political ideology is to keep people productive and docile. If this can be achieved, then who cares if the masses are actually having fun? China is a society where everyone is productive and docile. In that society, we tend to assume that the rulers do not care if the masses are happy; it is sufficient for them to be docile. But it is arguable that this is equally true of Western democracies. Western democratic politicians certainly spend a lot of time telling their citizens how much better off than everyone else they really are – a rather empty form of propaganda.

What I hope I have demonstrated is that no ideology is

fundamentally correct, but they all seem so because they are tautologies from the perspective of their believers. The idea that ideologies can be defined by measures of emotional wellbeing is false because the ideology alters the perception of the emotion that is the measure of its truth.

THE POLITICS OF KITSCH

The word 'kitsch' is often applied to objects of poor taste, for example garden gnomes or 1960s plastic furniture. However, this only captures part of its meaning because there is a wider sentimental meaning applied to the word. The word was originally German, but is now used in most Western languages. It originally referred to excessive sentimentality, but from the time that it entered the English language in the early twentieth century, its meaning has evolved. It is no longer necessary for something to invoke sentimentality to be kitsch. My favourite definition of the word is that used by the Czech writer Milan Kundera in his classic novel *The Unbearable Lightness of Being.*[225] "Kitsch," says Kundera, "is the denial of shit."

It is true that plastic garden gnomes are representative of a fake perfect world. 1960s kitsch plastic furniture is also representative of a consumerist dream, from a time when nobody imagined that there might be a downside to that lifestyle. The relevance of aesthetic ideals in this book arises because political ideology is a form of ideal. An aesthetic ideal is generally thought to be an ideal of beauty or, in Stendahl's words "the promise of happiness". Political ideology is about benefiting mankind on some measure, and what better measure than to promise happiness. There is no ideology that does not come with its own form of political kitsch; its own promise of happiness – a denial of shit.

Political kitsch is easier to detect in alien political ideologies than it is in the one in which you have been raised. Milan Kundera, a

Czech, considered the pinnacle of communist kitsch to be the May Day parade: girls dress up in red blouses, and the leaders beam idiotically and wave at the masses from their podium as the band marches by.

To me, the pinnacle of communist kitsch was the sculpture known as Worker and Kolkhoz Woman.[226] A young man and woman hold the hammer and sickle aloft. The man is square-jawed, tall and muscular. His singlet is cut low to show off the flex of his arm as he holds the hammer aloft. The woman has long wavy hair, and her dress floats in the breeze. She holds her sickle in a soft feminine hand. The pair of them gaze at a point just above the horizon, focussed on infinity – vaguely representative of lofty ideals. Both of them are physically attractive, but as they stand in their pose they do not touch. Sexual passion might be disruptive to productivity, and one's first duty is to further the glory of the fatherland.

It isn't hard to see that this image as kitsch – Soviet political kitsch. What then (in Kundera's use of the word) is the shit that is being denied? Real Soviets that carried hammers and sickles anywhere other than in propaganda art had torn clothes and stunk of sweat. Their skin was worn to creased leather by the sun and hard labour. Their nails were broken and their hair was lank and greasy. Their bodies were gnarly, but out of shape – the result of a combination of manual work and poor diet.

It is important to note that the political kitsch in this sculpture is ideology-specific. It would not work in America.

The political kitsch in propaganda art or a march-past parade is perhaps too obvious. However, political kitsch comes in many other forms. Clearly, it is the point of political kitsch that it is difficult to detect. The shit denied must be invisible or the denial isn't working. The whole point is that the foolish masses are presented with a vision of perfect happiness, and don't realise that this is a pretence.

POLITICAL KITSCH PERSONIFIED

Political kitsch in the form of a person can be both deliberate and unintentional. Deliberate political kitsch personified can be seen in almost any totalitarian state.

The posters of Chairman Mao seen all over China are a combination of propaganda and personality cult. This image, with its clean smooth skin and Mona Lisa smile, conceals the repulsive reality of the man: he was so suspicious of oral hygiene that his teeth were coved with a heavy greenish film and his gums oozed pus; and he spread his genital infections to dozens of young women because he couldn't be bothered to take precautions or have them treated.[227]

Kim Jong-il, the former leader of North Korea was officially known as "Dear Leader", which was pure, manufactured political kitsch. His official biography claims that his birth on a Korean mountain was foretold by a swallow, a double rainbow and a new star in the heavens. This seems an unlikely portent for a man who was rumoured to be a porno-flick aficionado. In fact, he was born in exile in the far east of Russia. I am eagerly awaiting the official kitsch of his son and successor.

It would be wrong, however, to presume that political kitsch in its human form is only found in totalitarian regimes. However, outside the world of totalitarian regimes, this political kitsch can never risk being obviously intentional.

Silvio Berlusconi of Italy always teetered on the edge of political kitsch. His nickname "The Great Seducer"[228] is a rival on the kitschometer for "Dear Leader" although unlike the latter it is not officially sanctioned. Why would it be? It is much more effective if it appears to have arisen spontaneously. However, Berlusconi controlled 90% of Italy's national television broadcasting.[229] This (on my calculation) is only 10% less than Kim Jong-il's, and Italy is supposed to be an advanced democracy. I cannot be sure whether or not Berlusconi's nickname first appeared on media he controlled, but I do wonder.

And then, of course, there is Sarah Palin, the hockey-moose with lipstick. Do an internet search of images of her and you will find that in almost all photographs she only has one expression – an unvarying beauty-pageant smile. The message is pure kitsch: believe in me, and you too can experience this vacuous happiness that is completely untroubled by doubt – it just takes a vote!

POLITICAL KITSCH INSTITUTIONALISED

Political kitsch can also take the form of an institution, or tradition. The communist May Day parade mentioned earlier is an example of this, while the British Queen is actually political kitsch personified. Every jubilee we get another biography published that promises to be truthful, but ends up being as cloyingly sycophantic as the previous one. This is clear denial of shit – if she had obnoxious habits, we wouldn't be told about them. However, the broader issue is that the institution of the British monarchy is kitsch. It is an irrelevant glitch of history. All that remains is waving from horse-drawn carriages, and smashing champagne bottles on warships built to control a non-existent empire.

Britain is defined by institutionalised political kitsch. The state opening of Parliament is one of the world's only events where allegedly heterosexual men wear tights and shiny shoes with buckles on them. Then, of course there is the British aristocracy. Some of them are by now impoverished. The only evidence of their former greatness is that their spoken English sounds like a sea lion with a clothes peg on its nose. Some have managed to hang on to real wealth (if not political power), which gives them the right to speak normally. Aristocrats like this embody a nostalgia for feudalism that is entirely kitsch. Old men in cloth caps live out a tableau of the old England seen in oil paintings by John Constable, so that the estate can be turned into a tourist theme park – the only way any aristocrat can afford the upkeep of the stately home.

Lastly, there is the House of Lords. The English Civil war ended in 1651, and this marked the start of the pre-eminence of the British

Parliament in wielding political power. However, it took until the House of Lords Act 1999 (almost 350 years) before aristocratic hereditary peers lost the right to sit in the House of Lords and exert a modicum of political power. That still has not stopped the House of Lords being a sentimental throwback to a glorious age viewed through rose-tinted spectacles. My favourite House of Lords eccentricity is that they have their own brand of Malt Whisky. It keeps them focussed on solving the problems of the nation. [I had a bottle of it myself. "Aged 10 years." It wasn't bad!]

POLITICAL KITSCH AS CULTURE

America does not do institutional political kitsch. Maybe they are trying, but it just takes a few more centuries to develop. Instead, Americans embed their political kitsch in culture. Consider the "I WANT YOU" Uncle Sam poster and the consumerist aesthetic of rosy-cheeked pin-up housewife advertisements of the mid-twentieth century.

What other nation has a national dream? Is there a Norwegian Dream, or a Bangladeshi Dream? Americans believe that having a national dream makes them stronger, but I would argue that it makes them more delusional. For some, who live in trailer parks, Native American reservations or urban ghettos, the American Dream is the false promise of the unobtainable. Denial of shit does not get crueller than this. While the American Dream was originally about enjoying the fruits of hard work, in reality, it is a work ethic, an economic stimulus of the mind. From its early origins, it has evolved into a consumerist fantasy – owning everything from your home to your pickup truck; that is, until the bank forecloses. Social mobility for the poorest in America is now the lowest of the developed nations, so the American Dream is statistically rudely awoken.[230]

Another American contribution to the world of political kitsch is "Manifest Destiny". Note that it is always written with capital letters as if it is necessarily a proper noun. Originally, a mid-nineteenth century political slogan; it morphed into a justification of the conquest of the Native American people, and by the late nineteenth century was being summoned as justification for colonisation of foreign lands. The belief kept on creeping, and by the 1920s it was being invoked by President Woodrow Wilson as the Manifest Destiny of the United States to spread democracy throughout the world. Today, in the age of global media, American politicians are loath to use the term for fear of being laughed at by the rest of the world. That does not mean that the expression is dead. Children in American schools are still taught about it, and it is difficult to know whether their little minds take it literally or if they know that today we should see it as an ironic throwback. However, even in the corridors of power, one gets the sense that it still lurks below the surface. It is part of the thinking, even if not spoken. Would America have invaded a Middle Eastern country, when the weapons of mass destruction were actually in the country next door, were it not for Manifest Destiny?

Why then is Manifest Destiny political kitsch? It is the blurring of the line between what is in America's interest and what it sees as its duty: "I didn't want to wipe out the Native American, but I felt that it was the right thing to do." "I didn't want to invade Iraq, but felt that it was our duty." It wouldn't take much of a tweak before Manifest Destiny could be invoked as the justification for genocide. A more contemporary version of the same thing is "American Exceptionalism", which is really no different to German Exceptionalism circa 1939 or British Exceptionalism in the nineteenth century. As political kitsch, it is comparable to the "Divine Right of Kings", an English notion of God-given power that was pretty much dead half a millennium ago.

POLITICAL KITSCH AS IDEOLOGY JARGON

The language of political kitsch is ideology-specific. For example, the word 'peasant' is a term of communist political kitsch. It is supposed to symbolise something noble about working the land –

serving the good of the "fatherland". America has always strongly identified itself as anti-communist, and therefore it rejects communist political kitsch. With that, comes the rejection of its jargon. If you called a poor American farmer a peasant, he would punch your lights out. The jargon of communist kitsch is derogatory in America.

The term "Fatherland" is Soviet political kitsch. However, Russian imperial kitsch tended to talk about "Mother Russia"; so with the Bolshevik revolution came a national sex change. It is strange that Chinese communists when trying to stoke-up nationalism and patriotism always talk about "Motherland". No land harbours parental instincts for the people that happen to live on it. All land is just a patch of dirt for humans to exploit. Would Mars become a "Motherland" if it were found that people actually lived there? Americans have never used a term like Motherland or Fatherland; indeed it would seem strange in a country stolen from Native Americans barely more than a century ago. However, shortly after 9/11 the term "Homeland" appeared in the lexicon of American political kitsch and was immediately institutionalised in the Department of Homeland Security. "Homeland" is just "Motherland" without the innate sexism. Political kitsch is becoming politically correct.

America has another piece of political kitsch that it can truly call its own: "The American People". Try saying "The Belgian People", and it simply does not have the same ring. The kitsch in this catchphrase is the suggestion that all Americans are a homogenous group with common values – invoking what the country "stands for". Americans do not have homogenous values. Whenever anyone points this out to a political pundit, there is an attempt to narrow the conversation down to "core values". Presumably, the longer the conversation continues, the smaller the set of "core values" becomes.

POLITICAL KITSCH AS REFERENCE TO FEELINGS

Political kitsch as a reference to feelings is a more recent phenomenon. Prior to the twentieth century, people in power would never have considered the feelings of their subjects to be relevant. One such example of this form of kitsch, commonly used by American politicians, is the idiom "Loved Ones". Referring to soldiers serving in Iraq and their "Loved Ones" in the same sentence makes any criticism of what is said seem petty. By the use of these words, a politician can reference the unknown feelings of the unseen masses. Feel their pain, without leaving the Oval Office! This is "caring about" at its most empty. Touch the button, and trigger their sentiments without having to bother to look into their eyes. It is a cheap linguistic reflex to make a politician appear to feel what the masses feel. It just trips out of the speechwriter's lexicon and straight onto the teleprompter. From there it mainlines from a politician's lips to your heartstrings. Aahhh!

There is however, a bigger word in the vocabulary of political kitsch; one that transcends all ideologies and cultures.

That word is "Freedom".

I have listed this under the subtitle of "political kitsch as reference to feelings" because the nature of freedom can be hard to define. There is a continuum, where at one end freedom is a physical state and at the other end it is pure feeling. The physical state simply means that you are not in prison. The feeling state of freedom is, for example, what you experience when you stand alone on a mountaintop and breath in the view below you. Between the extremes of physical and feeling state lie numerous hybrid states, including freedom to think and freedom to express. And there is a graduation of belief in the lack on constraint under which an individual operates. It is in this in-between zone that freedom tends to fall into the orbit of political kitsch. These are not physical states or feeling states, they are belief states.

Why then is "Freedom" political kitsch? Because all people operate under constraint, and the notion of freedom is in the denial of this constraint. Take the country that calls itself "The Land of the Free" – an expression of political kitsch in itself. This country has 5% of the world's population, but almost a quarter of the world's prisoners.[231] Over 1% of its adult population is in prison[232]; that is over 2.3 million people,[233] and this does not count over 4.8 million people on parole.[234] The total number of Americans in prison, on parole or on probation stood at one in 34 in 2011 and this statistic has been as high as one in 31.[235] For some demographics, this statistic is truly horrifying: for black men between 20 and 34, one in nine is behind bars[236] and I assume that many more are on parole. All the American lawyers that I have asked tell me that it is not actually illegal to be a black man in the USA. Are we to conclude that most of the consequences of being a black man are illegal? And then there is the problem of the mentally ill. One study found that 93% of people being admitted to prison had had a psychiatric disorder at some point in their life. Nearly two-thirds had had psychiatric disorders at least three times in their lives.[237] Is the prison system actually supposed to be a dumping-ground for all the unwanted of society; all the people who are not economically productive?

This is not the end of the restrictions on freedom that exist in the Land of the Free. The United States has (relative to other wealthy industrialised nations) very little social safety net, and very limited protection of employee rights. Taken together, this produces an astonishing pressure on Americans to conform. Step out of line, and all of the following could befall you:

- You lose your job;
- When your job goes, you lose your medical insurance;
- The bank forecloses your house;
- Your car is repossessed, meaning that you cannot drive to job interviews;
- Your credit rating is cut to the point where you struggle to rent an apartment and your credit cards stop working;
- Your children won't go to college; and
- If you steal to feed your children, you go to prison anyway.

Freedom means doing what you want. But conformity not only means doing what you are told, it means acting happy at the appropriate prompting. If you work for an American company, you cannot risk letting it show that you are bored with your work, so you act out contentment. However, there is one critical factor in the pressure to conform in the Land of the Free: it is the genius of American politics that none of the pressures for conformity come directly from government:

- Get sent to prison – Independence of the judiciary.
- Bank forecloses your house – Whose fault was it that you didn't make your payments?
- Your boss fires you – You should have toed the company line and worked harder!
- You lose your medical insurance – Why didn't you pay the premium?
- Your children won't go to college – You should have saved more!
- Your credit rating gets crushed – That's because you are not creditworthy.
- You cannot feed your children or pay the rent – Then get a job!

The pressure to live a corporate or institutional lifestyle is overwhelming. "Freedom" is the denial of this shit. At least, it is the transference of the means of oppression from the government to other forces in society. Step out of line, and you fall into oblivion. Avoid these pitfalls, and you can do just what the hell you want.

So in a book about how people conceive of emotional states and behave self-destructively, why is any of this relevant? The idea that freedom is an emotional state is the ultimate political myth because beliefs in emotional states are so easy to manufacture. The mythology is created with constant behavioural and verbal reinforcement – this is why American politicians talk about it so much. Politicians in Denmark, for example, rarely bother. Myths such as this can be manufactured in conjunction with any ideology. It is common for Islamic fundamentalists to say that "True Freedom" can only be achieved by the practice of Islam. If this can be said of any ideology, then the suggestion that *your* ideology uniquely confers freedom upon those that believe it is mere thought-fluff. Freedom means the right to have what you have been taught to want. People's desires are manufactured to suit a political objective, and because they are their desires they *want* to fulfil that political objective. In a capitalist country, you are taught to want a Digital-Microwave-Programmable-Cappuccino-Maker; in a communist country you are taught to want a society free of a class system. In the contemptible world of Nazi Germany you were taught to want a world uncorrupted by Jews, Gypsies, homosexuals, etc. and the kitsch of this was bound up in the romantic ideal of the great German "race": a cultured people that gave the world Goethe, Wagner and Beethoven.

Political kitsch is the cynical denial of negativity for the purposes of keeping people docile, productive and artificially contented.

"Man is born free; and everywhere he is in chains"[238] is perhaps the most famous saying in the literature of political thought. But the chains that Rousseau describes are not made of iron; they are made of words and, perhaps more importantly, systematic misrepresentation of emotional behaviour.

SCENARIO: A/B FREEDOM

In a sea of workstations, the girl hunched over her soldering iron. Deft, calloused fingers manoeuvred chips on to circuit boards. Her eyes were fixed on the point where the soldering iron touched the circuit board. She could not afford to look up. She had a production target to meet. The foreman urged her on; the company was under pressure from middlemen and markets that were far away – forces that, to the girl, were little more than a dream.

Every day, when she left the factory after dark, she passed a huge illuminated billboard – happy people smiled as they spoke into their mobile phones. There were no streetlights in the city where the girl worked. The billboard lit the street so that she could find her way back to her dormitory. She passed under the billboard, but she didn't look up. She didn't want to make any connection between herself and the people pictured on the billboard.

At her workstation, she was surrounded by other young people. These people were fulfilling exactly the same function as she was, but she didn't stop to talk to them. She didn't have time. She focussed on that single point at the tip of her soldering iron. She blotted out the world around her: the rodent scratching noises of her fellow workers; the clatter of the fan whose blade touched the protective wire cover. She stared, stared, stared at the tip of that soldering iron, and, gradually, she fell into a state of hypnosis.

She crouched over her work – a foetus on a chair – and she let the misty bubble descend over her. She entered the zone of suspended numbness where her fingers functioned automatically. She had no sense of any feeling, except the grip of her fingertips on the soldering iron. In this state she became free: free from boredom; free from loneliness and frustration; free from the sense of alienation that came from looking up and seeing the endless expanse of hunched backs that stretched out before her.

Sometimes, she could remain in her hypnotised state until she was sharply woken by the rude noise of the factory siren. She would look up dazed, and her colleagues would look at each other and smile in recognition. She knew that in that state, she was more likely to achieve her production targets, but more importantly she knew that she could retain her inner calm. These were the best days.

On other days, she was not so lucky. She had come to realise that the problem days often followed the days when she had looked at the billboard on her way to the dormitory; the days when she had permitted herself to see her role in the world of creation and consumption. Then, she would be unable to muffle her sensory perception. The noises that surrounded her on the factory floor became enhanced, internalised in her head so that they were a resonant intrusion; keeping her conscious of her dismal life, and the injustice of making cheap electronic goods that she could never afford.

These days were a torture, but she had even learned to turn this into production. When she could not enter her state of numb automata, she used her anger to fuel her work. She grit her teeth. She enjoyed the accidental burn of her soldering iron. It forced her to remind herself to believe that one day she would escape this world. She would be with her family, in her village, and she would not have to walk past the billboard to the dormitory.

On these days, when the factory siren sounded, she did not look up and smile at her colleagues. She knew that the ones who smiled were the ones who had succeeded in entering that hypnotic inner world. She had been angry, and she could not let anyone in the factory know that. As soon as she heard the siren, she would lean back and let her neck muscles go loose. She would stare at the ceiling and breathe deeply. Now it was her time, and there was so little of it that she could not let that time be spoilt with useless feelings.

Once a week, she had a half-day. She would leave the factory in the early afternoon, and she would buy some food from a street stall and sit in the park. Some of her friends from the factory would come with her. She thought of them as friends, but their friendship only went so far. Talking of their anger or frustration was pointless and dangerous; talking of their dreams would make them depressed. So mostly, they sat and exchanged few words – pleasantries about the weather, or asking after their families and their ailments. Anyway, this was her time; too precious to be spoilt. She needed to use this time, to focus on her calm, her inner peace, so that when she sat down at her workstation in the factory the next day she would be able to sink into that trance that enabled her to live her day in freedom.

This Scenario hypothetically constructs an illusion of freedom in a person that no Westerner would see as free. It is a modified form of the Generic A/B ideology that identifies freedom as the absence of all undesirable emotional states. She lives in a world where everybody is denying the presence of undesirable emotions by suppressing the behaviour that would naturally emanate from them.

VOTE FOR THE GESTURE

Imagine that you had just been elected President, and were settling into the Oval Office for the first time. What would be your first thoughts? Perhaps you would notice that your predecessor had disgusting taste in soft furnishings. All those tacky velvet curtains would have to go. But never mind, curtains can only stand about four years of being breathed on by foreign leaders, or being hidden behind by White House interns. You can replace these with some cream damask ones – practical enough to last four years.

Once you have sorted out the curtains, you might then start to think about policy. You could fiddle with the tax code a bit, and allocate some funds to build a new airport or a few bridges. You might up the benefits of military veterans, or designate a National Park or two. That ought to be popular. What about reform of the medical system? Nah! There really is no point, because anything you do will take at least six years before any effect is noticeable, and by then you may not be in office; so no point in touching that one then. You will just have to make do with expressing your concern, so everyone thinks that you really care about it. Reform of retirement finance? Again, no point! It would take at least twenty years for any change in policy to have a noticeable effect, and most of the people who elected you are either too young to care about their pension, or too close to retirement for anything you do to make a difference. So again: some well-chosen words, delivered with a furrowed brow should do the trick. Carbon emissions and reforestation? Forget it! Whatever you do there, you will be dead before it makes any difference. By then, everyone will have forgotten that it was your idea anyway. Best to skip that one too.

"It has been said that Democracy is the worst form of government, except for all those other forms that have been tried from time to time."[239] So Winston Churchill told the British Parliament. Democracy is one of our best ideas yet. But what happens if we forget its shortcomings?

Shortcomings, for example, like elected leaders being given a fixed time to make a difference. Any policy you implement must have a measurable benefit within a single term of office, or it is pointless to adopt it. As a result, all democratic countries gradually accumulate a whole host of problems where the fix will take decades. No elected politician has an incentive to tackle it. China, whose leaders expect to rule until oblivion, does not have this problem.

I am setting out a theory of how beliefs work. A political ideology is supposed to be a system of ideals that forms the basis of the political and economic management of a society. It starts out as a theory that is written down (generally quite a well thought out one – whatever you might think of Marx, Adam Smith or Lao-Tzu) but then it gradually morphs into a behavioural feedback loop where the written theory gradually disappears from relevance. Isn't democracy supposed to guard against this sort of ideological smoke and mirrors? A democratic election is nothing more than a crude process for measuring the average belief of the voting population. However, since most of us believe in democracy, democracy is actually a belief about beliefs. It is the belief that if the government reflects the beliefs of the people, then somehow everything will work out OK.

This belief is an illusion. I am arguing that *all* beliefs will ultimately become destructive to the people who believe them, so democracy will ultimately result in the masses voting for their own destruction.

If the beliefs of the people are determined purely by a mechanism of behavioural feedback, then to get elected all you need to do is play upon that behaviour in your campaign. Let us consider the generic ideology of the grotesques of the modern democratic age – Berlusconi, Putin, Obama, etc. It can be defined thus:

> *This is what I believe family means:* Hugs of wife and children on the stage, while scanning the back of the theatre for the TV camera;
> *This is what I think of my country:* Standing to attention with stern expression and jaw jutting determinedly; right hand on the wallet in your left breast pocket;
> *This is what I think about Freedom:* Firm gaze at the horizon with a single fist held aloft (but not so high as to look like a salute);
> *This is what I think about God:* Standing relaxed with eyes raised straight ahead in an expression of wonder about thirty degrees above the horizontal, and both arms spread out wide and raised about sixty degrees above the horizontal.

A man like this is considered to have *values*. But they are defined entirely by gesture – completely lacking analysis. They are devoid of analysis *by necessity* because the only question worth asking – "How does this benefit mankind?" – has become unanswerable. To answer this question, we would need to discover the emotional impact that such ideology had on humans, but this is impossible because everyone is acting out a tableaux of what they think their ideology implies a human nature ought to be. They do this because affecting the concept of human nature that the ideology implies is the best way to thrive within that ideology. Their leaders merely ape that with the added practised strut of looking "Presidential". Democracy can only protect against this sort of illusion if more than half of the population realise that it is occurring. Sometimes, this is not the case.

Emotions are mostly products of evolution by natural selection, and they have been selected over hundreds of millions of years to optimise our social interactions. A belief causes the behaviour to shift, and the optimisation is therefore compromised. A democratic campaign (as typically run by political grotesques of the late democratic age) causes this behavioural shift to be reinforced on national television. It becomes more important than any political theory, which is why modern electoral campaigns are so policy-lite. This results in a wholesale distortion of nature's mechanism for regulating our interactions. Democracy does *not* protect a society from self-destructing because a belief propagates and destroys this mechanism. The precise path of perversion of the original belief is almost impossible to predict. What happens if, for ideological reasons, pity is switched off for a subsection of mankind – the unemployed; Muslims; black people? Then we are rushing headlong towards Thomas Hobbes' vision of "warre, as is of every man against every man".

A democratic country's ideology gradually snowballs emotional behavioural distortion until its self-destruction is ultimately inevitable.

THE LOGIC OF THE IMAGINARY FRIEND

Verily the Messenger of Allah (may peace be upon him) said:
I have no concern with one who shaved her hair, lamented
loudly and tore her clothes in grief.
(The Islamic Book of Faith)

SCENARIO: THE ONLY FEELING THAT EXISTS
(THE GENERIC A/B RELIGION)

They led simple lives; emotions scythed to just above the root. Their clothes are plain earth colours without ornamentation: their beliefs do not permit them to participate in any extravagant celebrations or pastimes. Work is a duty; never a pleasure. In fact, pleasure, if felt, would never be shown.

On religious days, their faces are especially calm and expressionless. They greet one another outside their place of worship with barely perceptible smiles; displaying negligible pleasure regarding each other's companionship. Hands are shaken in token civility, and then they file inside.

During the religious ceremony, the preacher reads from the Book. The Book says that the only true joy comes from Him. Only through complete devotion to Him can fulfilment come. Earthly pleasures are nothing compared to His joy.

They listen, wrapped in calm concentration, their bodies relaxed; their eyes gazing upward. Concentrating inward, they seek a feeling; one that they know will come if they seek guidance from Him. This feeling will be proof of His goodness. His bliss is the reward of those who attain a state of total devotion to Him.

To display effusive emotion is to desecrate Him. People who behave this way are profane and are therefore shunned by the community. Any visible sign of lust and any expression of want is also suppressed, since such things must be subordinated to service to Him. Sadness is only permissible in certain circumstances, such as a death in the family; since sadness, without clear cause, shows that the sufferer is not being rewarded for devotion to Him, and therefore must be lacking in faith.

This leaves only guilt. If the feeling they seek does not come, it means that their devotion is insufficient because they are weak. However, guilt cannot be shared openly, since it carries the threat of rejection by the community. In this way, the community becomes an emotional vacuum where no feeling ever translates spontaneously into behaviour. They know nothing of emotion from each other because all the associated behaviour is suppressed.

What they know of emotion comes from the Book. But the Book is words. Even if the Book is His words, in the absence of behaviour how are they to attach a word for a feeling to the feeling itself? So how can they possibly recognise His joy, when it comes?

Should a feeling arise in one of them, and they are to think to themselves "this feeling comes from Him," how can they refute this thought? They have no basis for making a natural connection between the cause of the feeling, the feeling itself, and the behaviour naturally caused by it. The conceptual framework is missing. However, should they believe that the feeling comes from Him, then this is proof that He exists. This thought is irrefutable.

If no feeling comes, or if they doubt that the feeling comes from Him, then this means that their faith is incomplete. Absence of this feeling is the result of an insufficiency of belief. Of course, they could give up in their search for His joy, but this would bring rejection from the community. The community shuns the outside world because people there display a joy that does not come from Him, and this contradicts the belief that His joy is the only feeling that exists.

The community's use of the old-fashioned word "joy" itself is intended to distance them from people outside the community. People in the community therefore have no idea what life outside the community is like. Outside the community is oblivion.

So their path is fixed. Denial of emotion is what gives them their belief. And the search for His joy is their only path; the reward that will surely come from their denial.

This is an extreme version of Scenarios A and B converted into a belief system. However, note that it is *not* a version of The Generic A/B ideology; this is because it does not promise absence of undesirable emotions, it promises 'super-positive' emotions. These are mythologies of emotions that cannot possibly be imagined by mere mortals – not "earthly joy", but *"Heavenly* Joy". It is also not a version of the Generic C/D ideology; because it does not mythologise desirable emotions behaviourally, it mythologises them verbally. Verbal mythologising of emotional states only works in communities that void all natural emotional behaviour – suppression of natural behaviour makes you totally suggestible regarding the identity of an emotion. This is why all such religious groupings necessarily self-segregate – to preserve the behavioural integrity of the logic trap. In certain ways, this is a Scenario contrary to the normal flow of faking positive emotions and suppressing negative ones, in that there is an emphasis on the suppression of positive emotions. The Scenario is a presentation of the belief system of an orthodox religion that is completely stripped of all the specifics of theology. It demonstrates that it can be logical to believe in a fictitious religion. It is the stripped-down causality of a religious belief with the content of that belief removed.

THE INVENTION OF RELIGION

A lover, when the urge comes to him, whispers hyperbolic utterances into the ear of his mistress. A cynical seducer can whisper impersonated utterances into the ear of a woman and hope that she doesn't notice the cynicism. A scientist eavesdropping on these words should not be asking whether the whispered words are true, but rather "why is the man saying those words?", and "why do those words have an impact upon the woman?" Curiously, this is the same question that the woman should be asking. However, if she is asking this question then the words surely aren't working. A woman who has been cynically seduced will always ask the question, until, realising that the words will never work again, she cynically decides to ignore whether they might be cynically spoken or not.

It is almost certain that at least one person has cynically invented a religion – I'm not going to reveal my own suspicions. Of course, many people have cynically pretended to believe in a religion, including some religious leaders.[240] Jesus Christ, The Prophet Mohammed, Isaiah, Zoroaster, Siddharta Gautama, etc. were all historical figures who whispered hyperbolic utterances into the ear of mankind. It is probable that they did not do so cynically. What they set out to do was to teach mankind how to live. They whispered hyperbolic utterances to make their ideas exoteric to a society that was almost totally uneducated (indeed, at least three of these people were uneducated themselves, and most were illiterate). A scientist looking at a religion should not ask whether it is true, but rather why religions exist and how the belief works.

I am inventing religions in this book, not because I cynically want people to believe them, but because I want to explain how they work. I know that these religions are not *True* because I invented them. They are not hyperbolic but hypothetical – I am using thought experiments to demonstrate that truth can be invented. A belief *in*, to be believed, has to demonstrate that it causes human wellbeing. Human wellbeing is only measurable by observing emotional behaviour. But a belief *in* almost certainly alters how we project emotional behaviour. Someone who believes *in* will tend to display emotional behaviour that demonstrates compliance with the belief; and an unintended consequence of this is that the belief manufactures the evidence of its own truth. This is pseudo-empirical. A feedback loop is established which makes the belief an irrefutable thought. There is no theoretical difference between an ideology and a religion, but there is a practical difference: religions explicitly mythologise emotional states; whereas ideologies only do so implicitly. This is why scientists shouldn't ask whether religions are *true*, unless they are sure that they have no ideology – which I doubt is humanly possible.

So what is the relevance of theology? Suppose a rich man reads the passage in the Bible that says "it is easier for a camel to go through the eye of a needle than for a rich man to enter the kingdom of God."[241] He then gets into his Cadillac and drives to church. Clearly such a man isn't going to heaven; so what is the point of him being a Christian?

Socrates makes an illuminating distinction regarding belief. He discusses the discarding of beliefs, and points out that this can be done voluntarily or involuntarily.[242] In life, we are voluntarily deprived of things that are bad (example: we put out our garbage), but only involuntarily deprived of things that are good (examples: someone we love abandons us, or we have our wallet stolen). With regard to beliefs, we voluntarily discard beliefs that are bad. Generally speaking, bad beliefs are ones that are false. The involuntary discarding of belief, says Socrates, is when we discard beliefs that are good. Normally, this means beliefs that are true, and this only occurs when we are deceived.

Something that Socrates does not consider is that in the case of the involuntary discarding of beliefs, the deceiver can also be the believer. So what is going on with our Cadillac Christian is the involuntary discarding of a Christian belief, by a Christian. He reads the words, and denies them. The Freudian concept of denial is all very well, but you already know that I am no admirer of Freud. My stated assumption is that a human is a robustly logical computing device, and that it is incoherent to talk about irrational acts; so for me to accept denial as a concept, I need to explain the clear example of denial of a religious person who reads their religious book and is blind to what it says. The mechanism of the belief is a logical tautology, and this is an absolute, which is why it trumps the words of a religion.

There are many examples of such involuntary discarding of beliefs in Christianity, and in all other religions too. For example, "Love your enemies, do good to those who hate you, bless those who curse you, pray for those who mistreat you. If someone strikes you on one cheek, turn to him the other also."[243] In the George W. Bush White House, one staffer said that Bible study was "not quite unobligatory". But was the above passage followed on 9/11/01? Of course it wasn't! The actions that followed that date were the complete opposite of the teachings of the Bible. The President of the United States involuntarily discarded a Christian belief, despite being convinced that his Christianity guided his actions. Can anyone simultaneously believe the beatitudes of Matthew 5:1-11 and support the foreign policy of the United States since Vietnam, or of Britain during the nineteenth century? It is an historical irony that the most consistently belligerent nations of the past five hundred years have been dominated by a religion that preaches pacifism. The debate over whether Islam is a religion of peace or violence is irrelevant because the nature of the belief is different to what its believers think it is. Necessarily, it can be different for two believers of the same religion.

Of course, all religious texts are open to interpretation. But interpretation can only go so far before it becomes egregious. Can we interpret the Bible as being compatible with any lifestyle or political creed? Christians are all too ready to quote Leviticus on the immorality of homosexuality, but when considering the actions of Roman Catholic priests they conveniently ignore that Leviticus says that homosexuals should be put to death. They also conveniently ignore the fact that Leviticus forbids men to cut the hair on the side of their head, and to eat any fish that doesn't have fins; so Christians should grow ringlets like an Hasidic Jew and eat Kosher. On my reading of the Bible, a true Christian would live their life in a way that is imilar to the way the Amish live – pacifist, spurning modernity, non-interventionist, private, humble, etc. Practically all other

Christians are merely "Convenience Christians": people who read the Bible and go to church and then do whatever the hell they want to do.

Normally, if a book states beliefs that are diametrically opposed to your own beliefs, you would voluntarily discard the book. (You might do that to this one.) But why would you voluntarily discard the book, when you are already involuntarily discarding the words in it? Faith then, is not the ultimate act of belief; it is the ultimate act of denial. The irrefutability of the thought actually transcends the words in which it is expressed. You deny the belief, while still believing that you believe it.

SCENARIO: THE FEELING THAT DOESN'T EXIST (THE GENERIC C/D RELIGION)

They arrive at their place of worship in their best clothes. The women wear brightly coloured dresses, and the men wear expensively tailored suits. They beam wide smiles at each other. Handshakes are vigorous and double-handed. As they swarm inside for the religious ceremony they clap each other on the back and express themselves with effusive displays of communal bonding.

The preacher reads from the Book. The Book says that the Faith will release their souls and give them freedom. Only by following the Faith will they achieve release. Their time on Earth will be made beautiful by the feeling that comes from the Faith.

They listen, wrapped in fierce concentration. Their bodies tense; their eyes strain upward. Concentrating inward, they reach for a feeling; one that they know will come if they stay loyal to the Faith. This feeling will be proof of their commitment; the bliss will be their reward for following the Faith.

The preacher's voice rises as he speaks into the microphone. His pitch becomes frenetic; his words imploring. The crowd starts to moan, and then to shout. They raise their hands to the ceiling and they cry out together. Some of them are lost in oblivion; their mouths falling open, and their eyes roll upward so that only the whites show.

This is what fulfilment on Earth means! This is true freedom! The Faith is the path they must follow. They must stay together with the people that follow the Faith to ensure that their lives remain dedicated to this path. People that do not know the Faith are to be pitied because they will not know freedom. But they are never to be patronised because the Faith is to understand all people and their path to freedom and fulfilment. Of course, people who do not follow the Faith show emotion, some of it positive emotion. But this is not the bliss that comes from the Faith.

To the followers of the Faith, does the belief cause the feeling, or is the feeling the belief? Can the cause of an emotion be a belief, and that emotion not actually involve a feeling? Can an emotion still be an emotion if there never is or was a feeling? If, as I have argued, we cannot distinguish between an emotion and a belief in an emotion, then these questions become theoretically unanswerable. So, we can invent emotions without it mattering that there is no feeling attached, or we can manufacture emotions and assume that the feeling associated with another emotion is in fact the feeling associated with the emotion we have invented. We can create emotions in order to serve a particular human need. Should this emotion be a super-positive emotion that is manufactured by a belief, how can it be denied that the belief generates wellbeing for the humans that believe it? The belief is irrefutable to its believers.

This is a version of Scenarios C and D reconstructed in the form of a hypothetical evangelical religious belief. Unlike the previous hypothetical religion, which wasn't a version of either of the Generic Ideologies, this one is actually a version of Generic C/D ideology. Happiness might be a real emotion or it might be invented – we can't be too sure. However, this religion is a C/D ideology deliberately constructed to involve an invented behaviour representing a non-biological emotion. This is a difficult concept to grasp, and it is worth considering another form of this Scenario found in literature.

THE "FOUND SCENARIO"

Poets have a concept of the "found poem". Found poetry is an inadvertently written poem stumbled upon by a poet. For example, a technician might write the instructions for how to assemble a bookcase, or a lawyer might write a liability disclaimer on the packaging of some product. A poet will look at the words, and realise that with a small adjustment to the spacing and line breaks, they can reconstruct those same words into a poem.

I have been using a form of thought experiment to explain the relationships between feeling, behaviour, language and belief. I cannot claim to have invented this form of thought experiment because, like a poet stumbling upon found poetry, I stumble upon "found scenarios". One such found scenario also deals with invented emotion, though its writer did not call it that. Tolstoy's *War and Peace*[244] describes the conversion of Peter Kirilovich Bésoukhow to freemasonry. Bésoukhow meets a freemason who speaks to him in mystical tones and causes him to doubt his atheism. In the initiation ceremony, he is taken into a room blindfolded and led through a ritual where he is introduced to "important mysteries which have been handed down from the remotest past". This found scenario is of exactly the same structure as the Generic C/D religion. Found scenarios only exist in literature because novelists are doing the same thing that I am doing with the Scenarios in this book: creating a hypothetical mind and then thinking with that mind.

There is at least one other found scenario in *War and Peace*[245]: on the eve of battle Count Nicholas Rostow experiences a "sudden self-oblivion" as the Emperor rides past. His belief makes him overjoyed at the prospect of death. "How happy I would be if only he would bid me ride into the fire." Rostow suppresses all conventional flow of emotion and channels it entirely into his euphoric yearning to ride into battle. I think this is not invented emotion. If anything it is a version of Scenario A, where he is taking a real emotion and misidentifying it. He assumes that his feeling represents his love of

Emperor and country, and this is his own form of irrefutable thought. So overwhelming is this irrefutable thought, that he embraces the ultimate sacrifice and welcomes it. Which brings me to another form of religious irrefutable thought . . .

SCENARIO: THE FEELING OF THE AFTERLIFE (THE GENERIC A/D RELIGION)

They gather at their place of worship. The heavy beards of orthodoxy cover their clenched jaws and conceal their tension. Their beards partially conceal their expressions, but above this their eyes are a fixed stony grey. The women wear the veils of chastity. It doesn't matter what expression the women permit themselves because they are covered, but each must guard against careless expression lest their feelings show in their voice. They greet one another coolly with formal blessings as they prepare themselves for worship.

The preacher leads them as they read from the Book together. The Book tells of the ecstasy that comes from the Faith. The Faith prepares them to accept the ecstasy that will become complete after death. Only through death will they experience the eternal ecstasy that comes from union with Him.

They only permit themselves to express emotion when they read from the Book. As they read from the Book, their voices gather in a crescendo. Their bodies relax and flex upward like a dancer; their eyelids flicker shut, and their voices cry out in unison. They express emotion together; vocally; vigorously and with complete commitment. The eternal ecstasy comes from union with Him! Why then should they fear death, when death brings eternal ecstasy? The expression of the emotion of fear represents weakness – shown by those whose faith is insufficient.

The false joy of the Unbelievers is apostate: It must be a false emotion because it cannot come from Him to an Unbeliever. The Faithful must self-segregate because they cannot live with people who express emotion that is incompatible with the Faith. Unbelievers must be banned from the lands of the Faithful. But the Unbelievers continue to enter the world of the Faithful. The Unbelievers unknowingly mock them by demonstrating positive emotions that the Faith does not acknowledge. The Unbelievers' false joy is a blasphemy against Him.

How can the Faithful know that the behaviour they express when they read from the Book is the expression of an invented emotion – an emotional state that is pure belief? They systematically and habitually suppress all normal emotional response, and so their mechanism of response has over time become broken. To the Faithful, positive emotional response is only achievable by following the Faith. That the Faith brings ecstasy is irrefutable because the Faithful express positive emotion only when they read from the Book. But not only are they behaviourally mythologising positive emotions when they read from the Book, they are verbally mythologising super-positive emotions that will follow death. The mythologised emotions that follow death are better than the mythologised emotions that come from reading the Book

Emotions evolved as an instinctive survival prompter to animals. Language has destroyed man's instinct and therefore his ultimate aim is no longer survival, but the achievement of a higher emotional state. The Unbelievers and the Faithful cannot coexist because the Unbelievers express through their behaviour emotional states that the Faith denies. The Faithful can have no knowledge of it because they suppress the behaviour associated with all emotions except the virtual emotion that comes from reading the Book. To the Faithful, the presence of Unbelievers directly threatens their sole life purpose, which is the achievement of a higher emotional state by way of the Faith. The Faithful cannot achieve higher emotional states the way Unbelievers can because their behavioural response has been crushed by the requirement of the Faith that they only express emotion during worship.

An animal's fear causes it to flee instinctively and this can be explained in terms of natural selection. However, an animal has no fear of death. Only a human, with its language, has the ability to see its life as a concept in abstract time and space, and therefore can conceive of its life coming to an end. Humans, in evolutionary terms have inherited fear from animals, but language has transformed it. An animal fears the potential cause of its death without being able to conceive of that death; but a human fears death – the consequence of the threat.

People outside the Faith who see their life purpose as attainment of a higher emotional state can only achieve this if they stay alive. For the Faithful, the consequence of death is an eternal super-positive emotional state; so followers of the Faith yearn for death. It is to be welcomed, not feared. The fear of death in the Faithful is erased by the suppression of all behavioural evidence of that state. The collective euphoria that surrounds the reading of the Book is manufactured in parallel through behaviour. For the Faithful, their conception of the emotion of fear has been corrupted and they see death as positive, not negative; they are distorting a negative emotional state (fear of death) into a positive one.

The Faith is the only route to emotional fulfilment to the Faithful. But the Faithful have lost the yearning to survive because their life purpose does not require them to stay alive. Since the Faithful can only achieve ecstasy through the Faith, then the Faith must survive. The yearning to survive has therefore transferred from the Faithful to the Faith itself. It is only the Faith that must survive. The Faithful exist only to preserve it.

The Chosen One of the Faithful knew he was ready. He calmly prepared himself for the union with Him that would bring eternal ecstasy. He was relaxed; not fearful. He walked steadily to the place where the Unbelievers gathered; and as he mingled among them he quietly slipped his hand into his pocket and pressed the contact to the battery terminal.

This Scenario synthetically recreates the belief system that leads to suicide bombing. It is a synthetic representation of the causality of the belief, stripped of all the specifics of theology. It is not a representation of any particular religion, since suicide bombing has been a feature of many religious groups, including Muslims, Hindus and Christians. It contains a blend of several elements – the blanket suppression of all natural emotions, combined with the behavioural mythologising of a virtual emotion and the verbal mythologising of a "super-positive" emotion. It is therefore a hybrid of both the Generic A/B Religion and the Generic C/D Religion.

It is a synthesis of many sources: Robert Fisk's *The Great War for Civilisation*[246] quotes interviews with numerous Hizballah fighters, Islamist fighters in Algeria and returning soldiers from the Iran-Iraq War of 1980–88 (of which the most useful to me were interviews with Iranian Shia Muslim soldiers). These interviews provide descriptions of what martyrdom means for people for whom this belief system has been a particular feature. Fisk has been an invaluable source to me because (unlike most writers) he isn't shy about giving a naked quote, even if he doesn't understand what it means. He is therefore a source of raw data on belief that has not been reinterpreted by the writer and therefore corrupted by the writer's beliefs. V.S. Naipaul's two travelogues on the Islamic World[247] only deal fleetingly with the idea of martyrdom, but explore in depth the subordination of the self to the belief that is a repeating theme in Islam. Robert Baer's documentary *The Cult of the Suicide Bomber* produced for Channel 4 in the UK was also a valuable source. I also found several video interviews relating to martyrdom with guerrillas of Hizballah and the Liberation Tigers of Tamil Elam on YouTube.

THE NATURE OF FUNDAMENTALISM

The thesis of this book is that self-destructive acts are all rationally derived from manipulated emotional behaviour; and because beliefs *in* all cause their believers to distort emotions that are supposed to drive survival-enhancing actions, then all such beliefs will ultimately be destructive to their believers. This is a good point to examine the late stages of this process.

Suppose you hold a belief that is destructive to your wellbeing. Clearly, if that belief is widely held, then all sorts of things will be going horribly wrong in your society. But because you believe the belief, you cannot attribute any of these disasters to the belief itself. This is the most serious contradiction that you can face because it is central to everything you think and do. When the chaos becomes too blatant to ignore, a tipping point arises where someone suggests that it is not that the belief failed men, but that men failed the belief. This triggers a spiralling pursuit of a purer form of a belief system that has already failed – like a gambler who doubles his bets when he loses.

This tipping point probably occurred in the Muslim World long before 9/11. Increasingly, different Muslim sects are all involved in a fight with one another to prove that they are the purest form of the faith. Sunnis don't think Shias are proper Muslims, and Wahhabis are Sunnis that don't think other Sunnis are proper Muslims. And at the top of this pinnacle, Takfiris are Sunnis that don't even think Wahhabis are pure enough to qualify. There is a credible story that, back in bin Laden's Sudan days, the Takfiris tried to kill him for not being Islamic enough. A Kashmiri Muslim told me that there were seventy-two sects of Islam, and I wondered how they managed to count them. Then I realised that they need to count them because the other seventy-one sects present them with a serious problem.

Consider the history of terrorist atrocities in Pakistan since just before 9/11. At the beginning of that period, Muslim extremists were blowing up Hindus and Christians (each of which make up less than 2% of Pakistan's population). Within a few years of 9/11, they had switched to blowing up minority Muslim groups (Shias, Sufis, Ismailis and Ahmadis). After a decade had past, Taliban extremists (who are Sunnis) started blowing up Sunni mosques. We have now reached the point where the theological distinctions between the perpetrator and the victim have become imperceptible to Western journalists (and presumably to analysts at the US State Department). At this point the self-destructiveness is absolute.

We should not think that this problem is restricted to Muslims.

The fateful tipping point has recently occurred within the Amish, who have started attacking each other over a theological distinction that perhaps even the Amish don't understand. Religious groups that suppress all their emotional behaviour are particularly prone to self-destruction because they have switched off Nature's mechanism for regulating human interactions. They therefore lose the ability to judge moral nuance, and are entirely dependent upon religious teaching for their morality. This is the root of the extraordinarily high levels of corruption in Muslim countries. The Amish have managed to survive peaceably until recently only because they lived so simply. This reduced the possible range of nuanced moral issues that they had to deal with in daily life, but in effect they were delegating all the complex issues to the non-Amish people in the world around them. Although they appear to be self-sufficient, they are in reality highly dependent upon non-Amish to provide all elements of local government and infrastructure.

It would be unfair to pick on religious groups as being the sole form of fundamentalism. The Tea Party in the USA is a form of ideological fundamentalism that stems from exactly the same tipping point. Capitalism, as I have explained, has ceased to benefit the people who believe it: ideological collapse is becoming more evident; global economic dislocation is becoming more frequent; America is lapsing into increasing chaos. But rather than abandoning the ideology, the Tea Party wants to pursue a purer form of it – the ideology has not failed men, but men have failed the ideology. They fall over themselves to demonstrate loyalty to the strictest laissez-faire capitalism, despite this leading to environmental collapse and employee exploitation; they campaign for a fundamentalist interpretation of the US constitution, despite there being twenty-seven demonstrable errors and omissions in the original document.

The Tea Party and Muslim fundamentalists are as far apart ideologically as one could imagine, but they have the identical logical contradiction at their core.

SCENARIO: THE EMPIRICS OF SPIRITUALITY

Lying on the street was a dog. The girl could tell it was alive only because its chest moved. There was a living, luminous shine to its sores. The dog made no effort to chase away the flies that swarmed there. The girl looked. Something like revulsion surfaced, but she pushed it down and went on her way. There were things to do; places to see. The image of the dog kept surfacing in her mind like a still of bad pornography. Every time this occurred she drove the image away – a forceful diversion of the imagination.

Later, when she returned, the dog was still there. Was it still alive? She looked. She had to stand motionless to detect life because the movement of its ribs was so tiny. Its sores had changed – there was a developing dullness to them. Their colour was greyer than she remembered. Even the flies had lost interest. Suddenly, the dog's leg convulsed. Again, the girl had a feeling. Was this feeling revulsion or compassion? Revulsion should make her turn away, but she did not want to turn away. Compassion should make her reach down and save the dog, but this dog was surely beyond saving.

She stood there. Two emotions struggling for dominance, but the dominance they struggled for was not connected to the action that the girl should pursue – turn away or help the dog. She did neither. Instead, the emotions struggled for a dominance of identity. Gradually her perception became less about the dying dog and more about herself. She gazed inwardly at this emotional cocktail. Unidentifiable feelings merged together in the palette of her consciousness. The dog was a blur, but contemplating these emotions made her feel complete. She felt that she was a good person despite the fact that she did nothing. Morality had become a state that did not depend upon an action. It was a state of feeling. Was this the feeling of spirituality? This depth of emotion was something that defined her. It was a moral identity, and all that was required to be sure that she was good was to contemplate a feeling and wallow in the religion that was herself.

Action was irrelevant to goodness. Theology was irrelevant to belief.

THE ENGINEERING OF HUMILIATION

> I saw a man of simple origins, simply educated, but
> with a great sneering pride, deferential but resentful,
> not liking himself for what he was doing. He was the
> kind of man who, without political doctrine, only with
> resentments, had made the Iranian revolution.
> (V.S. Naipaul, Among The Believers, An Islamic Journey)

A few years ago, I was travelling on an urban metro train. I was minding my own business, sitting in my seat and reading a newspaper. Unexpectedly, the man sitting opposite me leant forwards and flicked the back of my newspaper with his finger. I peered over the top of my newspaper, but he was sitting back in his seat and pretending that nothing had happened. I carried on reading, and then he leant forwards and flicked the back of my newspaper again, so I asked him what he wanted. He said that he expected that I thought myself pretty clever, and then he started insulting me. It quite quickly became apparent that this was going to get nasty. People sitting next to me started to move away. I had the presence of mind to spot out of the corner of my eye the handle for the emergency brake, so I got up and stood by it. He followed, and with his face six inches from mine, his eyes flared and the veins on his temples throbbing, he hissed insults in my face to try to start a fight. I just stared him down until the train pulled into the next station, and then I pulled the emergency brake. Presumably, he realised that the train crew and the police were on their way, so he spat his last insults in my face and left.

In the chapter *The Evolution of Emotion* I described how humiliation and the revenge response had origins in evolution by natural selection. Uncorrupted, humiliation results from a threat to biological fitness, and the revenge response is directed at the threat. The genes that drive the revenge response were selected because they neutralise threats to biological fitness. The revenge response is biased towards males in humans because we are a polygynous species, which means that strong males tend to father children with more than one female and as a result, some weak males have no offspring. Males without a revenge response permit their biological fitness to be threatened and suppressed, and so they have no offspring and their genes are not selected. Males with a strong revenge response have more offspring, and so their genes gradually propagate throughout the population.

What I want to explore in this chapter is the perversion of this very basic element of our evolved emotional responses. I will explore ritual humiliation among humans. Humans know, without needing to be told, that to humiliate another human you need to attack their biological fitness. A simple way to do this to a man is to denigrate his virility.

My experience on the train probably lasted no longer than two minutes, and never got to the level of physical violence; but for some time after that, I had frequent fantasies of performing extreme violence on a man – not that man in particular, but some generic random man that existed in my imagination. I just wanted to slam my boot into his face. Good to know that my evolutionary response is still working – after a fashion! But, if my response to a two-minute verbal harangue was weeks of violent fantasies, what would have been my response if it had become physical, or had lasted two hours, or two decades?

Once I had stopped thinking about myself, I started thinking about my would-be assailant. Clearly, something had made him angry. Trust me! I saw it very close up. Equally clearly, the something that had made him angry *wasn't me*. And then I started wondering, not what makes a man angry (which isn't so difficult to imagine), but what makes a man's anger misdirected?

SCENARIO: THE INVENTION OF HUMILIATION

The Man lives in a world where everybody has a home and enough to eat. But the Man's People are unhappy. The People complain at every possible opportunity: "It wasn't like this before we lost the Homeland."

The People gather often. The elders talk at length about the beauty of the fields and orchards in the Homeland. They sing songs about the lakes and mountains, and read poems about the harmony of when the People lived there. When they meet for these gatherings, it brings them together. It is their identity: they belong not just to each other, but to the Homeland. And when they sing and remember, their eyes glow and they clasp one another's hands. As they look from one to another, they experience a feeling – an awakening that is like a religion.

The People talk constantly of the struggle of their ancestors when they were expelled from the Homeland. They believe that they feel the pain of their ancestors in their struggle. However, it isn't possible to invoke mental images of what suffering feels like, so they think of behavioural images of their ancestors emaciated and dying in their flight to exile. If the People concentrate on these mental images hard enough, eventually it causes a feeling; a dull ache that is not a recollection of their ancestors suffering, but is a compassionate response caused by forced recollection. But how can they know the difference? To the People, the suffering of their ancestors is continued generation after generation. They have no basis for knowing that their feeling is not the feeling of their ancestors, but something they themselves have created through collective imagination.

The Man's world also has fields and orchards. Beyond these are lakes and mountains. But this is not the Homeland. Sometimes, the Man thinks that his world is not a bad place at all. But only once had he spoken out loud of the beauty of their new world, and the reaction of the others had taught him that he should never do this again. The People were shocked. The elders' eyes had glowered, and they bore down on him forcefully. How dare he disrespect the injustice that had been done to the People! If he did not want to be a part of the fight for the People's justice and the return to the Homeland, then he should leave the People and go his own way. The suffering of the People must never be forgotten. People who did not feel the suffering of the ancestors were not of the People.

The Man often remembers his grandfather. His grandfather had been one of the original generation that went into exile. The Man remembers his grandfather's stories. He had sat with him for hours listening to his descriptions of their farm and their village until he felt that he knew it better than where he lived now. He can picture it in his head, despite the fact that he has never seen it. But the Man's grandfather was different to the elders of today. His grandfather had the humility of one who had suffered himself. His grandfather was grateful that he had survived; that he had come to the new land, and that his children and grandchildren were safe. Part of his grandfather's acceptance of the new land was that he knew that the Homeland had been destroyed by war and that the People couldn't live there anymore. His grandfather had fought, and he had used up the anger that was within him.

The elders of today have not suffered, and therefore have no humility. They have not fought, and therefore have not used up their anger. They are the next generation, and they cannot see that their efforts to maintain the culture of the People is manufacturing anger in a place where there is no natural cause. The injustice of which they constantly speak is not an injustice that has occurred to them. But ritualising it makes it feel as though it's theirs. Their unhappiness in the new land is acted out to create their anger. They need to manufacture their anger to keep their identity alive. The people who had forced their ancestors to flee are no longer alive, so they have no object for their anger.

Their belief in their right to their Homeland is irrefutable. An injustice needs to be righted. It does not matter that nobody is alive who has perpetrated that injustice, and none of the victims of that injustice are alive. They manufacture the feelings of despair through ritualised emotional behaviour. This makes them victims of the in-justice also; they create their own victimhood by acting it out to the point where they believe they themselves have suffered it. Happiness can only be achieved in the Homeland, despite the fact that living there is not possible. But the constant dream of living there fuels their sense of loss and creates their anger. This anger is targetless because the perpetrators are all dead, so it is redirected – to the new land; to the people who now live in the Homeland; to history; to people that no longer exist; to people who might never have existed; to hypo-thetical evil that is a construct of their own imagining.

The dominant source for this Scenario is Brian G. Williams, The Crimean Tartars.[248] Williams quotes numerous Crimean Tartars dis-cussing their concept of homeland and their concept of national identity following their exile by Stalin to the Soviet Far East. Impor-tantly, he quotes separately both the first and second generation of exiled people. In particular, the first generation of exiled people were relatively humble and philosophical about their situation but the second generation were much more angry and radicalised. We can also see this generational shift among Tibetans, where the generation born since the Chinese takeover and the flight of the Dalai Lama are much more prone to violent resistance than their parents.

SCENARIO: THE DENIAL OF HUMILIATION

Exhausted, the recruit plunges into the mud and scurries on his elbows under barbed wire. He is nearing the limits of his endurance, but he is nowhere near the end. The cold drizzle has taken away all the feeling in his feet and hands, and fatigue burns his muscles. But he cannot admit failure by stopping. His goal is to succeed, to belong with his colleagues as a member of the army brotherhood. The boot camp sergeant runs along the path beside the course screaming abuse at him, that he is fat, lazy and worthless.

The army tells him that endless assault courses are necessary to make him tough. But that is not the real reason.

Every morning, he is woken at 5am. He spends an hour polishing his boots and the buttons on his parade uniform. He makes his bed in the precise proscribed manner, and lays out his kit exactly as he is supposed to. On the parade ground, he is told to stand stiffly upright with his chest forced out. He is told to hold his face still and expressionless with his jaw locked with a determined jut. He does as he is told – stands there proud and strong. And then comes more abuse, that he is a mess, that he is sloppy. Despite being treated like an idiot, he shows the sergeant absurdly exaggerated respect. Every time he is abused by him, he shouts "Sir, yes Sir!" When his training is all over, he is told that he should be proud of what he has achieved, that what he has done is something great that will live with him for the rest of his life.

The army tells him that the parade drill is necessary to teach him discipline. But that is not the real reason.

How can a man know that he is humiliated if he suppresses the behaviour that would naturally be his response?

The process of infantry training is purposely a ritual humiliation: forced marches to the point of exhaustion; absurd muddy obstacle courses; screamed abuse for trivial misdemeanours; pointless work such as polishing what is already clean; having all power to act as an independent agent taken away from you; and finally having to pay undeserved respect to your abuser. However, it is essential that the deliberate humiliation is concealed from the recruit. The concealment occurs by forcing him to act, not as if he is humiliated, but as if he is proud. His humiliation is therefore unconscious. How can he have a concept of having been humiliated if his own behavioural response indicates the opposite?

Humiliation has an evolutionary origin, and its violent response is also an evolved response. But the humiliation of military training must be unconscious because otherwise the response would be directed against the humiliator. The point is that the violent response to humiliation is canned, put in a sealed receptacle to be released on cue. This is how the army makes a normal man a killer. A soldier is a man with intentionally stored revenge. It doesn't matter that the

*person he kills was not the person who humiliated him. The soldier
doesn't know that he has been humiliated because that fact has been
concealed from him, but the response is still there. To release this
response, all that is required is that you mythologise the person he is
to kill as the "Enemy". His emotional makeup wires him to respond
violently when humiliated, and direct his response at the threat to his
fitness. The origin of the threat must be concealed, so that the threat
can be reinvented.*

*A man whose behaviour has been forcibly manipulated in this
way is programmed to kill.*

THE ORIGIN OF MAN'S INHUMANITY

In the opening section of this chapter, I asked the question: How can
a man's anger be misdirected? In other words, if we look at the evolutionary origins of humiliation and revenge, how is it the process in
humans can become so corrupted? The previous two Scenarios
explain that humans (because they can tactically manipulate their
expression of emotion) can distort the revenge response but may not
realise that they are doing this. On the one hand, we can invent
humiliation – perhaps to reinforce a national or group identity – and
on the other hand, we can deny humiliation. Let us put the two prior
Scenarios into the context of the Scenarios of Part I.

The Invention of Humiliation is an example of Scenario D. When
a person lives in an environment where people affect an emotional
state (humiliation), they form beliefs that they experience the
emotion even though the feeling that would normally be associated
with that emotion is absent. However, in this case it comes with a
strange twist. The normal flow of things is that we have incentives
to affect positive emotions and suppress negative ones. This Scenario
presents the reversal of the normal flow. The People maintain their
sense of identity by the affectation of undesirable emotions. They
do this, despite the fact that they live in an environment where they
have everything they need to thrive.

The Denial of Humiliation is an adaptation of Scenario B: When a person suppresses the behaviour associated with their own emotional state, they cannot know that they experience that emotion. In Scenario B, I portrayed a man who suppresses the behaviour of anger and, once this becomes habitual, he loses the ability to know that he is angry. Not knowing that you are angry logically means that you are unable to identify the cause of your anger. In the chapter The *Myth of the Ghost in a Coma* I explained that the unconscious mind should be seen as the collection of all emotional states where the concept is absent. We have the word for the emotion, but the behaviour associated with that emotional state has been suppressed in certain circumstances and therefore the connection with the feeling is missing because the behaviour would be the only visible means of making the connection. The anger felt by the man in Scenario B is unconscious because he suppresses the behaviour, and therefore cannot identify it in himself. He does not ask himself where it comes from because he does not know it exists. Because he does not know that it exists he cannot cure it, and goes through life with the risk of the unconscious anger being triggered by circumstances where he is not used to suppressing it.

Let us apply exactly the same concept to humiliation and the behaviour that would normally result from it. Behaviour, in the sense in which I use the word in this book, means the behaviour that is immediately caused by the feeling. In the case of humiliation, this involves cowering, a look of defeat, expressions of subordination, inability to look your humiliator in the eye, etc. However, there is also another response – the need for revenge. This can be one of the most powerful and enduring yearnings in humankind. Consider what happens when the humiliated person suppresses the behaviour that immediately follows humiliation. When this is done systematically until it becomes habit, the person loses the ability to know that he is humiliated. Humiliation is unconscious. A disconnect arises and so the person detaches from the natural target for revenge, which is the threat to biological fitness. His yearning for revenge does not attach to the appropriate target of revenge.

This is how a soldier in every professional army in the world is made into a killer; it is the same way a soldier has been trained for centuries: you humiliate him, and then force him to suppress the behavioural response. You give him a sharp uniform and a shiny sword and make him raise a flag; you tell him that he is the greatest soldier alive; brave and proud.

His humiliation is unconscious.

His need for revenge is targetless.

He will kill anybody you want him to: coldly, silently, professionally, with no sense that anything is wrong, and with no remorse. All that is required is the key to unlock his revenge – a mythology of an *enemy* and their purported *evil*.

Of course, all armies will deny that this is how infantry training works. That is because they have to. Their training only works because the fact of the suppressed humiliation needs to be concealed from the recruit, or his humiliation won't be unconscious. In theory, any army recruit who reads this book should be able to immunise himself from the effects of his training, but he would likely hate the army because he would correctly see them as the source of his humiliation.

Having created killers, each with a canned unconscious revenge response, armies all over the world then have the problem of keeping this response contained. This is a continuous process. It only takes a momentary loss of vigilance and uncontrolled violence is released. This can either turn inward or outward and there are, sadly, numerous examples of this, whether in Chechnya, Gaza or Iraq.[249] There is usually excessive zeal in passing responsibility directly to the perpetrators, and silent foot-shuffling from the chain of command. In all cases, we should understand that the perpetrators were purposefully and deliberately created. I asked a former soldier about abuse within the US Army, and he answered "they want you to hurt yourself." Abuse can be constructed in astonishing ways that permit deniability, a skill in which most professional military organisations are adept.

The effect of suppressed humiliation in the military occurs in a relatively controlled environment. Let us look at this phenomenon in an uncontrolled environment. Adolf Hitler, leader of the National Socialist German Workers Party, *Führer und Reichskanzler* of Germany, had a vicious, tyrannical father who used to beat him almost daily. Hitler once said of his childhood,

> I then resolved never again to cry when my father whipped me. A few days later I had the opportunity of putting my will to the test. My mother, frightened, took refuge in front of the door. As for me, I counted silently the blows of the stick which lashed my rear end.[250]

Hitler trained himself in childhood to suppress the behavioural response of humiliation.

He had plenty of opportunity in early adulthood to put this skill into practice. His first choice of career was as an artist, but he failed to gain acceptance into art school. His second choice of career was as an architect, but he failed at this too. He also experienced the defeat in World War I as an infantryman, including being gassed. Before he rose to power, there was almost no period of Hitler's life during which he did not experience humiliation. Most importantly, however, Hitler's humiliation was unconscious. There can be little doubt about this. In *Mein Kampf* he eulogises his parents, despite the fact that his childhood was brutal:

> My father, a dutiful civil servant, my mother giving all her being to the household, and devoted above all to us children in *eternal, loving care* [my emphasis].[251]

Hitler was certain that his parents loved him, despite admitting in *Mein Kampf* that he has little memory of his childhood. His need for revenge was targetless and became detached from the source of his humiliation.[252] Hitler not only did this to himself, he actually thought this was morally praiseworthy. He encourages it in the German education system.

> The discouragement of whining complaints, of bawling, etc., also belongs in this province. If a system of education forgets to teach

the child in early years that sufferings and adversity must be borne in silence, it has no right to be surprised if later at a critical hour when a man stands at the front, for example, the entire postal service is used for nothing but transporting whining letters of mutual complaint.[253]

It is hard for someone who has not been brutalised to imagine a need for revenge of this magnitude, and it is logically impossible to imagine a humiliation that is unconscious, but consider this eye-witness report by the CBS correspondent William L. Shirer of the surrender of the French to Hitler. In 1918, the Germans signed their surrender to the French in a railway coach in Compiègne, Northern France. In 1940, Hitler, in a piece of political theatre that indicates a deep need for vindication, dictated that the French should surrender in the same place in the same railway coach:

> I observed his face. It was grave, solemn, yet brimming with revenge ... There was something else, difficult to describe, in his expression, a sort of scornful, inner joy at being present at this great reversal of fate – a reversal he himself had wrought.[254]

Hitler looked at the French memorial commemorating their victory over the Germans in 1918. Shirer observed:

> I have seen that face many times at the great moments of his life. But today! It is afire with scorn, anger, hate, revenge, triumph. He steps off the monument and contrives to make even this gesture a masterpiece of contempt. He glances back at it, contemptuous, angry – angry, you almost feel, because he cannot wipe out the awful, provoking lettering with one sweep of his high Prussian boot. He glances slowly round the clearing, and now, as his eyes meet ours, you grasp the depth of his hatred. But there is triumph there too – revengeful, triumphant hate. Suddenly, as though his face were not giving quite complete expression to his feelings, he throws his whole body into harmony with his mood. He swiftly snaps his hands on his hips, arches his shoulders, plants his feet wide apart. It is a magnificent

gesture of defiance, or burning contempt for this place now and all that it has stood for in the twenty-two years since it witnessed the humbling of the German Empire.[255]

The Holocaust was a perversion of an evolved emotional response that arose because the perpetrators had a stockpile of unconscious humiliation. Their revenge response became detached from the source of their humiliation and was misdirected. Once this is understood, it becomes plausible that there is no such thing as an unprovoked attack; only provoked attacks that are misdirected away from the provoker. This is *explanation*, and it should not be confused with *exculpation*. It is beyond the scope of this book to restate the entire history of the Holocaust. But I need to summarise it, and it is necessary to change the emphasis from how it is usually told.

MANKIND'S GREATEST ATROCITY

600 boys were led there in the middle of one bright day. 600 Jewish boys aged 12–18, dressed in very thin, long striped camp uniforms, with ragged boots or wooden clogs on their feet. The boys looked so beautiful and were so well built that not even those rags could make them look bad . . . 25 SS men, heavily loaded down led them in. When they reached the square, the *Kommandoführer* ordered them to disrobe . . . The boys saw the smoke belching from the chimney and realised instantly that they were being led to their death. They began running around the square in wild horror, tearing out their hair, [not know]ing how to save themselves. Many of them broke down in grievous weeping, a terrible lament [went up]. The *Kommandoführer* and his helper beat the defenceless boys mercilessly to make them disrobe. His club broke from that beating. So he fetched another one and kept beating them over the heads until his violence won out. The boys disrobed with an instinctive dread of death, and huddled together naked and barefoot in order to protect themselves from the blows, and they did not move. Many of the boys made a wild dash towards [the Jews]

from the *Sonderkommando* and threw their arms around their necks pleading for salvation. Others ran around that large square [to escape] death. The *Kommandoführer* called for the *Unterscharführer* to help with his rubber club . . . The clear young voices of the boys grew louder by the minute [until they changed into] bitter crying. That terrible lament carried far.

(Zalmen Lewenthal, Memoir of Auschwitz)[256]

The Holocaust was a genocide committed by Nazi Germany during the years of World War II. This is one of the most analysed and chronicled events in history, but I intend to look at it in an entirely new light. Different historians use the words 'holocaust' and 'genocide' to mean different things, and much confusion arises from this. So I need to explain how I will use these words, and then we can look at the events without being confused by the language.

The term 'holocaust' derives from the Ancient Greek *holos* meaning whole and *kauston* meaning to burn, and the term *holocauste* first appeared in the twelfth century to refer to the massacre of Jews. This derivation causes some historians to use the modern term 'holocaust' to refer solely to the genocide of Jews, and so they analyse the causes of the Holocaust predominantly in terms of anti-Semitism. This analysis either ignores the other victims, or assumes that their deaths were a completely separate set of events with a separate causality. This is totally unrealistic.

I use the word 'Holocaust' to refer to the entire programme of killing, so I include all victim groups that total about seventeen million people.

The term 'genocide' is frequently defined and redefined with microscopic precision. The United Nations defines it as "acts committed with intent to destroy, in whole or in part, a national, ethnical, racial or religious group".[257] However, the majority of genocide scholars are members of ethnic groups that have been victims of past genocides, and there is a tendency to redefine genocide in terms of what was done to their ancestors. Scholars bicker among themselves over the minutiae of one massacre versus another in unseemly squabbles which one scholar dubbed the "Suffering Olympics".[258] The debate reduces to a question of which massacres qualify as genocides and which do not. Causality is forgotten. This seemingly leads to the conclusion that we don't need to care about the massacres that the wordsmiths don't think are "genocides". I use the UN definition of the word.

The following is a list of the groups of people killed during the Holocaust, starting with the most numerous group and declining:

1. Slavs (Russians, Poles, Serbians, Ukrainians, etc.)
2. Jews
3. Romanies
4. Freemasons
5. Mentally ill and congenitally deformed people
6. Homosexuals
7. Jehovah's Witnesses
8. Political opponents (principally Marxists, trade unionists and other people from the political left, but also including dissenting priests).

The arithmetic of genocide is in theory straightforward. The number killed is the starting population, plus normal birth rates, less normal death rates, less the closing population. The Soviet Union had over twelve million civilian deaths (including over one million Jews). There are many difficulties with estimating the number of Slav deaths,[259] but they need to be identified as a group in any historical analysis of the Holocaust because that is how the perpetrator saw them – that is why they were killed. Despite these difficulties, there is little doubt that Slavs were the largest victim group and the number killed exceeded ten million.

A huge amount of scholarly research has enabled us to pinpoint the number of Jewish victims to between 5.8 and 6.0 million. There is a strong consensus about these numbers, with outlying estimates seemingly the product of dubious motivation. However, there were no pre-war Europe-wide demographic statistics for the Romanies, so we have to rely on crude methods of estimating the numbers killed.[260] The difficulty of counting the Romany dead is one factor that has led to their victim status being undermined.

All of the remaining victim groups were not ethnic groups, and were mostly German citizens.[261] We therefore need to rely on German records, and not demographic measures. The number of political opponents killed is difficult to quantify because there is no method of identifying them as a cohesive group or separating them from executed common criminals (which is how the Nazi regime saw them).

Germany during this period was a state as focussed on genocide as it was on war. During the final stages of military collapse, there was no slackening of the efforts applied to the continuation of the genocide, and this considerably diluted the German military effort. The disproportionate amount of research applied to the Jewish victims of this genocide has resulted in it becoming normal, including in scholarly writings, to refer to all the non-Jewish victims as the "other" victims. However, the Jews represent approximately a third of the total.

The tendency to place the Jews at the pinnacle of victimhood is based on an analysis of intentionality. There is no question that the evidence of intentionality is strongest for the Jews. In *Mein Kampf*, Hitler specifically mentioned only five victim groups: Slavs, Jews, Marxists, Freemasons and the mentally or congenitally ill. He focusses his hatred almost equally towards Jews and Marxists, and from about eighty pages into the book constantly tried to conjoin the two. "Marxism, whose goal is and remains the destruction of all non-Jewish national states."[262]

Hitler's idea of a Marxist appears to have been rather confused. In *Mein Kampf*, he argued in favour of trade unions, but then went on to smash the German labour movement, and the Nazis murdered many trade unionists. Although large tracts of *Mein Kampf* are unconstrained hate rants against Jews and Marxists, it does not specifically set out plans for killing them. Hitler proposed the enforced sterilisation of the mentally ill, but not killing them.[263] But he made no secret of his intention of spreading the German nation eastwards into Poland and Russia by military conquest. "The foreign policy of the folkish state must safeguard the existence on this planet of the race embodied in the state, by creating a healthy, viable natural relation between the nation's population and growth on the one hand and the quality of the soil on the other hand . . . Only an adequately large space on this earth assures a nation of freedom of existence."[264] This was in accordance with his principle of "Lebensraum", or "Living Space" which he deemed necessary for the German "race".[265] There is little doubt of the implied intentionality of Hitler's plans for Slavs, and it is also not open to doubt that he regarded them as inferior to "Aryans" and it was this supposed inferiority, he argued, that enabled them to be subordinated by the "Jewish doctrine of Marxism".[266]

Mein Kampf mentions the Freemasons in several places, but not Jehovah's Witnesses. This is curious, and perhaps is explained by tracing the path of a myth that flows throughout *Mein Kampf* that was generally known at the time as the *"Dolchstoßlegende"* or the "Stab in the Back Theory" that Germany lost World War I because Jews betrayed it. This myth was widely believed in post-WWI Germany and was derived from a forged document that conjoined Jews and Freemasons.[267]

Homosexuals are another victim group not mentioned in *Mein Kampf*, but Hitler did demonstrate a bizarre sexual prudishness. He devotes several pages to explaining that Germans must marry young because this would reduce prostitution and syphilis. Hitler also mentioned people of African descent with disdain, and it is troubling to speculate what might have occurred if large numbers of African American or African French soldiers had become German POWs.

The Romanies are the most significant victim group that gets no mention in *Mein Kampf*. The Romanies also got no mention in the Nazi Nuremburg Laws of 1935 that explicitly targeted Jews for segregation. (The Nuremburg Laws also did not target Slavs.) Once again, evidence of the intentionality towards the Jews is overwhelmingly strong. However, the evidence of intentionality cannot be used to segregate the Jews as a victim group because the ultimate fate of both the Jews and Romanies was almost identical, and the difficulty of quantifying the Romany dead should not permit this fact to be glossed over.[268]

Since the end of WWII, the fate of the Romanies has been immeasurably worse than that of the Jews. Romanies were mostly illiterate, and this made reuniting people with their families almost impossible. The Romany language was not then a written language, and only now is human rights law being written in Romany. Romanies, unlike Jews, had no representation at the Nuremburg trials. They relied on an oral tradition, so the loss of all their elders destroyed their culture. Today, they struggle with dire social conditions. The racial prejudice against Romanies continues unabated.[269] "They are at the bottom of every socio-economic indicator: the poorest, the most unemployed, the least educated, the shortest-lived, the most welfare-dependent, the most imprisoned, and yes, the most segregated."[270]

So if the fate of Jews and Romanies under Nazism was similar, how does the fate of Slavs compare? The key difference here hinges upon how the Nazis saw these "races" under their theories of eugenics. Jews were seen as an evil threat that was out to destroy the German "race". Romanies were seen as a source of pollution to German purity because of their perceived tendency to interbreed (hence the policy – introduced in 1933 – for their sterilisation).

Slavs, by comparison, were not seen as evil, but merely inferior. The Nazi theories of eugenics said that Slavs could be enslaved and made to serve their German masters. There were plans to prevent Slavs from marrying, and so the plan was that as Germany expanded to fill the newly conquered lands of Eastern Europe, Slavs would gradually die out. We can see the cruel logic of this theory if we look at the fate of Slavs in the Nazi camp system. Few of them were gassed, but huge numbers of them starved while working as slave labour. The genocidal intent of Nazi Germany towards Slavs cannot be denied – it was the expectation that over the course of 25–30 years, Slavs would cease to exist in the German-occupied world. The fact that the Nazis killed more Slavs than any other group was because they conquered more of them. The fact that the percentage of Slavs killed was much lower than the percentage of Jews and Romanies is that the plan was to exterminate them over a generation, and the plan was barely under way when the War ended.

There is an unfortunately common model of Jewish scholarship on the Holocaust that creates elaborate arguments about how the Nazis intentions towards Jews were worse than "other" victim groups, and then to explain the whole of the Holocaust in terms of anti-Semitism.[271] This is the victim creating a mythology about the mythology of the perpetrator – a pointless analysis. We cannot say that anti-Semitism was the cause of the Holocaust, when it was simply the reason that Jews were included in it. The Holocaust was a broad program of genocide that swept up every group that existed in the land occupied by Germany that was subject to *any* form of prejudice or discrimination. So we have to look for another explanation, something that accounts for all victims: a perversion of the evolutionary response of revenge misdirected because it was unconscious through suppression.

I have already discussed evidence of Hitler's humiliation, as well as evidence that this humiliation was unconscious. That suppressed humiliation is the main subtext is announced in the first page of *Mein Kampf*, when Hitler refers obliquely to "our Fatherland's deepest humiliation"; not daring to specify what this humiliation was. But we cannot look only to Hitler's humiliation, because he had armies of helpers. We therefore need to look at the humiliation of Germans more broadly.

It is undeniable that Germans of the time were humiliated. They were humiliated by the loss of WWI and by the terms of the Versailles Treaty that ended it. However, the humiliation of German-speaking people goes back much further than that:

squashed between all the competing forces of the Great Empires: Russian, French, Ottoman and British, they were constantly pushed around and divided. This was, however, political humiliation, and if we are to look to evolutionary theory for an explanation of the Holocaust, we have to find humiliation that is biologically relevant – i.e. a threat to biological fitness.

After the WWI armistice, Germany was forced to relinquish its navy, and then the British operated a naval blockade of Germany. Part of the justification of the blockade was the enforcement of the "War Guilt" clause of the Treaty of Versailles. Hostility towards Germany at the end of WWI meant that there was little pressure on Britain to lift the blockade and so it was maintained until March 1919. The blockade directly caused death by famine of hundreds of thousands of Germans, with a particular bias towards children. German estimates of deaths caused by the blockade were 762,000. A British government estimate at the time was 800,000. A more recent estimate was 424,000.[272] The journalist Walter Duranty visited Germany in 1919 and found people living on black bread and potatoes. They had no meat, butter, milk or eggs. Ninety per cent of children were malnourished and more than half had rickets.[273]

This was undoubtedly a threat to biological fitness, and in terms of evolutionary theory we should expect a revenge response. But was the humiliation suppressed? If it was, then we could expect the humiliation response of revenge to be misdirected. This is difficult to verify when we apply it to the nation of Germany as a whole, but Hitler certainly buried the fact. In *Mein Kampf*, he talks endlessly of trivial humiliations of Germany, but doesn't mention the blockade once. In fact, throughout the book he talks admiringly of the British despite the fact that they were the source of the real bio- logical humiliation of his country. (Compare his unconstrained admiration of the father who savagely beat him.)

It seems likely to me that Germans denied their humiliation. Hitler taught them how to do this. In the same way that the military teaches its army recruits to act proud when their training is a ritual humiliation, Hitler told them that they were the greatest race on

Earth. He spent huge resources on giving his soldiers the finest uniforms that money could buy and he applied this mentality to the entire nation. He built a cult of denial of true humiliation and replaced it with mythologies of humiliations that were marginal to the point of being tolerable. The result was an entire nation of people who were brimming with revenge but who had disconnected that response from the appropriate target. This revenge was applied to *all* the victims of the Holocaust, and the pattern of ritual humiliation applied to them was the same as the humiliation that the army applies to recruits during training: pointless marches, worthless work, the need for absurd respect to your abusers.[274] However, the difference between the humiliation of the Holocaust and that of soldiers is that the humiliator did not have any use for the victim once it was over.

THREE LEVELS OF HOLOCAUST DENIAL

Holocaust Denial has been a contentious issue ever since the full extent of the Holocaust became apparent. A Holocaust Denier is generally taken to be someone who states that the Holocaust did not occur, or that the numbers of people killed has been exaggerated, or even that it is a hoax or propaganda. However, there has been a recent trend towards revisionism that seeks to reduce the estimates of numbers killed (rather than deny them). I call such a person a "Level-One Holocaust Denier". Holocaust denial is a crime in many countries, but I think this is a mistake. Some people's Level-One Holocaust Denial is motivated by a political or racist agenda (former President Ahmedinejad of Iran falls into this category) but I think it plausible that some humane people fall into this category out of a form of cognitive dissonance – they have a concept of people as humane that simply contradicts the facts of the Holocaust.

We need to add to Level-One Holocaust Denial two further tiers of denial, and a complete acceptance of this history requires us to look in much more detail at what happened, and then to look at ourselves in a much more critical light.

A "Level-Two Holocaust Denier" is someone who admits that the events took place, but says that they were performed by "Nazis". In other words, they de-personify the perpetrators and blithely assume that the people who did this were "brainwashed" or subject to propaganda or "indoctrination". That propaganda was a major component of the Nazi Government is undeniable, but it is a component of most governments, including ones that don't commit atrocities. Hitler talks at considerable length in *Mein Kampf* of propaganda's necessity and how it should be executed. This does not mean, however, that the people who executed the Holocaust were mindless villains. I cannot find anybody who can describe how "brainwashing" or "indoctrination" is done anyway, and it is absurd to talk of it as if we understand its causality. Level-Two Holocaust Denial is the denial that this could have been done by people like ourselves unless they had had their minds mysteriously tampered with. I have sought to construct a causal path whereby rational people could execute the Holocaust as a corruption of a response that is a normal part of everybody's evolutionary makeup.

Until recently, it has been standard for Holocaust scholars to be Level-Two Holocaust Deniers.[275] I was overwhelmed by a sense of it when I visited the United States Holocaust Memorial Museum. Although hundreds of thousands of Germans were involved in the execution of the Holocaust, the USHMM mentions almost none of them by name, gives little clue as to who they were or how they lived. It gives no sense that they were ordinary people. By contrast, much detail is given (including names) of people who risked their lives to save victims. The Level-Two Holocaust Denier wants to deny that perpetrators were people, but is happy to celebrate heroes as people. It is perhaps understandable that a museum peddles this line, otherwise nobody would want to visit it, but the risk is that it panders to people who want to "care *about*" the Holocaust without bothering to understand it: a generic form of political kitsch – the denial of shit. At the time of my visit (July 2010) there was a special exhibit on Nazi propaganda, and visiting the museum it is hard to avoid the conclusion that the whole thing could only have occurred if the executers were somehow duped or acting under duress. There is almost no attempt to describe the motivations of the Holocaust's foot-soldiers.[276]

The bubble of Level-Two Holocaust Denial was spectacularly and controversially burst in 1996 by Daniel Goldhagen's *Hitler's Willing Executioners*.[277] Goldhagen demonstrates that the Holocaust was executed by large numbers of ordinary Germans, and not a small group of ideologically indoctrinated Nazis. The idea that Hitler indoctrinated the Germans is false; he merely exploited prejudice that was already there.[278]

Goldhagen establishes several important points: the perpetrators were ordinary Germans; they were people with moral consciences; they lived normal lives; and they acted willingly.

The perpetrators were ordinary Germans: Goldhagen demonstrates that police battalions recruited ordinary German men.[279] Generally, they were too old for normal military duty, but were otherwise fairly average. They went through very little ideological indoctrination.[280] The men of these battalions included members of the SS and the Nazi Party in only slightly higher percentages than the German national average. However, during the period before the establishment of the death camps, the police battalions operated throughout the area of the former Polish-Lithuanian Commonwealth and were the Nazis' principal agents of genocide.

The perpetrators had moral consciences: Goldhagen opens the book with an anecdote about Captain Wolfgang Hoffmann, a commander of a police battalion that executed thousands of civilian Jews; yet he was outraged that he was asked to sign a declaration that he would not steal from Polish people. Not only did he find it morally objectionable that his superiors implied he might steal, he refused a direct order to sign the declaration.[281]

Another example of moral conscience is the outrage at the Nazi government's euthanasia program for the mentally ill or congenitally defective. This program was called the T4 program, after its Berlin headquarters at Tiergarten Strasse 4. "Germans (1) recognised this slaughter to be wrong, (2) expressed their views about it,

(3) openly protested for an end to the killing, (4) suffered no retribution for having expressed their views and for pressing their demands, and (5) succeeded in producing a formal cessation of the killing program, and saving German lives."[282]

A bizarrely ironic example of German moral conscience is their treatment of animals. Goldhagen gives the example of the commander of Police Regiment 25. Goldhagen quotes his information sheet: "One should with renewed strength take measures against cruelty to animals . . . Special attention is to be devoted to beef cattle, since through over-crowding in the railway cars great losses of the animals have occurred." [283] This compares to the treatment of Jews in similar cattle cars. Goldhagen quotes a member of Police Battalion 101: "The cars were stuffed so full that one had to labour in order to close the sliding doors. Not seldom did one have to lend aid with one's feet."[284]

The perpetrators had normal lives: Goldhagen demonstrates that the Germans executing the Holocaust went to the movies, drank, sang and danced. They went to church, and the Catholics took confession. Goldhagen describes that they openly took their wives and girlfriends to witness massacres of Jews. A Captain Julius Wohlauf of Police Battalion 101 took his pregnant wife Vera to an "action".[285] His officer was outraged that he took her to a massacre of Jews *while pregnant*. He was not at all bothered that other non-pregnant wives witnessed the same thing.

The perpetrators acted willingly: Goldhagen goes to great length to demonstrate that some Germans chose not to participate. There were very few, but by demonstrating that they were not punished, Goldhagen proved that they did not act for fear of punishment should they refuse. Goldhagen found evidence of at least eight different police battalions where "the men had been informed that they would not be punished for refusing to kill."[286]

Goldhagen quotes Erwin Grafmann, a member of Police Battalion 101. When asked why he and the other men did not take up the sergeant's offer to excuse themselves from a killing squad, he replied, "at the time, we did not give it any second thoughts at all."[287]

Another member said, "The Jew was not acknowledged by us to be a human being."[288]

Goldhagen, despite extensive research, fails to answer the fundamental question: why did this happen? He simply resorts to the all-too-common model of Jewish scholarship: downplay the suffering of "other" victims and explain what is left in terms of anti-Semitism. "The one explanation adequate to these tasks holds that a demonological anti-Semitism, of the virulent racial variety, was the common structure of the perpetrators' cognition and of German society in general."[289] To conclude this, he had to ignore the Romanies – a form of Level-One Holocaust Denial. He refers to them only three times in a 600-page book, and only admits their treatment was similar to the Jews in an endnote that most readers will miss. This endnote says that, "Germans' policies towards the two people [Jews and Romanies] differed in important ways."[290] If these differences are important, why does he not explain them?[291]

Goldhagen's analysis reduces everything to factors unique to German culture at the time, and this is an example of what I call "Level-Three Holocaust Denial" – the belief that although ordinary Germans could do this, ordinary people from your own culture could not. We all need to maintain the belief that we could not do this, and this means that we have to find some feature of the people who did it that distinguishes them from ourselves. Many historians have tied themselves in knots trying to do this without being racist themselves.

The circumstances that gave rise to the Holocaust were a basic human element of emotional makeup – revenge – and a pattern of behaviour manipulation by the perpetrators that caused that revenge response to be unconscious. This was a perversion of our evolved nature that resulted in the revenge being executed against someone other than the humiliator, and every group that was subject to prejudice was swept up in the dreadful path of a simple belief – an irrefutable thought. This is something that could happen to anyone, including you, dear reader, and all that separates you from a genocide perpetrator is that your humiliation hasn't been severe enough, or that you have never had cause to deny or mythologise it.

So, once you have embraced the concept of Level-Three Holocaust Denial and admitted that you were until now such a denier, should you have compassion for the perpetrators of the worst crime in the history of humanity? Are we ready to reach out to the place where forgiveness can be total? All humans are innocent, but for some it isn't possible to understand how.

Consider this story told by Primo Levi. He does not tell the story in one place. You have to piece it together from snippets in his writings spread over decades.[292] Levi worked in Auschwitz III, Monowitz as a slave labour research chemist, and the most senior civilian German he dealt with was a chemist. One day, the German asked Levi if he was OK, and Levi was utterly stunned. Levi thought silently to himself "What is the man thinking?" What common meaning could be found for the expression "OK" in a conversation between a German and an Auschwitz inmate? The German gave Levi a chit to get a new pair of shoes. An insignificant act you might think, but Levi explained its significance in an interview years later. When you arrived at Auschwitz, you were stripped and showered, and then you were given a striped uniform and two shoes. These shoes could be both left shoes, and would be in random sizes. What you would quickly realise is that you must find someone with two right shoes, and then if your shoes are too small, you must find someone else who had shoes that were too big. Everybody would trade until they had two shoes (certainly not a matching pair) that approximately fit. But what if the pair you ended up with were worn out or caused you to have blisters? Bad shoes meant that you ended up unable to walk, and therefore unable to work. And in Auschwitz if you couldn't work, you were gassed. Bad shoes, says Levi, *killed* you. So the German chemist quite possibly saved Levi's life. Levi admitted this (only indirectly in other writings) but he never showed gratitude. Years later, after the War, Levi met the German. Perhaps this wasn't by chance because the world of European research chemists wasn't large at that time. The German and Levi corresponded briefly, and the German told Levi "compassion was not tolerated".

Let us examine these two men, thrust together by an unfathomable set of circumstances. Levi was struggling with his perception of the German's compassion, but he simply couldn't reconcile it with his daily treatment by Germans. We can tell that the event had a huge impact on him because it crops up over and over in his work, but in no one place does he tell the whole story. Levi could not put all the pieces together in one place because that would force him to admit that the German had compassion.

Consider the German. He said that compassion was not tolerated, but how was this order to be obeyed? Easy! All he had to do was suppress the behavioural response of compassion in himself. Doing this on its own seems innocent enough; it could even be portrayed as a coping strategy. Over the course of the War (and perhaps some of the years before) it became a habit and then he forgot he was doing it. Gradually his concept of his own compassion dims until it is barely perceptible to him. There he was, years after the War, trying to reconcile his past and his morality and pretending that life was normal – when suddenly Primo Levi walks back into his life. Ask yourself if you really have no pity for this German. You cannot shed a tear? Are you really so certain that you are not suppressing your own emotional response? Is there some history of yours that you need to think about? Consider the giving of the shoes – in many ways a pathetic gesture – and think about what it means. It should not be seen as an act of kindness because this action is *all* about the German. He is looking into himself and asking "why do I have this sudden urge to help a strange Jew?" He is reaching out, not to Levi, but within himself. He is grappling to try to regain the concept of his own compassion, and he is unable to do so. Suppression of the behaviour has made his recognition of his own emotion a hazy blur, and all that he can find within himself is this pitiful floundering.

WORSE THAN GENOCIDE

If you are unable to feel pity for a genocide perpetrator, then you are unable to acknowledge that you are capable of holding such destructive beliefs yourself. This is unfortunate because it is quite possible that you do. If mankind collectively destroys the ability of this planet to support the diversity of life that exists here now, then why would it matter that the Holocaust killed seventeen million people? What's going to be left to care about?

The loss of human life that man-made changes occurring on our planet are likely to cause will make the slaughter of the Holocaust seem like a footnote of history. Even this is to disregard the loss of life to other species, much of which has already occurred.

Comparing man's environmental destruction to the Holocaust might appear controversial, but I am looking at belief through a wide lens that must encompass all instances of humanity's capacity to self-destruct. Beliefs by their nature are considered to be right by their believers, and it is only through some level of Holocaust Denial, that we can think that Germans during WWII *must* have known that something was wrong. *They did not know.* They believed that Nazism would enhance human wellbeing, and most of us believe that unconstrained consumption enhances human wellbeing. Let us compare these beliefs in the lead-up to their respective catastrophes. In the years immediately preceding the Holocaust the following were actually believed by the people who became the perpetrators:

- "Science demonstrates that Aryan people are superior to other races, and Jews and Romanies are sub-human";
- "Jews were responsible for the humiliation of Germany in WWI"; and
- "Bolshevism is a Jewish conspiracy".

Regarding environmental destruction, consider the following general beliefs that are widely held today:

- "Climate science is pseudoscience and climate scientists are liars";
- "Climate scientists are corrupted by research grant money and governments pay it to them so that they can raise taxes";
- "The theory of man-made climate change is a socialist conspiracy".[293]

Let us examine these general beliefs and look at some specific examples. For somebody like myself who is interested in belief, an interesting source is online blogs and public comments posted on news websites. People who post on these do so anonymously, and appear to feel uninhibited in saying exactly what is on their mind.[294] Here is a group of postings representing the beliefs about climate change that I selected more or less at random. 'Kicker3' writes:

> This used to be the forum you would come to hear the wackiest wackaloons spouting world class AGW [Anthropogenic Global Warming] hysterics. Amazing that in a matter of 6 months or so the majority of the posts are now heavy with skepticism. Even the author who is visibly a hairy-armpit liberal, uses a modest and restrained tone, where once we would have gotten wild propaganda . . . Bye Bye Global Warming. Thanks for raping science before you left...[295]

One might imagine that The Economist attracts a more thoughtful readership. Sadly, this does not appear to be the case. 'obusquets' writes:

> Wow, I'm truly scared after reading this article. You are really good at fear-mongering . . . You are a really good for a fiction book, or maybe comics [sic]. Would you have lived during the times when the bible was written, you would have had a chapter in the apocalypse . . .[296]

The BBC regularly has an on-line 'Have Your Say' forum for environmental issues. 'europhile' writes: "Here we go again, eco fascists, it is total utter rubbish."[297]

It would be easy to dismiss the views of Kicker3, obusquets and europhile as those of a few oddballs until you start to notice the simple statistic of the people who click the "recommend" button next to their comments. For example 'dryrot' got twice as many recommendations for his comment "More brainwashing – more thinly disguised propaganda by the AGW alarmists" than any other comment on one particular thread.[298] So this rather crude method of online democracy implies that such beliefs are common. Widespread belief in the falsity of science is alarming. There is wide disbelief in the theory of evolution by natural selection.

The Pew Research Center for the People & the Press employs robust statistical analysis. Their research found that the percentage of Americans who think that there is no solid evidence that the Earth is warming has risen from 17% in 2006 to 28% in 2011, despite the fact that the evidence is actually increasing.[299] This belief has strong correlation with party affiliation: 77% of Democrats think there *is* solid evidence compared with 43% of Republicans. And the percentage decreases to 30% for people identifying with the Tea Party. Most of the people on the right who think there is evidence of warming think it is not caused by humans. This is truly extraordinary.

These views are propagated by some best-selling commentators. Ann Coulter says, "A sparrow does not a spring make, but in the Druid religion of environmentalism, every warm summer's breeze prompts apocalyptic demands for a ban on aerosol sprays and plastic bags."[300] Coulter goes on to denigrate the statistics by picking individual months in individual US states, and she denigrates the Intergovernmental Panel On Climate Change because it is affiliated with the UN, and the UN concluded that there was not enough evidence that Saddam Hussein was a threat. Well actually, the statistics (when you consolidate all of them in a rigorous fashion) *do* prove that the Earth is warming, and news clearly hasn't reached Coulter that the UN was right on Saddam Hussein.

It could be argued that Coulter is a wingnut like Kicker3 and his ilk, but some very sober and educated commentators have made similar arguments. Nigel Lawson, a former British Cabinet Minister argues[301] that global warming isn't certain and would actually benefit humanity if it occurred. How does he claim to know this? He dismisses the computer modelling of climate scientists, but did no modelling at all in reaching his conclusion. Some of Lawson's language is just as extreme as Coulter and the bloggers: comparing "eco-fundamentalism" to a religion. Who does he think practices this religion? Where is their church? The evidence is found in the dry mathematical consolidation of statistics and the numbers have been checked over and over again.

Climate change denial has given birth to a hodgepodge of people passing themselves off as experts. One of the leading lights of this pseudo-expertise is Lord Christopher Monckton. He is quoted as an expert by the Wall Street Journal, and he has addressed the US Congress on behalf of Republicans. However, his formal scientific education ceased halfway through high school.[302] It is perhaps no coincidence that he is related by marriage to Nigel Lawson.[303] Much of the doubt in climate science is created by a symbiosis between British commentators (most climate denial originates in Britain) and the US media. US media rules purporting to support objectivity require the disclosure of dissenting views even if those views are a tiny minority. The US media therefore often suggests there is doubt, even though the scientific community is close to unanimous. In addition, US news sources tone down climate change reporting because they are so dependent upon advertising revenues from corporations that are CO_2 emitters.

If we look at the accredited scientists who doubt climate science (and they are a shrinking group), we find a few that can easily be dismissed as what a criminal judge would call "unreliable witnesses". These are scientists that appear to be corporate stooges: they have sided with Big Business against the majority of the scientific community on more than one issue. For example there are climate-sceptic scientists who previously argued that smoking did not cause lung cancer, that there was no hole in the ozone layer, and that CFCs did not cause atmospheric damage.[304] Many of these have direct connections with the fossil fuel industry either as employees or consultants.[305] The remainder of the doubting scientists have one surprising unifying quality: they almost all agree that the Earth is warming – that is because statistics don't lie. These doubting scientists argue that the Earth is warming, but *not* because of the release of greenhouse gases. But I cannot find one of them that has produced hard analysis. Climate scientists who believe that global warming is man-made have performed detailed modelling, and the doubters are relying upon hand-waving arguments.

Rick Perry, the Texas governor and one-time Republican presidential candidate, insists that climate change theory has been created by "a substantial number of scientists who have manipulated data so that they will have dollars rolling into their projects".[306] There is no evidence of this manipulation.[307] But there *is* evidence that the reverse is the case: the worst corporate polluters have been making huge donations to environmental lobbyists. This has effectively bought their silence. When the BP gulf oil spill occurred in 2010, everybody agreed that it was an environmental disaster – including climate change deniers – but the environmental lobby was almost silent because they depend upon polluter donations.[308] The inverted logic of all this is quite stunning. Oil companies (e.g. Chevron) have advertising campaigns that have nothing to do with making people consume their product, but with suggesting people should consume less of it – the subtext being that they are responsible corporate citizens and so there is no ethical problem with consuming their product.

It seems unlikely that climate scientists are making a mistake because doubters have made them redo the calculations many times more than any normal scientific best practice would require. Recent opinion polls among working climate scientists reveal that 97% of them think that global warming is a serious risk.[309] However, even if they *have* got it all wrong, we have so many other problems to face:

- Garbage that we have dumped into the sea all floats to the point where the currents meet, and the Atlantic and Pacific Oceans each have a floating garbage pile that some scientists have estimated to be as large as Germany.

- We continue to destroy forest at an alarming rate. In aggregate, we have destroyed half the world's tropical forests, and for particularly endangered forests (e.g. in Indo-Burma, African Coastal, etc) cumulative deforestation is 95%. Nobody understands what the environmental impact of this will be, but it is conceivable that large areas that were previously forested will turn into desert wasteland.[310]

- Over 30% of the CO_2 that we emit into the atmosphere dissolves into the sea. This creates H_2CO_3, a mild acid, and the oceans (which are actually slightly alkaline) are being acidified. Since the start of the Industrial Revolution, we have added 500 billion tonnes of CO_2 to the oceans.[311] Ocean acidification is already damaging the world's coral reefs[312] and 80% of some reefs have died due to a combination of acidification and increased temperature.[313] Natural volcanic emitters of undersea CO_2 off the coast of Italy and Papua New Guinea give scientists a natural lab to study the effect of ocean acidification, and what they are finding is that crustaceans and molluscs cannot survive acid seas because they cannot form shell.[314] We are only just starting to ask what the impact of this would be upon plankton – which forms a larger biomass than the world's forests. At a certain level of acidification, it is conceivable that plankton could become extinct, and that could be the beginning of the end of life on this planet.

Nobody denies the trash heap and nobody denies the deforestation because it isn't deniable, but people have proved to be very adept at ignoring it. But denial of ocean acidification is already appearing in on-line forums. How is this possible? The chemistry involved is so staggeringly simple that even Lord Christopher Monckton could understand it.

I am not writing about environmental destruction or climate change, but about belief. We have a conflict between evidence and ideology that produces extraordinary confusion at all levels of this debate. Of Tea Party supporters, 64% say there is no evidence of warming, but only 47% think there is no problem.[315] That means that approximately 17% both think there is no problem, but something to worry about nonetheless. This conflict even exists in the scientific community. Craig Idso is a climate-sceptic scientist. So then why is he a leading researcher in carbon sequestration? He is devoting his professional career to seeking solutions to a problem he is denying. Richard Lindzen is another climate-sceptic scientist who appears unable to accept reality. He believes that changes in cloud cover will offset warming, but whenever his peers blow apart his research papers he continues to peddle his hypothesis.[316] He appears to be engaging in wish modelling: tweaking his model to produce the results he hopes for.

How can we (including scientists) be so confused about overwhelming empirical evidence? This question is *not* about the evidence, but about the nature of the beliefs involved.

COGNITIVE DISSONANCE

Cognitive dissonance is the term used by psychologists to describe the holding of contradictory beliefs. Psychologists tell us that people resolve this conflict by accepting whatever belief makes them feel good about themselves. But they cannot explain why. The theory in this book permits us to do this. If a belief *in* is a logical tautology, then this trumps a belief *that*. It is rational that logic should trump empirical evidence because we can always be mistaken about empirics. But if the logic starts with a false behavioural assumption, then it does not make the belief right.

It seems implausible that cognitive dissonance could arise from two conflicting beliefs *that*. These are all in theory empirically verifiable, although some are difficult to verify for practical reasons. In both normal life and science, conflicting beliefs *that* prompt us to try to find out by an empirical process which of the beliefs is mistaken or to try to resolve the conflict. If you had evidence both that your child is at school *and* that he or she is playing truant, would you not set out to find out what was really happening? Similarly, theoretical physicists have been burning their grey cells for half a century trying to resolve the conflict between relativity and quantum theory. Nobody would say that physicists have cognitive dissonance, despite two of their most important theories conflicting. However, scientific theory is belief *that*.

It is also difficult to imagine a conflict occurring in one person between two beliefs *in*. This would seemingly involve them manipulating their behaviour in different ways at the same time. How could this occur? Cadillac Christians fudge their concurrent belief in Christianity and consumerism by a process of denial and it ultimately becomes a belief virus – what Socrates would call the involuntary discarding of beliefs. They adopt a form of Christianity that bears no relation to what the Bible says, but they would disagree if you pointed this out.

So if climate science is a belief *that*, and the denial of this is the result of a cognitive dissonance, what is the belief *in* that subordinates the empirical evidence?

SCENARIO: C/D FREEDOM

The Woman lived in a world of plenty. People had everything they needed, but to keep themselves happy they went out and bought more of it. Shopping wasn't a chore; it was a hobby. It gave structure to their lives – a cultural ritual that made them feel at one with their fellow man. People who drove old cars were teased and people who wore last year's clothes weren't invited to social gatherings. New things made them happy. They made them proud and whenever they went to work wearing a new coat, they felt an extra spring in their step. The people in the Woman's world had been programmed to think this by a relentless campaign of behavioural indoctrination. All their waking hours they were beamed images of good-looking people pretending to be happy while consuming products. The Woman could never escape it: neither in her home, in elevators nor the backs of taxis. She had a good job that paid well, but consumption was her freedom; so she spent all the money she earned, and therefore was utterly dependent upon her marginal dollar. Beautiful people with happy lives told her that she could buy more on credit, and since consumption was freedom, what reason was there to do otherwise?

Gradually, she fell further and further into debt. But how could she stop without relinquishing freedom? Freedom was the right to consume and total freedom was unconstrained consumption. A new image was added to the behavioural indoctrination of good-looking happy people consuming unnecessary things: serious, sensible-looking people told her that she could manage her debts. She could refinance and consolidate, and this seemed to be like making them go away. And this meant that her illusion of freedom could continue on its spiralling path to her destruction.

It's easy to say that she could have "taken responsibility". But we devote the entirety of our lives to a single project: figuring out what makes us happy and free. We think that we are listening to our feelings, but we can only identify our feelings by comparing our behaviour to that of other people. So what hope do we have if the behaviour of other people that we observe includes a relentless and systematic campaign of lying? We derive our concept of what makes us happy from deliberate behavioural misinformation.

IDEOLOGY TRUMPS SCIENCE

History makes clear that when ideology subordinates science or when ideology poses as science that the consequences are catastrophic.

The Dark Ages were a period in which all the philosophy of ancient Greece was buried under Christian orthodoxy. Mankind lived a life of brutal religious suppression for a millennium until it awoke again under the Renaissance. This lasted until Marx told us that his political theories were scientific. They weren't! His opening statement "The history of all hitherto existing societies is the history of class struggles" is empirically refuted by basic anthropology – Amazonian Indians don't have a bourgeoisie or a proletariat. Yet Marx held that there was no such thing as a human nature, and from this it naturally follows that there cannot be such a thing as an *apple* nature or a *wheat* nature. Consequently, Soviet scientists in the 1950s rejected Mendelian genetics. A human, said Marx, could be trained to exist in any ideology. And so Soviet scientists "trained" apple trees to grow in Siberia by repeatedly freeze-thawing their seeds prior to planting. Wheat was "trained" to grow with high density planting by pressure treating the seeds. The consequence of this phoney science was a famine that spread from Ukraine to China claiming forty million lives.[317] Nazism was similarly based on a phoney theory of eugenics that was little more than racism posing as science.

Climate science *is* science, and the campaign to discredit it comes from an ideological belief that human wellbeing is determined by unconstrained consumption. This ideology, like all beliefs *in* ultimately becomes destructive to the people who believe it. Humans, as the totally dominant species have learned to conquer all other species and all environments. So there is nothing to hold our population in check. It has doubled in less than fifty years. Each of us has doubled our resource consumption in an even shorter period, so our aggregate resource consumption has quadrupled. And just when we arrive at the point of identifying freedom with unlimited consumption we realise that our planet is not only a finite breadbasket, but is actually approaching exhaustion. Demographers expect our population to peak at around nine billion sometime in the 2040s or 50s.[318] If I live into my 80s, the world's population will have trebled in my lifetime.

We face the total contradiction from which fundamentalism is born: consumerism will exhaust our planet and we cannot accept that what we believe will kill us, so we say that we have failed our ideology. And we chase after a purer form of an ideology that is failing us. To escape this total contradiction, the lesser contradictions pour forth: your right to life begins at conception and ends when you hold a belief that threatens me; the right to life of a fertilised egg is based on the theory of genetics but we reject the theory of evolution; consumption means freedom but we have to work sixty hour weeks just to stay in the same place; we want religious freedom but only for our religion; we want more ideological war, lower taxes and no deficit; we want to be energy independent but place no constraint upon energy consumption. These are contradictions that a child could spot, but an adult cannot. It is often said that believing such contradictions is irrational, but a rational human is like water flowing through rock – it simply finds the path of least resistance and these contradictions are nothing compared to accepting that your own ideology is destructive to your own interest.

We face the perfect storm of the planet's ability to support human existence collapsing at the time when our numbers become ungovernable. All constraints on consumption are removed just as our consumption consumes us, and Consumption Fundamentalism sends us hurtling towards oblivion.

Genocide is nothing compared to this.

THE SELF-REFERENCING BIOLOGICAL MACHINE

The time has come to step back from the brink of political advocacy. The purpose of this book is not to invent a new ideology, but to explain how a human functions. We cannot do this without explaining what a belief is, why we have them and how they work. It is an inevitable consequence of their structure that they become destructive to their believers. That humanity is on a self-destructive path is not a new observation, but perhaps it is a new idea to explain why this is so hard to avoid. We need the sharp realisation of where our nature has led us to act as a catalyst for ideological renewal. So, let me now sum up the entirety of this book.

That humans have emotions isn't proof that we are not machines – the emotions *are* the machinery. In higher vertebrates, they are primary action drivers. If a chimpanzee didn't have emotions, it would slump in a blob until maggots (that don't have emotions) reduced it to crumbling bones. Emotions in a chimpanzee are products of evolution by natural selection. They drive survival-enhancing actions, and should be regarded as biological phenomena by scientists – including psychologists.

Attempting to understand human nature is one of our oldest enquiries. Since the Age of Enlightenment, it has been symbolically split between the views of Hobbes and Rousseau. Both lived before Darwin, but Rousseau was probably acquainted with the idea of evolution because one of his contemporaries, Georges-Louis Leclerc, was the first to propose it as a scientific hypothesis. Leclerc's descriptions of the great apes likely influenced Rousseau's idea of primitive man. Rousseau would have been fascinated by Darwinian theory had it been around in his day. But I suspect that Hobbes would have regarded it as heresy.[319]

The debate about whether humans are fundamentally good or fundamentally bad has raged ever since we first came up with a concept of a human nature. Evolutionary theory now permits us to answer this question. Kinship theory and theories of reciprocity enable us to describe the evolution of altruism. We can study this in chimpanzees, and can compare the results with Rousseau's conception of a primitive man. What we find is that the moral emotions (pity, sympathy, guilt, gratitude, etc.) are a product of evolution by natural selection and seem to operate in chimpanzees in the way that Rousseau would have us believe. When Rousseau argues that primitive man was peaceable, he is saying that our fundamental nature grants us the ability and the desire to cooperate. And he is right!

Altruism only works if we have mechanisms for detecting cheaters who do not reciprocate. Anger therefore is a product of evolution by natural selection and we can see it directed at cheaters in chimpanzees. The Darwinian theories of parental investment and sexual selection also demonstrate that humiliation and its violent response is a product of natural selection; so too is the emotion of jealousy. When Hobbes argues that without the Leviathan of the state to intervene we would be constantly in a state of "warre as of every man against every man", he is saying that anger and our response to humiliation is central to our nature, and the chain of humiliation and violent retaliation is never-ending. And he is right!

Hobbes and Rousseau are both right about human nature, but they are each only looking at that part of human nature that suits their political theories.

Consciousness isn't understood by either scientists or philosophers. However, it is clearly a mechanism whereby an animal self-reviews. That is a problem because self-referencing in a mechanism is a prerequisite to circular causality. It isn't clear that this can happen in a chimpanzee, but it certainly does in humans. Language is unique

More comple
violence, evoluti
should recognis
response. We are
threats to biolog
source of the thr
tion does not su
rects it. Hitler su
Germans suppre
and the response
target of discrim
ating others is th
consequences is
manipulation of
uncontrolled. W
who suppresses
formation is a cei
thology of hum
Egypt), and Am
reading a versior
Christians has b
everything" as tl
lims have been ar
need to rearm wi
is to gain an unde

Hobbes is cori
us at peace with
the right to viole
that the state has
humiliate their o
ingly prevalent ir
law: strip-searchi
cies; or exportin
countries that ens
the weapon of ch

to humans; so is the ability to contemplate future emotions and fluently deploy tactical deception with emotional behaviour. We can think about thinking, and we can understand that affecting emotional behaviour impacts upon the thinking of others – Rousseau's *Pitié*. Thereby, we can alter their responses towards us in ways that benefit us. However, such benefits are only short term. Eventually, this tactical deception alters how the emotion functions. The emotion was supposed to drive a survival enhancing action but no longer does so, and the gradual slide into self-destruction begins.

The ability to impersonate our own behaviour is the critical self-referencing mechanism that leads to circular causality in humans. A word for an emotion indirectly references the cause of the behaviour associated with that emotion. However, when we affect that behaviour, the cause is no longer a biological emotion, but the reason for the affectation. Humans modify their behaviour to demonstrate their compliance with the cultural group to which they identify, and this establishes a vortex that gradually gathers momentum: the culture causes the emotional behaviour; the meaning of the word for the emotion references the cause of the behaviour, i.e. the culture. It is irrefutable to people caught in this vortex that the culture causes emotional outcomes. If this outcome is bad, the feedback loop breaks. If it is good, then a belief is born. The belief exists because of circular causality of which the believer has no awareness. Logically, all beliefs are tautologies that the believer cannot escape – they are irrefutable thoughts. The pressure to modify behaviour to demonstrate compliance with the belief becomes stronger, and for entire societies a biological emotion no longer drives a survival-enhancing action. Self-destruction becomes a mass phenomenon, as the belief increasingly becomes destructive to the people who believe it. What I hope I have demonstrated is that *all* forms of belief *in* work this way. Bin Laden was in such a trap, and so was Hitler. Every Indian who thinks he needs more children is in such a trap, and so is every American who can only live with a massive carbon footprint. It is logical to believe in a fictitious religion. Once you understand its ingredients, inventing one is as easy as baking a cake. This is a form

of reductio
that you ar
of some for
mentally th
tance of th
tolerant of

A moral
should act
twenty-firs
tionary the
the unified
This is a vi
into the tw

I have de
and a mora
or affected
moral belie
secular soci
ones. This
scientific ey
as scientists
ideology, h
scientific hi
derive an id

The mo
Like Rouss
trust our m
These emo
and Menciu
us to the r
bombarded
emotions t
add to Rou
affecting o
become self

The only way to diffuse past humiliation is to apologise. Germany has done a substantially unqualified mea culpa for the Holocaust, but Japan's apology for the atrocities it committed in Asia during the same period has been weak and qualified. However, the winners of wars never apologise. Had Britain apologised for the naval blockade of Germany, the Holocaust might not have happened. Had America apologised for all the depleted uranium that they sowed across Iraq, 9/11 might not have happened.

The next Holocaust will occur when the political kitsch of a country becomes insufficient to cover up the shit that is being denied. People will have a destructive irrefutable thought. And someone will mythologise the cause of the destruction, and the anger and revenge will escalate in an unpredictable direction.

Let us review the principle objective of this book: to demonstrate that a human is a robustly logical computational device. What I have demonstrated is that if we make this assumption, we can still account for most of the craziness of human nature. This of course doesn't prove the case, it merely makes it a highly plausible hypothesis. But let us consider the alternative hypothesis. Most prior theory has said that because a person can perform a self-destructive action, that they are capable of "irrationality". In effect this is saying that because the output of human thinking can go awry, that there must be something wrong with the brain's processing. I am simply suggesting that the brain's processing is working just fine, and all the problems with the output are due to problems with the input. This is a garbage-in-garbage-out argument that any computer scientist should greet with a shrug. I have demonstrated that self-destructive actions are rational. Human actions are generally dependent upon beliefs, but beliefs are logical because they all take the form of logical tautologies. There remain some holes in my argument, but I'll leave you to search for them and, hopefully, you won't work them out before I fill them with my future work.

Can you accept that you are a robustly logical computational device? If that is all you are, then your life has no point. The origin of

there wasn't an anomaly in Mercury's orbit. The truth was something unimaginable at the time – Newton's Theory of Gravitation was wrong.

Albert Einstein's theories of Special and General Relativity are theoretically derived from a very small number of empirical phenomena. Observation of the mutual orbit of twin stars demonstrated that the speed of light is constant in space irrespective of the relative motion of the source of propagation. This simple fact was inconsistent with everything that physicists thought about space and time. Einstein worked out his theory almost entirely by thought experiment and mathematics.

An unexpected consequence of Einstein's theory was that light must bend when it passes through a gravitational field. Nobody had thought about this before. However, the effect is so small that to be observable we need a very large gravitational force such as the one that the Sun produces. We can only observe this during total solar eclipses because otherwise the light from the sun blots out the ray of light that we are trying to observe being bent. The astronomers Eddington, Cottingham, Crommelin and Davidson demonstrated Einstein's prediction by observing the positions of fixed stars (that is, stars so far away that they appear never to move) during such an eclipse. Since the light of those stars had all been bent inward by the sun's gravitational field, they all appeared to be further away from the sun than we would normally have expected to see them. This was Einstein's eureka moment. Scientists could no longer doubt the Theory of Relativity.

Let us stop for a moment and think about this irrelevant little planet that we love because it feeds us. Let us hypothesise about how a trivial meteorological change on our planet might have affected the destiny of our species. Some of the time, clouds enclose us such that we cannot see beyond them. Let us imagine that this occurred all the time. We would never have seen twin stars, and so we would have no law of propagation of light, and therefore we would have no law of relativity. We would never have seen another planet, and so we would not know what an orbit is. Therefore, we would have no theory of gravitation. It really isn't clear to me that we would have yet realised that our little planet wasn't flat. In fact we wouldn't know it was a little planet; it would be the entirety of our observable universe. We couldn't have built a telescope in space because we couldn't have got it up there without a theory of gravitation. In any case, we would first need to know that there was something out there to see. Otherwise, we would lack the curiosity.

Data is the life-blood of science. Science without data is like a plant without water; it cannot grow and eventually withers.

I have produced a philosophical theory of how a human algorithm works. I have explored the relationship between four phenomena: feeling, behaviour, language and belief. For two of these phenomena, language and behaviour, the data is visible for all to see. Scientists can construct experiments and can develop theories about them. However, I have also demonstrated that language and behaviour are affected by the other two phenomena, feeling and belief. In fact, each of the four phenomena is affected by the other three, with the possible exception of feeling, but this is the one phenomenon that poses the greatest metaphysical problem – what exactly is it? Sometimes we can mistake a belief for a feeling; it simply isn't possible to be sure, so we can't even make consistent observations about our own feelings. The scientists developing theories about the observable phenomena (language and behaviour) are going to be in a similar position to the pre-Einstein astronomers looking at Mercury: behavioural deception is corrupting the data they are trying to explain. However, the almost infinite variability of feeling and belief means that these scientists are going to be in a much worse position. The data that they observe is going to be pulled every which way in a pattern that appears to be random. It is no surprise that this had led some of mankind's greatest thinkers to produce laughably absurd theories about souls, unconscious minds, irrationality and free will.

The two phenomena that are somehow internal, feeling and belief, are only represented to the outside world through behaviour and language, but both can be misrepresented. A scientist can examine his own beliefs and feelings, but how can he conduct experiments on them if he doesn't know which beliefs are true? How can he conduct experiments on his feelings if he cannot measure them, or cannot be sure he remembers them accurately? He cannot be sure he can distinguish between feeling and belief, or that he correctly names his feelings.

Einstein worked out the Theory of Relativity from a very small number of observed phenomena. I too have a small number of observed phenomena: I have noticed that you occasionally make the same face that I make when I feel worried. From this, I deduce that you must be worried, but I cannot really be sure. Let us suppose that you and I agree that we will call the feeling "worry" when either of us makes that face. I know that when I feel worry, if I suppress the face, then you have no way of knowing that I am worried. I know this by hypothetical reasoning. I do not need to put human beings into a laboratory to check this. Similarly, without conducting any experiment, I know that if I affect the face, you cannot know that the feeling isn't there. Once I have deduced a few relationships like this, is it possible that I can deduce the algorithm that determines every human action?

The method of hypothetical reasoning in this book has been philosophical thought experiments. Theoretical physics uses mathematical thought experiments, but I suspect that a better mathematician than I am could fully mathematicise this book. However, for this book to be scientific, it would need to be possible to use it to make predictions about human actions that can be tested by experiment. Maybe with a bit more analytical horsepower, it could be developed to the next level. And it could be predicted that at the moment the next lunar eclipse became total, a man would walk into a tobacconist on a certain street corner in Prague, pull out a Gauloise cigarette and ask a girl in a blue dress for a light. Astronomers and psychologists could team up for a famous experiment. They could set up listening equipment and sensitive instruments to test the colour of the dress and the chemical composition of the cigarette smoke. And when the prediction was found to be true, this theory would have its eureka moment. There would be ticker-tape parades, and nice people from Sweden would invite me to an awards ceremony. But don't worry! I know this isn't going to happen.

The only phenomenon I can currently predict is that because we have become so mesmerised by absurd hypothetical idols such as God, happiness and freedom that our entire species could self-destruct. Sadly, from a scientific point of view, the best that I can hope for is that this theory will be proved right after everyone is dead.

So some white-trash intellectual comes along. He tells you that some of your feelings are figments of your imagination; that you can be made to believe in anything, so some of your most axiomatic beliefs about yourself are probably crap anyway. Why should you care? Mankind might self-destruct, but it is unlikely to happen in your lifetime. It might happen in your great grandchildren's lifetime, but they aren't even born yet, and chances are you won't meet them anyway. All that matters is that you are happy now.

If you are happy, you can ignore this book. You can join forces with all the Holocaust deniers and climate change deniers. You can raise your arms to heaven and sing praise to God. You can allow yourself to be swept up in the orgy of eye-swivelling virtual emotion and dance yourself into a frenzy as the wonderful light that is our species fades out to a dot. You can do this, but despite all the pseudo-ontological arguments about the existence of God, we have to determine our destiny on our own. The more we gaze into space through telescopes, the more we know that nobody will come to our aid.

If all of mankind is snuffed out in a cataclysmic instant then it actually only matters if someone is left to care about it. But the problem that does actually matter is not that we might ultimately self-destruct. It is the process of self-destruction that we need to worry about. This process is almost certainly going to become more evident during your lifetime.

Trivial meteorological events could dramatically alter the destiny of our species. Certain areas of our insignificant little planet that were previously able to support life might cease to be able to do so. As a result there would be colossal regional famines and mass-migrations of people, which in turn would cause warfare on a hitherto unknown scale. Many of those who survived famine or war would be eliminated in inter-ethnic or inter-religious genocide of hideous brutality.

The theory of this book cannot be scientifically proven; it is just a tool for hypothetical reasoning. Our science permits us to predict the colossal events in our universe such as the tides, the appearance of comets and the timing of eclipses, but we cannot predict the insignificant little events like the extinction of our species. I have tried to explain that this could occur. It could occur because, since we developed language, we lost sight of our instincts, and ultimately this caused us to be driven by how we feel about ourselves and not by our survival.

We can only alter this course by the use of our rationality, but I cannot demonstrate to you that you should use your rationality. It is a strange fact that nobody can prove that rationality is a better course than simply trusting emotion because nobody can conclusively define the objective of human life. Darwinism tells us only one thing about the meaning of life – survival is all that matters. All other meanings are mythologies built from pretended emotional behaviour. We should therefore abandon all ideologies of emotional wellbeing and be satisfied with the modest objective of survival.

Let us be nostalgic for our future. Consider your children and your grandchildren and the great grandchildren that you might never meet. Think of how your beliefs are actually a product solely of your emotional aspirations as moulded by your cultural environment. Consider whether you could live another way. Could a simpler life bring you contentment? Because ultimately, all I can ask of you is that you consider these things and ask yourself: how does it make you feel?

APPENDIX I:
THE ALGORITHM AS A FLOW CHART

Concentrate now! Yes, you at the back ... This appendix sums up the entire theory of Part I of the book. However, don't think that by reading it you can save time and not bother reading the book because, if you try that, you won't have a clue what it's going on about.

This is how our understanding of our emotions is supposed to work: circumstances in our environment cause us to have a feeling; this causes us to exhibit a certain behaviour; anyone can observe the behaviour but the feeling is private; only the fact that the behaviour is public enables us to form a concept of the emotion, and collectively an ability to name it; we use the word as though it refers directly to the feeling, but in reality it refers indirectly to the unseen cause of the behaviour (whatever that might be).

Tactical deception with the behaviour disrupts this process. Firstly, it causes us to form an incorrect concept of the emotion: suppressed behaviour disrupts identification of an emotion, and affected behaviour creates false beliefs as to its cause. When we goal-seek an emotional outcome with a disrupted concept of the emotion, we rationally choose a self-destructive action.

- Scenario A involves suppression of emotional behaviour by third parties;
- Scenario B the suppression is by the protagonist;
- Scenario C involves affectation by the protagonist; and
- Scenario D involves affectation by third parties.

We can construct a 2x2 matrix: one axis is affection or suppression; and the other axis is first person or second/third person. Respectively: they suppress; I suppress; I affect; they affect.

(1) When we remember emotions, we think we remember the feeling, but our memory tricks us by recalling surrogates of the feeling (such as the behaviour) (BEHAVIOUR IS THE ONLY CONSTANT);

(2) Human action is driven by goal-seeking the achievement of positive emotional states and the avoidance of negative ones (INTENT);

(3) Humans implicitly form theories that certain sets of circumstances cause certain emotional states (BELIEF);

(4) Humans act on the belief (3) to establish sets of circumstances that cause positive emotional states, and avoid the sets of circumstances that cause negative emotional states (DERIVE AN ACTION).

The action is rationally derived from the concept of the emotion, and this remains the case even if the concept is distorted; so from here the theory reduces to: "How is the concept derived?"

(5) Words for feelings reference whatever causes the behaviour. It is merely an assumption that this is caused by a feeling, so the metaphysics of the feeling becomes irrelevant. The word is a derivative of behaviour (CONCEPT AND LANGUAGE);

(6) Tactical deception with the behaviour, results in the concept of, or the word for, an emotion being derived from false data:

   a. When the behaviour is suppressed, the evidence of the feeling is absent:
      i. If the subject suppresses the behaviour, then they will interpret the word for the feeling as meaning just the behaviour; so if the feeling arises in themself (which will not trigger the behaviour) they will have no knowledge that they have the feeling associated with

that behaviour. (ABSENCE OF BELIEF THAT OWN FEELING IS THE EMOTION THAT CAUSES BEHAVIOUR IN OTHERS) [Scenario B];

ii. If people in the subject's world suppress the behaviour, then the subject has no mechanism to allocate the word to the feeling. If a feeling arises in themselves and they hypothesise a name for that feeling, they have no mechanism to refute the hypothesis, so it is irrefutable. (A HYPOTHESIS AS TO FEELING IDENTITY AUTOMATICALLY BECOMES A BELIEF IN THE IDENTITY OF THE FEELING) [Scenario A];

b. When someone tactically affects the behaviour, the behaviour is caused by something other than the feeling (usually, in the first instance, by a belief about how modified behaviour will alter how others perceive them):

i. If the subject affects the behaviour (and therefore their own behaviour is not caused by the feeling) then the subject assumes the presence of the emotion without the feeling. (FALSE BELIEF OF WHAT CAUSES THEIR EMOTION) [Scenario C];

ii. If people in the subject's world affect the behaviour, then the subject will identify a false cause of the emotion in others. (FALSE BELIEFS OF WHAT CAUSES EMOTION IN OTHERS) [Scenario D];

(7) Each of the four circumstances described in (6) gives rise to an incorrect belief, so the simple derivation of action in (2) through (4) gives rise to a rationally derived self-destructive action, respectively:

a. With respect to suppression:

i. The self-suppressor will be unable to identify the causes of their feelings and will be unable to take corrective action. (CANNOT DETERMINE

ACTION THAT ACHIEVES EMOTIONAL
GOAL);

ii The person living in an environment of suppression
will, upon hypothesising the identity of a feeling, be
unable to refute that hypothesis. This will draw a false
conclusion as to what emotional goal they have
achieved. (CONTINUE A COURSE OF ACTION
BASED ON FALSE BELIEF OF EMOTION
ATTAINED.)

b. With respect to tactical affectation of behaviour:
   i. The self-faker will continue to pursue a course of
   action that they believe will lead to an emotional
   outcome without being able to know whether they
   achieve that outcome. (REPEAT ACTION
   WITHOUT ABILITY TO DETERMINE
   SUCCESSFUL OUTCOME);
   ii. The person living in an environment of affectation
   will pursue an incorrect course of action in the mistaken belief that it will lead to an emotional outcome.
   (PURSUE ACTION BASED UPON FALSE
   ASSUMPTION OF OUTCOME.)

NOTES

1. Chimpanzees can perform tactical deception but, as we will see later, they have a very limited ability to do it with their emotional behaviour.
2. Ludwig Wittgenstein, *Lectures & Conversations on Aesthetics, Psychology and Religious Belief* (Oxford: Blackwell, 1966). The "waste of time" remark was made in 1914 to Rush Rhees, one of Wittgenstein's pupils, p41.
3. Karl Popper, *Conjectures and Refutations: The Growth of Scientific Knowledge* (London: Routledge & Keagan Paul, 1963), pp. 33–39. Popper held that Freud's theories could not be refuted by scientific experiment and therefore could not be considered to be scientific.
4. Gilbert Ryle, *The Concept of Mind* (London: Hutchinson, 1949), Chapter X, Psychology. This is one of the twentieth century's most important books on the philosophy of mind. It was one of the first to attack the notion that a "mind" was a separate entity that lacked physical form.
5. Ray Monk, *Wittgenstein, The Duty of Genius* (London: Jonathan Cape, 1990).
6. Ludwig Wittgenstein, *Tractatus Logico-Philosophicus* (London: Routledge and Keegan Paul, 1992). This work first appeared in the original German and was first published in English with an introduction by Bertrand Russell.
7. Monk, *Wittgenstein*.
8. Ludwig Wittgenstein, *Philosophical Investigations*, trans. G.E.M. Anscombe (Oxford: Basil Blackwell, 1953) This work was written between 1945 and 1949, but was first published in 1953 after the author's death.
9. Ibid, §I 571 (italics as in the original).
10. Ibid, §II xiv.
11. Ibid, §I 107.
12. Fiona D Zeeb, et al., "Serotonergic and Dopaminergic Modulation of Gambling Behavior as Assessed Using a Novel Rat Gambling Task,"

Journal of Neuropsychopharmacology (June, 2009): 34(10) 2329–43.

13. Stephen Pinker, *The Blank State – The Modern Denial of Human Nature* (New York: Viking Penguin, 2002), p24.

14. A designer friend of mine (who has to remember colours because that is her job) tells me that she has trained herself to break colours down into their component basic colours. She can remember colours because she remembers that they are x parts white, y parts blue and z parts orange. She is therefore interpreting colours using language in a way that permits her to remember them more reliably than other people. Wine connoisseurs remember taste in much the same way.

15. Throughout this book, I focus entirely upon the conscious experience of feelings and emotions. Since the connection between conscious experience and neurophysiology is not understood by either scientists or philosophers, it would be a distraction and perhaps lead to confusion for me to try to explain any parallel in brain activity (which is lucky because my knowledge of such things is just sufficient to be dangerous). However, it is interesting that nerve scientists can distinguish sharp and dull pains. Myelinated nerve fibres conduct sharp pain messages to the brain. These fibres conduct messages at high speed, which provides a benefit to survival in that it permits rapid reflex recoil from a source of pain. Unmyelinated fibres conduct dull pain messages to the brain at much slower speed, and provide a constant reminder to the brain that something in the body is wrong. See Ian Glynn, *An Anatomy of Thought – The Origin and Machinery of the Mind* (Oxford: Oxford University Press, 1999), Chapter 8.

16. David E. Cooper, *Philosophy and the nature of language* (Westport: Praeger, 1987), Chapter 5. It turns out that the Inuits' forty words for snow is an urban myth, which is a shame because it was a great story.

17. Coffee shops in America are trying to make coffee like wine, presumably so they can sell it at a higher price. My local café in Brooklyn had four varieties of bean and tried to educate me using weird jargon about what they all tasted like. This annoyed me and so I always bought the cheapest one.

18. A.A. Gill, *London Times*, 15 March, 2009. This is one of the most epically vituperative reviews I have ever read, so the emotion of pity causes me to withhold the name of the restaurant.

19. I have a tenuous connection with the great man, and also with the economist John Maynard Keynes. Darwin had a granddaughter Margaret Darwin who married Keynes' younger brother Geoffrey. He shared big bro's not-too-shabby intellect, being an eminent surgeon and literary critic. My parents met Sir Geoffrey Keynes when he was 91, and he lived to 95. Margaret Darwin and he possessed a small

eighteenth-century French sofa. When this became worn, it was chucked into the back of a garage. My mother asked if she could restore it in her upholstery classes, and it has now passed to me. So I am now in possession of a sofa that was almost certainly sat upon by John Maynard Keynes and quite possibly by Charles Darwin. We clutch at straws in our bid to touch greatness, but I am sticking to my story. And if I ever find bedbugs in that sofa I am definitely blaming Darwin.

20. Charles Darwin, *The Origin of the Species by Means of Natural Selection* (London: John Murray, 1859), Chapter IV Natural Selection. All my Darwin references are sourced from the edition edited by E O Wilson, *From So Simple a Beginning: Darwin's Four Great Books* (New York: W. W. Norton & Company, 2005)

21. Richard Dawkins, *The Extended Phenotype* (Oxford: Oxford University Press, 1982), Chapter 10. Dawkins points out that biologists have used the word "fitness" with five subtly different technical meanings. This level of distinction is beyond the scope of the limited overview of evolutionary theory that I include here.

22. Our ability to relate to the emotions of other species is deeply entrenched in the emotions of our own species. This fact has not escaped the notice of Hollywood. In a fantasy movie where humans interact with other intelligent species, the "goodies" always demonstrate humanoid emotional behaviour, and the "baddies" always have no emotional behaviour at all. Examples of goodies that demonstrate humanoid emotional behaviour include E.T., Jah Jah Binks and certain characters in Planet of the Apes. Examples of baddies that are devoid of all emotional expression include Darth Vader (who doesn't even have a movable face). This is of course completely unrealistic because an intelligent creature from another planet would have completely different emotional expressions. Hollywood could create characters that had completely distinct behaviour, but Hollywood (not known for a shortage of imagination) is probably correctly taking the view that it would be impossible for us to relate to newly invented emotional expression, and the movie would become hopelessly confusing. These problems do not apply in literature, and the Hitchhiker's Guide To The Galaxy gleefully describes the emotions of Vogons, including their ghastly poetry. Consequently, this great book, despite working brilliantly on radio, did not translate well to the screen. The total absence of emotional expression extends to human baddies that are inexplicably evil (e.g. every baddie in a James Bond movie, and this is parodied by Dr. Evil in the Austin Powers series).

23. A possible exception is the emotion of revulsion that drives us to recoil from noxious substances.

24. The sense in which biologists use the term "altruism" differs from normal usage. Biologists use the term to mean the *effect* of providing benefit to another with expense to itself, not the *purpose* of so bene-fiting.

25. Robert Trivers, *Social Evolution* (Menlo Park, CA: Benjamin Cummings, 1985), Chapter 3 Elementary Social Theory.

26. Dawkins, *Extended Phenotype*, p185.

27. Kinship theory was probably first described by William Hamilton in "The Genetical Evolution of Social Behaviour," *Journal of Theoretical Biology* (1964). The theory is further developed in Richard Dawkins, *The Selfish Gene* (Originally published in 1976, but I use the Oxford University Press 30th anniversary edition 2006, with additional chapters) and in Trivers, *Social Evolution*.

28. Both of these examples come from Trivers, *Social Evolution*.

29. Dawkins, *The Selfish Gene*, p97.

30. Trivers, *Social Evolution*, Chapter 7 Parent – Offspring Conflict, p162.

31. Dawkins, *Selfish Gene*, Chapter 10 You scratch my back, I'll ride on yours, p184ff.

32. Quoted in Stephen Pinker, *Blank State*, Chapter 14 The Many Roots of Our Suffering, p243.

33. Trivers, *Social Evolution*, Chapter 15 The Evolution of Cooperation, p377.

34. Trivers, *Social Evolution*, p388.

35. Frans de Waal, *Chimpanzee Politics: Power and Sex Among Apes*, (New York: Harper & Row, 1982).

36. Martin Daly and Margo Wilson, *Homicide*, (New Brunswick, NJ: Transaction Publishers, 1988), p5.

37. Charles Darwin: *The Descent of Man, and Selection in Relation to Sex*, (London: John Murray, 1871), Chapter VIII, Principles of Sexual Selection. In: Wilson, E O. (ed.) *From So Simple a Beginning: Darwin's Four Great Books*. W. W. Norton & Company (2010).

38. Nobody is quite sure how long Moulay Ismail lived, but if you do the arithmetic, he had a child at least once a month, including his infancy and old age. Presumably at his peak he was producing offspring every ten days or so. On one estimate, he could only achieve this great feat if he had sex 4.8 times a day. But I doubt this because, as the thinking man's sex addict, he had a cleverer strategy: he had the menstrual cycles of all his concubines monitored. This is fortunate because having sex that often quickly becomes a boring. I know this because I once maintained that rate for a whole 12 hours.

39. Daly and Wilson, *Homicide*; also Trivers, *Social Evolution*, pp215–219.

40. Daly and Wilson, *Homicide*. Daly and Wilson specifically refute the

research of Margaret Mead who in 1935 claimed to have found primitive tribes where females were more violent or where there was no distinction between the sexes (see p149–152). In fact, a male human is roughly 50 times more likely to murder another male than a female is to murder another female, and this is true in every society that has been studied in a rigorous statistical manner.

41. Martin Daly and Margo Wilson, "Evolutionary Psychology of Male Violence," in *Male Violence*, ed. John Archer (London: Routledge, 1994).

42. There is an interesting statistical anomaly that springs from this. Human couples of high social status or high libido have a higher probability of producing sons than those of low social status or low libido who are most likely to produce daughters. A classic illustration of this is Moulay Ismail, the Moroccan king who is acknowledged as the human with the most offspring. He was obviously high social status and clearly had quite a lot of sex. He produced 1.54 sons for every daughter, a ratio that is almost inconceivable if the probability of an individual birth was 50/50 boy/girl. The evolutionary theory is as follows: evolution selects for genes that maximise their own propagation, and since humans are polygynous, high status males with high libido have the most offspring, so if you are high status and high libido then you will propagate your genes more if you produce sons. However, females tend to produce similar numbers of children whether they are high or low status, so if you are low status and low libido then you are more likely to propagate your genes if you produce daughters. Low status couples with low libidos will produce sons who are very unlikely to have further offspring, but their daughters have about the same chance as a daughter of Moulay Ismail.

43. Mark Teismann, "A study of verbal interaction and labelling of jealousy among dating couples involved in jealousy improvisations," (doctoral dissertation, New London: University of Connecticut, 1975), quoted in Daly and Wilson, *Homicide*, p183.

44. There is an argument at the pinnacle of academia regarding whether the language capability of humans is a product of evolution by natural selection or not. Noam Chomsky is of the view that it is not, and Steven Pinker is of the view that it is. I have nothing new to add to the debate, and so I shall not enter it. However, the outcome of the debate does not have an impact on the argument that I am constructing in this book, and hence I only mention it in this note. For the record, I agree with Pinker. For a clear (but clearly frustrated) summary of the debate, see Daniel C. Dennett, *Darwin's Dangerous Idea – Evolution and the Meanings of Life* (New York :Touchstone, 1995), Chapter 13, Parts 2

and 3. For a more complete explanation of the theory that language is a product of evolution, see Steven Pinker, *The Language Instinct – How the Mind Creates Language* (New York: William Morrow, 1994), Chapter 11, Big Bang.

45. Whilst I love making fun of scientists, I try to resist making obnoxious accusations. However, it appears to me that animal behavior scientists are guilty of systematic bias towards making animals seem cleverer than they really are. If you spend months in the freezing rain studying some critter and the evidence points to the fact that they are really stupid then you wasted your time, but coming to the conclusion that they are very smart gets you a nice article in the New York Times or a documentary slot on the BBC. Often, scientists come to the conclusion that animals are smarter than philosophers would think possible because they fail to ask the philosophical questions. For example, scientists trained monkeys to play a computer game where they clicked on buttons marked "yes", "no" or "pass" and when they got the right answer they got an edible treat. [I always roll my eyes heavenward when a research paper includes the words "monkeys were trained to . . ."] The scientists concluded that because the monkey often selected "pass" that monkeys are capable of self-doubt. But they failed to notice that the monkeys couldn't read what the button said. Self-doubt is a very complex cognitive capability that requires thinking about thinking – something that philosophers assume requires language. A more realistic interpretation is that the monkey figured out the algorithmic pattern of button pushing that produced edible treats with the highest frequency. They could do this without self-doubt, and the scientists' conclusion is in my opinion utter codswallop. "Some scientists were trained to teach monkeys to . . . Etc."

46. Most of us think of hunger as an unpleasant sensation, and being replete as a pleasant sensation, but anorexics and bulimics almost certainly think of these sensations the other way around. I cannot work out the cause of eating disorders, but I have a suspicion that the explanation is nothing more than a distorted aesthetic judgment about whether a sensation is pleasant or not. That just leaves the thorny question of how such a circumstance arises and how it can be reversed.

47. Two examples of goal-seeking in computing:
The computation of the yield of a bond from its price:
- If I know the yield of a bond (Y), I can compute its price (P) by discounting the coupons and principal payment of $100 of that bond at a yield of Y. This is a close-ended mathematical function.
- If I know the price, but I want to compute the yield, then I am doing the calculation backwards. This cannot be computed by a

close-ended function, so I have to create the following goal-seeking computer program:

1. Input the degree of accuracy (A) of my intended yield (say to the nearest 0.001%)
2. Compute the price (P_1) of the bond at a "guessed" yield (Y_1) (say $Y_1=10\%$)
3. Compute the price (P_2) at a second "guessed" yield (Y_2) (say $Y_2=5\%$)
4. Input n = 2
5. Compute n = n+1
6. Interpolate or extrapolate a new yield $Y_n = Y_{n-1} + \{((Y_{n-1} - Y_{n-2}) \times (P - P_{n-1})) / (P_{n-2} - P_{n-1})\}$
7. If $Y_n - Y_{n-1} < A$, then Y_n is an approximation of Y within my intended degree of accuracy, otherwise go to step 5 and repeat.
• This program will keep repeating the loop interpolating or extrapolating a new "guessed" yield until it generates an estimate that is closer to the previous one by less than the target degree of accuracy, and then it will stop.

Mathematicians since the time of Euclid have being trying to find a close-ended computation of a square root (S) of a positive number (N). Here is how your pocket calculator goal-seeks it:

1. Input the degree of accuracy (A) of my estimation of S (say to the nearest 0.0001)
2. Calculate a first "guess" of S as follows: $S_1 = N/10$.
3. Calculate a second "guess" of S as follows: $S_2 = N/100$.
4. Input n = 2
5. Compute n = n+1
6. Interpolate or extrapolate a new estimated $S_n = S_{n-1} + \{((S_{n-2} - S_{n-1}) \times (S_{n-1}^2 - N))/(S_{n-1}^2 - S_{n-2}^2)\}$
7. If $S_n - S_{n-1} < A$, then S_n is an approximation of S within the intended degree of accuracy, otherwise go to step 5 and repeat.

48. In New York City, it is common to find dog owners who treat their pets with Prozac because they believe them to be anxious. It occurs to me that the more effective treatment would be for the owner to take the Prozac, not the dog. Sadly, veterinary surgeons are only permitted to give prescriptions for animals and not for their owners.
49. Wittgenstein, *Investigations*, §II i.
50. Soren Kierkegaard, *Works of Love,* trans. and ed. H.Hong and E.Hong (Princeton NJ: Princeton University Press, 1998), volume 16.
51. *Gilgamesh*, ed. Stephen Mitchell (New York :Simon & Schuster, 2004).
52. Charles Darwin, *The Expression of the Emotions in Man and Animals*

(London: John Murray, 1871). He states this in respect of monkeys in Chapter V, 'Special Expression of Animals', and makes it unclear that he perceives the distinction in humans in Chapter VIII 'Joy, High Spirits, Love, Tender Feelings, Devotion'.

53. Aeschylus, *The Oresteia, Agamemnon*, trans. George Thomson (London, New York, Toronto: Everyman's Library, 1938), line 24.

54. Aeschylus, *The Oresteia, Agamemnon*, trans. Anne Carson (New York: Faber and Faber, 2009).

55. Aeschylus/Thomson, *Agamemnon*, line 752.

56. Aristotle, *Nichomachean Ethics*, trans. Terrence Irwin, 2nd edition (Cambridge: Hackett, 1999).

57. Aristotle, *Nicomachean Ethics*, Book 1, Chapter 9.

58. For example: Karl Popper in Popper, K. and Eccles, J C., *The Self and Its Brain* (London/New York: Routledge & Keegan Paul, 1963), Chapter P5, p44.

59. Aristotle, *Nicomachean Ethics*, Book IV, Chapter 9.

60. Plato, *Charmides*, §173e. All Plato references are drawn from *Plato, Complete Works*, eds. J M Cooper and D S Hutchison (Cambridge: Hackett, 1997).

61. Plato, *Clitophon*, §410e and *The Republic*, §I.354.

62. Democritus, *On Cheerfulness* (*Peri Euthumies*), in P Curd and R D McKirahan Jr, *A Presocratic Reader: Selected Fragments and Testimonia* (Cambridge: Hackett, 1995).

63. Diogenes Laertius, *Lives of Eminent Philosophers*, trans. R D Hicks in the Loeb Classical Library (Cambridge MA: Harvard University Press, 1925).

64. Arthur Waley, Translator's preface to Confucius, *The Analects* (London, New York, Toronto: Everyman's Library, 2001).

65. Waley, *Analects*.

66. Confucius, *Analects*, III §26.

67. Ibid, VII §15.

68. Ibid, IX §28.

69. Waley, *Analects*.

70. James Behuniak, *Mencius on becoming human*, (Albany: State University of New York, 2005).

71. Ibid.

72. Ibid.

73. Mencius, quoted in Behuniak, *Mencius*, pp87–88

74. Sometimes it is misinterpreted as such by Western practitioners of Buddhism.

75. Darwin, *Expression*.

76. Glynn, *Anatomy of Thought*, Academic Apes p302–6

77. There is some very cute, but sadly fallacious "research" where chimpanzee trainers claim to have taught language to their charges. Some of them refuse to submit their data to scientific peer review. These researchers get lots of media attention, but when the chimpanzee predictably refuses to perform on cue, the reason given for the predictable dumb show is some human emotional explanation such as "he is moody", or whatever. [That old chestnut: "Some scientists were trained to teach a chimpanzee to write their research papers."]

78. Quoted in Trivers, *Social Evolution*, Chapter 16 Deceit and Self-Deception, p411.

79. The psychologist Gordon G. Gallup invented this experiment in 1970.

80. Scientists have observed apparent tactical deception in squirrels. Squirrels bury nuts for later consumption, but if a squirrel knows it is being watched, it will dig a hole and pretend to put a nut in, but in fact it keeps the nut in its mouth. Two things should be noted: firstly, this is deception, but not of emotional behaviour; and secondly, it is conceivable that such behavior could evolve in the squirrel without it being truly tactical. In other words, this could be instinctive behavior that has the *effect* of tactical deception without the squirrel having the *intent*. The intent would seem to require the squirrel to have a concept of its own behaviour, and this is difficult to explain without language. (Compare W.D. Hamilton's explanation of the evolution of altruism, where the behaviour evolves without requiring the intent.) See Michael A. Steele, et al., "Cache protection strategies of a scatter-hoarding rodent: do tree squirrels engage in behavioral deception?" in *Animal Behavior*, volume 75, issue 2 February, 2008. Apparent non-emotional tactical deception has also been observed in crows.

81. This story may be apocryphal. It is possible that Galileo performed the experiment by rolling balls of different mass down a slope, but there is no doubt that he did the related thought experiment. There is also little doubt that Stevinus performed the physical experiment earlier from a church tower in Delft.

82. John von Neumann, "The Mathematician," originally published in *Works of the Mind,* volume I no. 1 (Chicago: University of Chicago Press, 1947), 180–196.

83. As any good scientist knows, a laboratory experiment needs to be constructed under controlled conditions. This ensures that no unforeseen causal force intervenes in the experiment to corrupt the result. A thought experiment is performed in the laboratory of your mind, and this also needs to be constructed under controlled conditions. When we perform thought experiments in physics and mathematics, the stuff in your head is unlikely to corrupt the thought experiment unless you

are too stupid to understand it, which sadly is a problem that all of us encounter at some level. However, with the scenarios in this book, we have no such certainty that the laboratory of your mind is a controlled environment. If the scenario describes a behavioural manipulation that happens to be a feature of your own environment, then it is unlikely that you will be able to understand the thought experiment in the way that was intended, and this will not be because you are too stupid. To understand what would be going on in *your* head, we would need to construct a thought experiment cubed. That would be amusing, but beyond the scope of this book.

84. Daniel Dennett, "Quining Qualia," originally published in *Consciousness and Contemporary Science,* eds. A. Marcel and E. Bisiach, (Oxford: Oxford University Press, 1988). I use as my source, the reprint in *Philosophy of Mind, Classical and Contemporary Readings*, ed. David Chalmers (Oxford: Oxford University Press, 2002).

85. Dennett, *QQ.*

86. Ryle, *Concept of Mind.*

87. René Descartes, *Discours de la Méthode*, trans. Desmond M. Clarke (London: Penguin Classics, 2000).

88. Democritus was a rare exception.

89. David J. Chalmers, "Facing up to the Problem of Consciousness," reprinted in *Explaining Consciousness, the Hard Problem*, ed. Jonathan Shear (Cambridge, MA: Bradford Books, 1995).

90. Leibniz, *The Monadology*, trans. Robert Latta (Oxford: Oxford University Press, 1923), §17.

91. E.g. Popper and Eccles in *The Self and Its Brain.* I myself fall into the category of people who think the Hard Problem will never be solved.

92. E.g. Daniel Dennett, "Facing Backwards on the Problem of Consciousness," and Kieron O'Hara and Tom Scutt, "There is no Hard Problem of Consciousness," both reprinted in *Explaining Consciousness, the Hard Problem*, ed. Shear, (Cambridge MA: Bradford Books, 1996).

93. David J. Chalmers, *The Conscious Mind, In Search of a Fundamental Theory* (Oxford: Oxford University Press, 1995), Chapter 4 pp161, 168, "The Logical Geography of the Issues". Chalmers admits that some of the possible theories don't actually seem to have any real world practitioners, so perhaps seventeen separate theories is a slight overstatement.

94. Thomas Nagel, "What is it Like to be a Bat?" *Philosophical Review,* No. 83, p435–450, in *Philosophy of Mind, Classical and Contemporary Readings,* David Chalmers, (Oxford: Oxford University Press, 1974).

95. I recently read an interesting article that suggested that blind people

can train themselves to echolocate. But I don't imagine that they can spot a flying insect!

96. J.Y. Lettvin, et al., "What the Frog's Eye Tells the Frog's Brain," *Proceedings of the IRE* 1959. In *The Mind: Biological Approaches to its Function*, eds. William C. Corning and Martin Balaban, (New York: John Wiley & Sons, 1968).

97. Sir William Temple, "An Essay on the Original and Nature of Government," quoted in C. B. Macpherson, "Sir William Temple, Political Scientist?", *The Canadian Journal of Economics and Political Science / Revue Canadienne d'Economique et de Science politique*, (Canada: Blackwell, 1943), Vol. 9, No. 1: pp. 39–54.

98. Karl Marx and Frederich Engels, *The Communist Manifesto,* opening line.

99. The one exception to this is Schopenhauer, who alone amongst major Western philosophers was influenced by Eastern religions. See Bertrand Russell, *A History of Western Philosophy* (London: George Allen & Unwin, 1945).

100. As a slightly bizarre aside, it is an odd, repeating feature of history that the losing side in major wars always does best in the immediate aftermath. Germany significantly outperformed Britain in the three decades after WWII, and Japan outperformed the USA over the same period.

101. Hildegard von Bingen, *The Book of the Rewards of Life*, trans. Bruce W. Hozeski (New York: Garland Publishing, 1994), The First Part, §122.

102. Ibid, The First Part, §121

103. Ibid, The Second Part, §11 and §12

104. Thomas Hobbes, *Leviathan*, Chapter 13, p184. For my source, I use the Penguin Classics (1968) edition with an introduction by C. B. MacPherson (spelling, punctuation and capitalisation as in contemporary editions).

105. Ibid, Chapter 13, p185.

106. Ibid, Chapter 13, p186.

107. Ibid, Chapter 6, p127.

108. Ibid.

109. Ibid, p129.

110. John Locke, *An Essay Concerning Human Understanding*, ed. P H Niddich (Oxford: Oxford University Press, 1975), Book II, Chapter XXI §29 (spelling, punctuation and italics as in contemporary editions).

111. Ibid, Book II, Chapter XXI §29.

112. Ibid., §39.

113. Ibid.

114. David Hume, *A Treatise of Human Nature*, edited and with an intro-

duction by Ernest C Mossner (London: Penguin Classics, 1969) The quotation comes from a facsimile of original title page.

115. Ibid, Book II, Part III, Sect. III, "Of the influencing motives of the will".

116. Ibid.

117. Ibid.

118. Ibid.

119. Jeremy Bentham, *Introduction to Principles of Morals and Legislation*, in *The Classic Utilitarians,* ed. John Troyer, (Cambridge: Hackett, 2003), Chapter 1.

120. Jean-Jacques Rousseau, *Discourse on the Origin and Basis of Inequality Among Men.* Rousseau references are to *The Social Contract and the Discourses,* with an introduction by Alan Ryan, translated by and with a preface by G.D.H. Cole, (London, New York, Toronto: Everyman's Library).

121. Alan Ryan, introduction to *The Social Contract and the Discourses.*

122. I follow G.D.H. Cole's preface here in using the word "sentiment". Alan Ryan's introduction uses the word "emotion", which I think is a mistake; perhaps I am being unfair to Ryan since I am using the word "emotion" in an almost technical sense and Ryan has no reason to be concerned with my purpose.

123. Using the expression used by G.D.H. Cole.

124. Rousseau, *Origin of Inequality*, The First Part. This passage bears interesting comparison to the passage in Mencius of how seeing a child falling into a well, we are compelled to act without needing to reason.

125. Rousseau, *Origin of Inequality*, The First Part.

126. Ibid.

127. Ibid.

128. Rousseau, *Origin of Inequality*, The Second Part.

129. Ibid.

130. Ibid.

131. Rousseau, *Discourse on the Moral Effects of the Arts and Sciences*, The First Part.

132. In a letter to Rousseau in response to *The Social Contract*, Voltaire in 1755 wrote "no one has ever been so witty as you are in trying to turn us into brutes: to read your book makes one long to go on all fours."

133. Russell, *History of Western Philosophy*, Chapter XIX, Rousseau.

134. Ryle, *Concept of Mind*, Chapter X, Psychology.

135. Wittgenstein, *Aesthetics,* p41ff Conversations on Freud and p51.

136. Ibid, p44.

137. In a bizarre twist to the Popper-Freud dispute, Popper himself was something of a Ghost in the Machine dogmatist. He pledged his faith

to the Ghost in *The Self and its Brain* co-authored with John C. Eccles, a neurophysiologist.

138. Popper, *Conjectures and Refutations*, Chapter 1, Science: Conjectures and Refutations.

139. This might seem like a novel idea, but it is not original. The wise man Ludwig Wittgenstein thought of it, but doesn't seem to have considered it worth delving into: "Now someone tells me that *he* knows what pain is only from his own case! – Suppose everyone had a box with something in it: we call it a 'beetle'. No one can look into anyone else's box, and everyone says he knows what a beetle is only by looking at *his* beetle. – Here it would be quite possible for everyone to have something different in his box . . . The thing in the box has no place in the language-game at all; not even as a something *for the box might even be empty* [my emphasis]." Wittgenstein, *Investigations*, I §293.

140. Albert Einstein, *Relativity, the Special and General Theory*, trans. Robert W. Lawson (New York: Henry Holt & Company, 1920), Chapter 8 On The Idea of Time in Physics.

141. Paul Valéry, *Aesthetics* (London: Routledge & Keegan Paul, 1964) pp46–47. This book contains some very sensible observations about aesthetics, so maybe he had drunk too much espresso when he wrote that extract.

142. I gave two examples in the chapter *The Language of Feeling and Emotion*.

143. George Orwell, "Politics and the English Language," in *Essays*, (London, New York, Toronto: Everyman's Library, 1946), p959.

144. Stendahl's famous quotation "beauty is nothing but the promise of happiness" isn't a definition; it is a correlation between two concepts that we struggle to understand. This quotation gives the impression of explaining something, when actually nothing is explained.

145. One art critic referred to Renoir's paintings as "cotton-candy nudes". Blake Gopnik, "Philadelphia's Reopened Barnes Foundation Puts Its Masterpieces in a Better Light," *The Daily Beast*, 18 May 2012

146. John Williams, *The Compleat Strategyst* (New York: Macgraw Hill, 1954), p5.

147. *The Economist* magazine, cover headline 10 June, 2004.

148. Forbes, *Special Report – The World's Billionaires*, accessed 18 July, 2013, http://www.forbes.com/lists/2010.

149. Boney M made a cute folksy song out of Psalm 137 "By the rivers of Babylon, we sat down and wept." However, they edited out this last verse of this Psalm "Happy is the one who seizes your infants and dashes them against the rocks." When you point this out, you tend to be accused of taking things out of context. But would somebody please

explain the context in which smashing children against rocks is such a great idea?

150. Edward W. Said, *Orientalism* (London: Vintage Books, 1978).

151. Said quotes Karl Marx as saying of Orientals, "They cannot represent themselves; they must be represented"; and claims that John Stuart Mill, the writer of *On Liberty* and *Utilitarianism* considered that his theories of social justice did not apply to them. In fact, the Marx quotation was said of French peasants, and Mill (a long-time employee of the British East India Company) argued that foreigners were unsuited to ruling colonies; so Said's quotations are at best out of context and at worst recklessly dishonest.

152. V.S. Naipaul, *An Area of Darkness* (London: André Deutsch, 1964); *India: A Wounded Civilisation* (London: André Deutsch, 1977); and *India: A Million Mutinies Now* (London: Heinemann, 1990) – Original publishers, but I use the Picador editions as my source.

153. V.S. Naipaul, *Among the Believers: An Islamic Journey,* (London: André Deutsch, 1981); *Beyond Belief: Islamic Excursions Among the Converted People,* (New York: Random House, 1988) – Original publishers, but I use the Picador editions as my source.

154. Naipaul, *Wounded Civilization*, p92.

155. Naipaul, *Area of Darkness*, p45.

156. Ibid, p76 (emphasis is Naipaul's).

157. Ibid, p76.

158. Mahatma Gandhi, *An Autobiography, or The story of my experiments with truth,* (Ahmedabad: Navajivan Publishing House, 1927) Part III, Chapter XIII, In India Again. Note that I describe Gandhi as an outsider because he left India in his late teens to study law in England, and then worked for many years in South Africa where he first became a political activist. He did not return to India until he was in his forties.

159. Lao-Tsu, *Tao te Ching*, trans. D.C. Lau (London, New York, Toronto: Everyman's Library,).

160. Confucius, *Analects*, XV §23. Jesus Christ had the same maxim without the double negative (Luke 6:31). The presence or absence of the double negative is the fulcrum on which the difference between Eastern and Western thought hinges. In the East, human wellbeing is defined as the avoidance of negative emotional outcomes (hence the double negative), and in the West, it is the achievement of positive emotional outcomes (hence the absence of the double negative).

161. Ren Changhong and Wu Jingyu, *Rise and Fall of the Qin Dynasty* (Singapore: Asiapac Books, 2000).

162. Dr. Li Zhisui, *The Private Life of Chairman Mao* (New York: Random House, 1994), p480.

163. Wang Jian Shou, (blog), http://wangjianshuo.com.

164. Ibid.

165. Jasper Becker, *Hungry Ghosts: Mao's secret famine* (New York: Henry Holt, 1996)

166. Becker, *Hungry Ghosts*. This famine occurred between 1958 and 1961.

167. Deng is reported to have said this in a speech to the party secretariat in 1962, but it was not original. It is a Sichuan proverb.

168. My visit was to a textile factory in Suzhou in 2004. The Chinese seemed keen to show this factory off to me, so I suppose they thought it rather a nice one. I have worked in some pretty grim factories in the West, but in those there was a cynical *esprit de corp* among the workers, whereas in the Chinese factory I visited emotions were suppressed almost to the point of entering a state of hypnosis.

169. David Barboza of the *New York Times* has been instrumental in bringing this to light. His articles for the NYT include: "Another Death at Electronics Supplier in China," 21 May, 2010; "String of Suicides Continues at Electronics Supplier in China," 25 May, 2010; and "In China, Human Costs are Built into an iPad," 25 Jan, 2012 (co-authored with Charles DuHigg).

   The *Center for Research on Multinational Companies* and *Students & Scholars Against Corporate Misbehaviour* conducted research into the treatment of employees at Chinese electronics manufacturers and found that employees had been forced to sign pledges not to commit suicide.

   See also, Gethin Chamberlain, "Apple's Chinese workers treated 'inhumanely, like machines'," *The Guardian*, 30 April, 2011.

170. Jasper Becker, *The Chinese* (New York: Simon & Schuster, 2000).

171. Adam Smith, *An Enquiry into the Nature and Causes of the Wealth of Nations,* (first published 1776). I use as my source the Everyman's Library edition with an introduction by D.D. Raphael. It is important to get the right edition because some of them have had bits edited out, including bits that don't conform to the ideological dogma of the editor.

172. David Ricardo, *The Principals of Political Economy and Taxation* (London: John Murray, 1817).

173. The New Deal might have been a US phenomenon, but the ideology of mixed economies is now more typical of Europe. France and Germany have far outstripped the US in terms of the percentage of total spending that comes from government.

174. Steve Schifferes, "The end of the American Dream?", news.bbc.co.uk/2/hi/business/5303590.stm.

175. Matt Krantz and Barbara Hansen, "CEO Pay Soars While Workers' Pay Stalls," *USA Today*, 4 April, 2011.

176. Mike Spector and Tom McGinty, "The CEO Bankruptcy Bonus," *Wall Street Journal,* 27 January, 2012. Bless their cotton socks! That beacon of socialist journalism the WSJ, after years of denial, is finally raising the question (but by implication only) that something might be wrong with capitalism as an ideology. Other business newspapers such as the Financial Times and the Economist have been discussing this for years. Questioning whether capitalism might be broken does not make you left wing; it makes you someone capable of interpreting statistics. Statistics are not ideology. They are fact!

177. Bill Perkins, a trader at Centaurus Energy, quoted in *Trader Monthly*, April/May 2007, p83. Trader Monthly was a lifestyle magazine for the financial trader community in publication between 2004 and 2009.

178. Meena Krishnamsetty, "Best Hedge Funds: Jim Simons Medallion Fund's Returns and Alpha," *Insider Monkey*, 30 December, 2010. http://www.insidermonkey.com/blog/best-hedge-funds-jim-simons-medallion-fund%E2%80%99s-returns-and-alpha-1679/.

179. Many institutional investors now understand that these fee structures are damaging to their interests. Today, it is difficult to launch a new fund with such fee arrangements. However, there are many individual investors who are still mesmerised by the hedge fund aura. Many of them put their money in after all the big gains were already made, so they take the risk without the upside.

180. *Trader Monthly* magazine, April/May 2007 and April/May, 2006.

181. Gretchen Morgensen and Louise Story, "Investor Who Made Billions Is Not Target Of Suit," *New York Times*, 16 April, 2010.

182. DealBook column (author unknown), "2007, A Vintage Year For Mortgage Bears," *New York Times,* 8 April, 2008.

183. Eamon Javers, "A Subprime Bet for Paulson," *Business Week*, 12 October, 2007

184. HFR Global Hedge Fund Industry Report - Second Quarter 2013. https://www.hedgefundresearch.com/?fuse=products-irglo

185. Jenny Anderson, "Betting on the Weather and Taking an Ice-Cold Bath," *New York Times,* 29 September, 2006.

186. David Ellis, "US takes another crack at AIG rescue," *CNN News,* 9 March, 2009. http://politicalticker.blogs.cnn.com/2009/03/02/us-takes-another-crack-at-aig-rescue/.

187. Gary Duncan, "IMF warns global crunch losses to hit $1 trillion," *The Times,* 8 April, 2008.

188. Paul Davidson, "Fannie, Freddie bailout to cost taxpayers $154 billion," *USA Today,* 22 October, 2010.

189. Ann Davis, "How Giant Bets on Natural Gas Sank Brash Hedge-Fund Trader," *Wall Street Journal,* 19 September, 2006.

190. Matthew Leising, "Morgan Stanley Sues Peak Ridge Over $40.6 Million Loss," *Bloomberg News*, 30 November, 2010. http://www.bloomberg.com/news/2010-11-09/morgan-stanley-sues-peak-ridge-fund-over-40-3-million-gas-loss.html

191. Ann Davis, *Wall Street Journal*, 19 September, 2006.

192. Jenny Strasbourg, "Long-Term Capital's Rosenfeld Opens Fund, Person Says," *Bloomberg News*, 9 May, 2007. http://www.bloomberg.com/apps/news?pid=newsarchive&sid=aCz8EcJBd5RA

193. Sylvia Nassar, *A Beautiful Mind* (New York: Simon & Schuster, 1998).

194. As a reminder: in evolutionary theory, an evolutionarily stable strategy is a Nash equilibrium point where no gene mutation can invade a population.

195. There are several examples of prisoner's dilemma in the real world – one such is steroid abuse among professional athletes, where cooperating means agreeing not to take steroids, and betrayal means taking them on the sly. They would all be better off if they cooperated because taking the drugs damages their health, but each of them can individually improve their position by betrayal, so they all betray. The cold war arms race was also an example of prisoner's dilemma; it was only solved by removing the constraint of not being able to communicate.

196. Just to prove the utter lunacy of American law: Phillip Garrido, who kidnapped Jaycee Dugard, was sentenced to 431 years in prison. The last 400 years of this sentence are pointless. However, it could be argued that the value of a prison term could be measured in terms of the emotional response of the *victims*, who might get more value out of a 150 year prison sentence (or a 400 year one), even though most of it is purely symbolic.

197. Naipal, *Area of Darkness*, p215.

198. "India and pollution: Up to their necks in it," *The Economist*, 27 July, 2008.

199. This hypothetical bias is not as ridiculous as it sounds. The social psychologist Jonathan Haidt, in a talk given at the annual meeting of the Society of Personality and Social Psychology, San Antonio, 27 January, 2011, pointed out that social psychologists looking at the phenomenon of social biases (racism, sexism, etc.) are themselves highly correlated to the political left, and so are subject to the very bias that they study.

200. This was the title of an article, *The Economist*, 18–24 July, 2009

201. de Waal, *Chimpanzee Politics*.

202. Oblivion can be relative, as demonstrated by Greg Smith, who gave his reasons for quitting Goldman Sachs in a *New York Times* Op-Ed "Why I am leaving Goldman Sachs," 14 March, 2012.

203. Richard Easterlin, *Does Economic Growth Improve the Human Lot?*

Some Empirical Evidence, in *Nations and Households in Economic Growth: Essays in Honor of Moses Abramowitz*, eds. Paul A. David and Melvin W. Reder (New York: Academic Press, Inc., 1974).

204. Betsey Stevenson and Justin Wolfer, "Economic Growth and Subjective Well-Being, Reassessing the Easterlin Paradox," *Brookings Papers on Economic Activity*, Spring 2008. Wharton, University of Pennsylvania.

205. Source: Betsey Stevenson and Justin Wolfers, 'Subjective Well-Being and Income: Is There Any Evidence of Satiation?' American Economic Review: Papers & Proceedings 2013, 103(3): 598–604. Reproduced by kind permission of Prof. Justin Wolfer.

206. Daisy Dumas and Kristie Lau, "Carrie's Sex and the City house sells for a cool $9.85 million," *Daily Mail*, 24 April, 2012.

207. Andrew Oswald, "The hippies were right all along about happiness," *Financial Times*, 19 January, 2006.

208. Kate Pickett and Richard Wilkinson, *The Spirit Level: Why More Equal Societies Almost Always Do Better* (London: Allen Lane, 2009).

209. Diener, E. et al. "Factors Predicting the Subjective Well-Being of Nations," *Journal of Personality and Social Psychology*, 1995, 69(5): 851–64.

210. John Helliwell, et al., eds., *World Happiness Report*, (Columbia University).

211. Ed Diener, "Guidelines for National indicators of subjective well-being and ill-being," *Journal of Happiness Studies*, vol 7, no. 4 (2006), 397-404.

212. Sigmund Freud, in a letter to Lou Andreas-Salomé, November, 1914: "I do not doubt that mankind will survive even this war, but I know for certain that for me and my contemporaries the world will never again be a happy place. It is too hideous. And the saddest thing about it is that it is exactly the way we should have expected people to behave from our knowledge of psycho-analysis."

213. Ben Shephard, *A war of nerves; Soldiers and psychiatrists, 1914–1994* (Cambridge, MA: Harvard University Press, 2003).

214. Adam Curtis, *The Century of the Self,* a BBC four part documentary, 2002.

215. The Public Relations Museum (author unknown) http://www.prmuseum.com/bernays/bernays_1915.html

216. Ibid.

217. Ibid.

218. Ibid.

219. Curtis, *Happiness machines*, also quoted in Al Gore, *The Assault on Reason* (New York: Penguin Press, 2007).

220. Ibid.

221. Brian Wilcox, et al., *Report of the APA Task Force on Advertising and Children*, American Psychological Association, 2004. http://www.apa.org/pi/families/resources/advertising-children.pdf

222. Vance Packard, *The Hidden persuaders*, 2nd edition (New York: Pocket Books, 1980).

223. Eric Weiner, *The Geography of Bliss: One Grump's Search for the Happiest Places in the World* (New York: Hachette Book Group, 2008).

224. This term was actually coined by Jigme Singye Wangchuck, who was king of Bhutan from 1972 until he abdicated in favour of his son in 2006.

225. Milan Kundera, *The Unbearable Lightness of Being* (London: Faber & Faber, 1984)

226. The sculpture was by the Soviet artist Vera Mukhina, and it was constructed for the 1937 Paris expo, where (at 78m tall) it was situated opposite a similar monstrosity put up by Nazi Germany. It was subsequently moved to Moscow. Despite being a rather cumbersome symbol of Soviet days, it was recently accorded a very expensive restoration.

227. Zhisui, *Chairman Mao*, p99, 363–4, 490–1

228. John Follain, "Seducer Silvio Berlusconi to shower women with cabinet jobs," *The Times*, 3 February, 2008.

229. The Economist, *Fit to run Italy?*, 26 April, 2001.

230. Jason DeParle, "Harder for Americans to Rise From Lower Rungs," *New York Times*, 4 January, 2012. There is one earlier study that suggest that the UK may actually be worse than the USA in terms of social mobility.

231. Adam Liptak, "Inmate Count in US Dwarfs Other Nations," *New York Times*, 23 April, 2008.

232. The Pew Center on the States, *One in 100: behind bars in America in 2008*, 28 February, 2008. Data as of 1 January, 2008. http://www.pewstates.org/uploadedFiles/PCS_Assets/2008/one%20in%20100.pdf.

233. Ibid.

234. U.S. Department of Justice, Office of Justice Programs, Bureau of Justice Statistics. *One in 34 U.S. Adults Under Correctional Supervision in 2011, Lowest Rate Since 2000*, http://www.ojp.usdoj.gov/newsroom/pressreleases/2012/ojppr112912.pdf.

235. Pew, *One in 31, the Long Reach of American Corrections*, March, 2009.

236. Ibid.

237. Donald W Black, et al., "Borderline personality disorder in male and female offenders newly committed to prison," *Comprehensive Psychiatry*, September–October, 2007, 48(5) p400–5.

238. Rousseau, *The Social Contract*, Chapter 1, opening line.
239. Winston Churchill, speech to the House of Commons, *Hansard*, 11 November, 1947.
240. Daniel Dennett and Linda LaScola, "Preachers who are not believers," *Evolutionary Psychology*. See http://newsweek.washingtonpost.com/onfaith/Non-Believing-Clergy.pdf
241. There is little doubt that the words of Jesus Christ are correctly quoted – we have three versions: Matthew 19, Mark 10 and Luke 18.
242. Plato, *Republic* §412e and §413.
243. Again, these words cannot be in doubt, since they occur in Luke 6 27–29, and only in slightly different form in Matthew 5.
244. Tolstoy, *War and Peace,* trans Constance Garnett (Everyman, 1939), Chapters 87 and 88 of Book Five. However, many contemporary editions have modified the division into chapter and sections. Some have even introduced chapter titles (which were absent in the original) so this reference might not correspond to your edition.
245. Tolstoy, *War and Peace*, Chapter 58 of Book Three of my very decrepit edition.
246. Robert Fisk, *The Great War for Civilisation, the Conquest of the Middle East* (New York: Knopf, 2004).
247. Naipaul, *Among the Believers*, and *Beyond Belief*.
248. Brian G. Williams, *The Crimean Tartars – The Diaspora Experience and the Forging of a Nation* (Boston: Brill's Inner Asian Library, 2001).
249. In the British army, random revenge turns inward rather than outward, with a long-running history of abuse, suspicious death and suicide. (bbc.com, "Timeline: Deaths at Deepcut barracks," 29 October, 2002.)

   Random revenge in the Russian army turns outward with a history of atrocities in Chechnya and elsewhere. (Sebastian Smith, *Allah's Mountains: The Battle for Chechnya* (London: I.B.Tauris, 2006) p188ff. Nicholas Griffin, *Caucasus: Mountain Men and Holy Wars,* (New York: St. Martin's Press, 2001) p100 also lists abuse from prior campaigns.) It also turns inward with a shocking record of internal abuse and deaths caused by hazing. (Pravda, *3,000 Russian recruits die of army hazing every year*, 22 February, 2005.)

   The Israeli army has faced serious allegations of brutality against Palestinians from its own soldiers, usually officially denied. (Ethan Bronner, "Israel Disputes Soldiers' Accounts of Gaza Abuses," *New York Times*, 27 March, 2009.)

   In the US Army, one of the most notorious was the massacre at Mai Lai in Vietnam. (Seymour Hersh, "The Massacre at Mai Lai," in *Tell Me No Lies: Investigative Journalism that Changed the World*, ed. John Pilger (London: Jonathan Cape, 2005). Also, Telford Taylor,

Nuremberg and Vietnam, an American Tragedy (New York: Quad-rangle Books, 1970).) A more recent example is the abuse at Abu Ghraib prison. (Scott Higham and Joe Stephens, "New Details of Prison Abuse Emerge," *Washington Post,* 21 May, 2004.)

250. John Toland, *Adolf Hitler, The Definitive Biography* (New York: Anchor Books, 1976) p12.

251. Adolf Hitler, *Mein Kampf,* trans Ralph Manheim (1943) p4 (Volume 1, Chapter 1). http://www.nazi.org.uk/political%20pdfs/AdolfHitler-MeinKampf-ManheimTrans.pdf .

252. It is easy to provide evidence of the humiliation of the other great sadists of the twentieth century: Josef Stalin was brutalised by his step-father; Saddam Hussein by his father; Pol Pot failed his university exams three years in succession. It is harder to find evidence of concurrent suppression of this, since no biographer of any of these people could have conceived that the suppression of this humiliation could have been the key to what they became. However, consider the swagger of Saddam and Stalin in later life. Look at the absurd bombast of Saddam as he faced his nemesis and reconsider "Scenario: The Moral Logic of Tyranny". How could Saddam have known he was ridiculous? The sycophants that surrounded him denied him the evidence he needed to establish this benchmark. There is almost no film evidence of Pol Pot, but some evidence indicates that he had stone busts carved of himself in the style of the kings of Cambodia's golden era when Ankgor Wat was built.

253. Hitler, *Mein Kampf,* p416 (Volume 2, Chapter 2).

254. William L. Shirer, *Berlin Diary: The Journal of a Foreign Corre-spondent, 1934–1941* (New York: Alfred A. Knopf, 1941).

255. Ibid.

256. Memoir of Zalmen Lewental, Auschwitz inmate, quoted in *Auschwitz – the residence of death,* eds. Teresa and Henryk Swiebocki and Adam Bujak (Auschwitz-Birkenau State Museum: Bialy Kruk).

257. United Nations, *General Assembly Resolution, 1948 260 (III) "Preven-tion and Punishment of the Crime of Genocide."*

258. Roger Cohen, "The Suffering Olympics," *New York Times,* 30 Jan-uary, 2012. The academic referred to here is Anthony Polonsky, a professor of Holocaust studies at Brandeis University.

259. For example: 1. Whether to count Slav prisoners of war who were often ethnically selected to be killed; 2. Ensuring that Jewish victims from Slavic countries are not counted in both victim groups; 3. Consolidating statistics from different Slavic nations (e.g. the Soviet Union and Yugo-slavia); and 4. segregating deaths between genocide and other wartime privation (e.g. victims of the sieges of Stalingrad and Leningrad).

260. Estimates range from the tens of thousands to 1.5 million, with estimates based on the most thorough statistical analysis being approximately three to five hundred thousand.

261. On a strict interpretation of the UN definition of genocide, the mentally ill, homosexuals and political opponents don't count, but let's not get into the Suffering Olympics ourselves.

262. Hitler, *Mein Kampf*, p168 (Volume 1, Chapter 5).

263. Ibid, p402 (Volume 1, Chapter 5).

264. Ibid, p642-3 (Volume 2, Chapter 14).

265. Compare the mythology of Homeland in *Scenario: The Invention of Humiliation*.

266. Hitler, *Mein Kampf*, p65 (Volume 1, Chapter 3).

267. The origin of the myth was not Hitler. General Ludendorff, who was joint commander of Germany's WWI military effort, introduced the legend into Germany in his post-war memoirs and political writings. The link with Freemasons is that the "Stab in the Back Theory" almost certainly had an earlier source in the "Protocols of the Elders of Zion". This was an anti-Semitic text published in Russia in 1903, setting out a stab in the back theory that blames Jews and Freemasons for Russia's loss of the Russo-Japanese War. In 1921, two years before Hitler wrote his book, the London Times exposed this text as a forgery (possibly by the Russian secret police). It plagiarised a French satirical piece that attacked not Jews or Freemasons, but Napoleon III. Hitler refers to it as a source in *Mein Kampf* (p307 – Volume 1, Chapter 11), and he explicitly denies that it was a forgery.

268. *Both groups were subject to prejudice before Nazism.* This could be identified as early as the nineteenth century. In 1880, the Reichstad debated revoking Jewish rights, and there were calls for the extermination of Jews in the 19th century. During WWI, it was common to speak of the *Judenfrage* or "Jewish Problem". Romanies were also subject to prejudice before the Nazis. The Bavarian Police established a "Gypsy Affairs Section" in 1899, and this became a national institution in 1929 (see Myriam Novitch, "Half a Million Gypsy Victims of the Nazi Terror," *Unesco Courier* 1984).

    Both groups were subject to specific control by the Nazis before the War. The Nazis regulated Jews, principally under the Nuremburg Laws, but they had a program for enforced sterilisation of Romanies from 1933.

    Both groups were subjected to state-inspired pogroms. For the Jews, this was *Kristallnacht* or the "night of broken glass" (10 and 11 November, 1938), when the Hitler Youth and members of the SS destroyed Jewish homes and businesses. The pogrom against the

Romanies was *Zigeunerauf-räumungswoche* or "Gypsy clean-up week" 13-18 June, 1938 (see Ian Hancock, "The Romanies and the Holocaust: A Re-evaluation and an Overview" in *The Historiography of the Holocaust*, edited by Dan Stone (Basingstoke/New York: Palgrave-Macmillan, 2005)).

Both groups were subjected to Nazi orders for their elimination. "The earliest Nazi document referring to 'the introduction of the total solution to the Gypsy problem on either a national or an international level' was drafted under the direction of the State Secretary Hans Pfundtner of the Reichs Ministry of the Interior in March, 1936, and the first specific reference to the 'final solution to the Gypsy question' was made by Adolf Würth of the Racial Hygiene Research Unit in September, 1937. The first official Party statement to refer to the *endgültige Lösung der Zigeunerfrage* [final solution to the Gypsy question] was issued in March, 1938, signed by Himmler." Ian Hancock cites the Nazi reference number of this document as Reichsfuhrer-SS-Dokument S-Kr. 1 Nr. 557/38.

Both groups suffered the same fate. In the early phases of the war, both groups were hunted down and shot by the *Einsatzgruppe*. Later, they were both herded into Ghettos. And once the extermination camp system was established, both were transported to extermination camps in cattle cars (the Romanies, almost exclusively to Auschwitz) where they were either used as slave labour until they died, or they were gassed. There were no Romanies on the death marches that took place when the German defeat became inevitable because all adults had been gassed previously. The only Romanies surviving at liberation were children (principally twins) kept alive to be used in medical experiments.

269. Henry Kamm, "End of Communism Worsens Anti-Gypsy Racism," *New York Times,* 17 November, 1993.

270. The Economist: *Europe's Spectral Nation*, 10 May, 2001.

271. One example is the academic Guenter Lewy, who specifically argues that what Nazi Germany did to the Romanies was not genocide (G. Lewy, *The Nazi Persecution of the Gypsies* (Oxford: Oxford University Press, 2000)). Another example is Daniel Jonah Goldhagen, discussed in more detail later in this chapter.

272. Jonathan Glover, *Humanity – A Moral History of the Twentieth Century* (New Haven: Yale University Press, 2001) p64ff.

273. Glover, *Humanity*.

274. An alarming comparison can be made between the German experience and modern China, where children are taught obligatory history lessons about the "Century of Humiliation" that China experienced at the hands of colonial powers. However, it is forbidden to teach that

Mao's policies during the Great Leap Forward caused the death by famine of thirty million Chinese. The "Century of Humiliation" is a mythology whose purpose is the denial of the real biological humiliation: the threat to biological fitness perpetrated by a misguided tyrant.

275. It remains the case today that scholars who study suicide bombing have an equivalent form of denial: they talk of "radicalisation" and "brain washing" as if we understand how those processes work. The implication is that the only reason for a suicide bombing is that the perpetrator had their minds meddled with by a mysterious force.

276. It is a little unfair to criticize the USHMM for sanitizing history, when Auschwitz-Birkenau itself is now rather too manicured. Most of Birkenau is like a rather pleasant municipal park with some very tidy huts in it. A more powerful experience for me was a recent visit to a disused KGB prison in Estonia, where my boots crunched over broken glass, as I felt my way down unlit corridors. I could open drawers and pick through medical instruments. Old Russian newspapers and cheap novels were lying around precisely where they had been abandoned.

277. Daniel Jonah Goldhagen, *Hitler's Willing Executioners – Ordinary Germans and the Holocaust* (London: Abacus, 1997).

278. Goldhagen, *Hitler's Willing Executioners*, Chapter 2.

279. Ibid, Chapter 6.

280. Ibid.

281. Ibid, p3.

282. Ibid, p119.

283. Ibid, p269.

284. Ibid, p270

285. Ibid, p243.

286. Ibid, p278.

287. Ibid, p279.

288. Ibid, p280.

289. Ibid, p392.

290. Ibid, note 83 on p577.

291. In a later 600-page book on genocide *Worse Than War* (New York: Perseus Books, 2009), Goldhagen manages to boost his admission that the Romanies were victims to a whole three-quarters of a page. At least by the time he wrote that book he had learned to call them Roma and Sinti, rather than using the term "Gypsy" that the Romanies themselves consider racially derogatory.

292. Elements of this story can be found in the following Primo Levi books: *If this is a Man,* (New York: Little Brown, 1947); *The Periodic Table* (New York: Schocken Books, 1975); *The Drowned and the Saved*

(New York: Little Brown, 1989); and *The Voice of Memory*, edited by Marco Belpoliti & Robert Gordon (New York: The New Press).

293. This belief is locally adaptable into a conspiracy by any group of people who are easy to dismiss; for example in parts of the developing world the belief is that climate change is a *right*-wing conspiracy to prevent poor people benefiting from development.

294. Mainstream newspapers in Britain tend to permit this routinely on their websites, but this is much less common in the US. In the US, online comments are usually restricted to specialist web news sources (e.g. thedailybeast.com). Why does the New York Times and the Los Angeles Times not routinely permit online comment on their articles?

295. Comment in response to an article by Kate Shepperd, "The US freezes on climate change," *The Guardian*, 3 September, 2009.

296. Comment in response to The Economist, *The Curse of Carbon*, 30 December, 2008.

297. Comment posted on a bbc.co.uk *Have Your Say* forum posted 22 September, 2009.

298. Comment in response to an article by Lyn Gardner in the Guardian 16 February, 2011.

299. Pew Research Center, *Modest Rise in Number Saying There Is 'Solid Evidence' of Global Warming*, 1 December, 2011. Fortunately, this statistic is slowly drifting lower. The number saying that there was no solid evidence peaked at 33% in 2009.

300. Ann Coulter, *Godless, The Church of Liberalism* (New York :Three Rivers Press, 2007).

301. Nigel Lawson, *An Appeal to Reason: A Cool Look at Global Warming* (London: Duckworth Overlook, 2008).

302. His resumé, until recently posted on the UK Independence Party website, disclosed that he does not have a single O-level in a science subject. When Monkton was at school in England, an O-level was an exam usually taken at the age of fifteen or sixteen, so he presumably gave up formal science education some time before that.

303. His sister is married to Nigel Lawson's son.

304. Naomi Oreskes & Erik M. Conway, *Merchants of Doubt: How a Handful of Scientists Obscured the Truth on Issues from Tobacco Smoke to Global Warming* (New York: Bloomsbury Press, 2010).

305. Ross Gelbspan, *Boiling Point: How Politicians, Big Oil and Coal, Journalists, and Activists Have Fueled a Climate Crisis – And What We Can Do to Avert Disaster* (New York: Perseus Books, 2004). In addition, leaked documents from the Heartland Institute – a non-profit think tank that denies climate science revealed that they directly fund climate-sceptic scientists.

306. Editorial, "The Land of Denial," *New York Times*, 7 September, 2011, page A34.

307. Fred Pearce, *The Climate Files – the battle for the truth about global warming* (London: Guardian Books, 2010). Emails of climate scientists at the University of East Anglia were hacked and leaked in a scandal that became known as "Climategate". Climate-sceptic activists claimed that this "proved" that climate scientists manipulated data. However, detailed analysis of these emails demonstrated that nothing of the kind took place, and all the scientists involved were exonerated.

308. Joe Stephens, "Nature Conservancy faces potential backlash from ties to BP," *Washington Post*, 24 May, 2010.

309. Justin Gillis, "Clouds' Effect on Climate Change Is Last Bastion for Dissenters," *New York Times,* 30 April, 2012.

310. During the 1970s and 80s, I travelled extensively in tropical forests in Guatemala, Mexico, Burma, Thailand and Borneo. In 2010, I spent a day retracing my steps on Google maps, and I found that all the rainforest in which I travelled no longer exists, except for some of the teak forests in Burma near the Thai border. Chinese logging companies have indiscriminately logged Burmese teak. Before the thawing of military rule in Burma, the generals junta were happy to sell anything to the Chinese to retain power.

311. Mark Bittman, "What is worse than an oil spill?" *New York Times,* 19 April, 2011.

312. Richard Black, "Climate Targets 'Will Kill Coral'," *BBC*, 2 September, 2009.

313. Karl Ritter, "Climate Goal May Spell End For Some Coral Reefs," *Associated Press*, 7 December, 2010.

314. Richard Black, "Natural Lab Shows Sea's Acid Path," *BBC*, 8 June, 2008 and "Bubbling sea signals severe coral damage this century," *BBC*, 29 May, 2011.

315. Pew Research Center, *Modest Rise*. 30% say there is no evidence, 64% say there is evidence and 6% don't know.

316. Gills, *Clouds' Effect on Climate Change.*

317. Becker, *Hungry Ghosts.*

318. United Nations report, *World population to 2300*. 2004. http://www.un.org/esa/population/publications/longrange2/WorldPop2300final.pdf

319. Hobbes was accused of being an atheist, and was terrified of being branded a heretic. In the seventeenth century, a person could be considered an atheist if they believed in a God of a form that differed from that approved by the church authorities.

320. Every war fought by America since Vietnam has been in a former

Ottoman province. Genocide of Muslims in these territories started with the Greek uprisings of the 1820s and ran right up to the Kosovo and Bosnia wars (see McCarthy, J. *Death and Exile: The Ethnic Cleansing of the Ottoman Muslims, 1821-1922*. Princeton: Darwin Press, 1996). Stalin made his contribution, with the ethnic cleansing of Muslims from all the former Ottoman provinces that lay within the Soviet world. Arguably, the USA and Britain have contributed too with half a million deaths caused by depleted uranium from the first Gulf war.

BIBLIOGRAPHY

Aeschylus. *The Oresteia*. Translated by G. Thomson. Cambridge: Cambridge University Press, 1938.

Aeschylus. *The Oresteia, Agamemnon*. Translated by A. Carson. New York: Faber and Faber, 2009.

Anderson, J. "Betting on the Weather and Taking an Ice-Cold Bath." *New York Times*, 29 September, 2006.

Anderson, M M. *Hidden Power: the palace eunuchs of Imperial China*. Amherst: Prometheus Books, 1990.

Aristotle. *Nicomachean Ethics*. Translated by T. Irwin. 2nd edition. Cambridge: Hackett, 1999.

Baer, R. *The Cult of the Suicide Bomber*. Channel 4 documentary, London, 2005.

Barboza, D. "Another Death at Electronics Supplier in China." *New York Times*, 21 May, 2010.

Barboza, D. "String of Suicides Continues at Electronics Supplier in China." *New York Times*, 25 May, 2010.

Barboza, D and DuHigg, C. "In China, Human Costs are Built into an iPad." *New York Times*, 25 January, 2012.

BBC. *Timeline: Deaths at Deepcut*, 2008. Accessed at: http://news.bbc.co.uk/2/hi/uk_news/3743131.stm on 18 July, 2013.

Becker, J. *Hungry Ghosts: Mao's secret famine*. New York: Henry Holt, 1996.

Becker, J. *The Chinese*. New York: Simon & Schuster, 2000.

Behuniak, J. *Mencius on Becoming Human*. Albany: State University of New York, 2005.

Bentham, J. (1789). "Introduction to Principles of Morals and Legislation." In: *The Classic Utilitarians*, edited by J. Troyer, pp 1–90. Cambridge: Hackett, 2003.

Bittman, M. "What is worse than an oil spill?" *New York Times* Op-ed, 19 April, 2011.

Black, D. W., Gunter, T., Allen, J., Blum, N., Arndt, S., Wenman, G. and Sieleni, B. "Borderline personality disorder in male and female offenders newly committed to prison." *Comprehensive Psychiatry*, September-October, 2007, 48(5):400-5.

Black, R. *Natural Lab Shows Sea's Acid Path*. June 8, 2008. Accessed at: http://news.bbc.co.uk/2/hi/science/nature/7437862.stm on 18 July, 2013.

Black, R. *Climate Targets "Will Kill Coral"*. 2 September, 2009. Accessed at: http://news.bbc.co.uk/2/hi/science/nature/8233632.stm on 18 July, 2013.

Black, R. *Bubbling sea signals severe coral damage this century*. 29 May, 2011. Accessed at http://www.bbc.co.uk/news/science-environment-13569442 on 18 July, 2013.

Bronner, E. "Israel Disputes Soldiers' Accounts of Gaza Abuses." *New York Times*, 27 March, 2009.

Chalmers, D. J. "Facing up to the Problem of Consciousness." In: *Explaining Consciousness, the Hard Problem*, edited by J. Shear, pp 9–31. Cambridge, MA: Bradford Books, 1995.

Chalmers, D. J. *The Conscious Mind, In Search of a Fundamental Theory*. Oxford: Oxford University Press, 1996.

Chalmers, D. J., ed. *Philosophy of Mind, Classical and Contemporary Readings*. Oxford: Oxford University Press, 2002.

Chamberlain, G. "Apple's Chinese workers treated 'inhumanely, like machines'." *The Guardian*, 30 April, 2011.

Changhong, R. and Jingyu, W. *Rise and Fall of the Qin Dynasty*. Singapore: Asiapac Books, 2000.

Cohen, R. "The Suffering Olympics." *New York Times* Op-Ed, 30 January, 2012.

Confucius. *The Analects*. Translated by A. Waley. London, New York, Toronto: Everyman's Library, 2001.

Cooper, D E. *Philosophy and the nature of language*. Westport: Praeger, 1987.

Corning, W. C. and Balaban, M., eds. *The Mind: Biological Approaches to its Function*. New York: John Wiley & Sons, 1968.

Coulter, A. *Godless, The Church of Liberalism*. New York: Three Rivers Press, 2007.

Curtis, A. *The Century of the Self*. A documentary in four parts: "Happiness Machines"; "The Engineering of Consent"; "There is a policeman inside all our heads. It must be destroyed"; and "Eight people sipping wine in Kettering." BBC2, London, March 2002.

Daly, M. and Wilson, M. *Homicide*. New Brunswick, NJ: Transaction Publishers, 1988.

Daly, M. and Wilson, M. "Evolutionary Psychology of Male Violence." In: *Male Violence*, edited by J. Archer, pp 235ff. London: Routledge, 1994.

Darwin, C. *On the Origin of the Species by Means of Natural Selection.* In: *From So Simple a Beginning: Darwin's Four Great Books,* edited by E. O. Wilson New York: W. W. Norton & Company, 2005.

Darwin, C. *The Descent of Man, and Selection in Relation to Sex.* In: *From So Simple a Beginning: Darwin's Four Great Books,* edited by E. O. Wilson. New York: W. W. Norton & Company, 2005.

Darwin, C. *The Expression of the Emotions in Man and Animals.* In: *From So Simple a Beginning: Darwin's Four Great Books,* edited by E. O. Wilson. New York: W. W. Norton & Company, 2005.

Davidson, P. "Fannie, Freddie bailout to cost taxpayers $154 billion." *USA Today,* 22 October, 2010.

Davis, A. "How Giant Bets on Natural Gas Sank Brash Hedge-Fund Trader." *Wall Street Journal,* 19 September, 2006.

Dawkins, R. *The Selfish Gene.* 30th anniversary edition. Oxford: Oxford University Press, 2006.

Dawkins, R. *The Extended Phenotype.* Oxford: Oxford University Press, 1982.

Democritus. "On Cheerfulness." In: *A Presocratics Reader: Selected Fragments and Testimonia,* edited by P. Curd, translated by R. D. McKirahan. Cambridge: Hackett, 1995.

Dennett, D. C. *Brainstorms – Philosophical Essays on Mind and Psychology.* Cambridge, MA: The MIT Press, 1978.

Dennett, D C. *Elbow Room: The Varieties of Free Will Worth Wanting.* Cambridge, MA: The MIT Press, 1984.

Dennett, D C. "Quining Qualia." In: *Consciousness and Contemporary Science,* edited by A. Marcel and E. Bisiach, pp 42ff. Oxford University Press, Oxford, 1988.

Dennett, D C. *Darwin's Dangerous Idea – Evolution and the Meanings of Life.* New York: Touchstone, 1995.

Dennett, D C. "Facing Backwards on the Problem of Consciousness." In: *Explaining Consciousness, the Hard Problem,* edited by J. Shear, pp 33–36. Cambridge, MA: Bradford Books, 1996.

Dennett, D C and LaScola, L. "Preachers who are not believers." *Evolutionary Psychology.* 2010. Accessed at: http://www.epjournal.net/wp-content/uploads/EP08122150.pdf on 18 July, 2013.

DeParle, J. "Harder for Americans to Rise From Lower Rungs." *New York Times,* 4 January, 2012.

Descartes, R. *Discours de la Méthode.* Translated by D. M. Clarke. London: Penguin Classics, 2000.

de Waal, F. *Chimpanzee Politics: Power and Sex Among Apes.* New York: Harper & Row, 1982.

Diener, E. "Guidelines for National indicators of subjective well-being and ill-being." *Journal of Happiness Studies*, vol 7, no. 4 (2006), 397-404.

Diener, E., Diener, M. and Diener, C. "Factors Predicting the Subjective Well-Being of Nations." *Journal of Personality and Social Psychology*, 1995, 69(5): 851–64.

Dumas, D. and Lau, K. "Carrie's Sex and the City house sells for a cool $9.85 million." *Daily Mail*, 24 April, 2012.

Duncan, G. "IMF warns global crunch losses to hit $1 trillion." *The Times*, 8 April, 2008.

Easterlin, R. "Does Economic Growth Improve the Human Lot? Some Empirical Evidence." In: *Nations and Households in Economic Growth: Essays in Honor of Moses Abramowitz*, edited by Paul A. David and Melvin W. Reder. New York: Academic Press, Inc., 1974.

Economist. *Fit to run Italy?* 26 April, 2001.

Economist. *Europe's Spectral Nation*. 10 May, 2001.

Economist. Cover headline 10 June, 2004.

Economist. *Happiness (and how to measure it)*. 23 December, 2006 to 5 January, 2007.

Economist. *Economics discovers its feelings*. 23 December, 2006 to 5 January, 2007.

Economist. *Briefing on rural China*. 13–19 October, 2007.

Economist. *India and pollution: Up to their necks in it*. July 27, 2008.

Economist. *What Went Wrong With Economics?* 18–24 July, 2009.

Edgeworth, F. Y. *Mathematical Psychics: an Essay on the Application of Mathematics to the Moral Sciences*. New York: Augustus M Kelly, 1881.

Einstein, A. *Relativity, the Special and General Theory*. Translated by Robert W. Lawson. New York: Henry Holt & Company, 1920.

Ellis, D. *US takes another crack at AIG rescue*. 2 March 2009. CNN News. Accessed at: http://politicalticker.blogs.cnn.com/2009/03/02/us-takes-another-crack-at-aig-rescue/ on 18 July, 2013.

Engels, F. and Marx, K. *The Communist Manifesto*. Translated by Samuel Moore, (1888). London: Penguin Classics, 1967.

Fisk, R. *The Great War for Civilisation, the Conquest of the Middle East*. New York: Knopf, 2004.

Follain, J. "Seducer Silvio Berlusconi to shower women with cabinet jobs." *The Sunday Times*, 3 February, 2008. Accessed at: http://www.thesunday times.co.uk/sto/news/world_news/article79968.ece on 18 July, 2013.

Forbes. *Special Report: The World's Billionaires*, 3 October, 2010. Accessed at: http://www.forbes.com/lists/2010/10/billionaires-2010_The-Worlds-Billionaires_CountryOfCitizen_19.html on 18 July, 2013.

Freud, S. *Letter to Lou Andreas-Salomé*, November, 1914. Accessed at: http://romuluscomplex.tripod.com/romulus7.htm on 18 July, 2013.

Gandhi, M. *An Autobiography, or The story of my experiments with truth*.

Ahmedabad: Navajivan Publishing House, 1927.

Gelbspan, R. *Boiling Point: How Politicians, Big Oil and Coal, Journalists, and Activists Have Fueled a Climate Crisis – And What We Can Do to Avert Disaster.* New York: Perseus Books, 2004.

Gide, A. *The Fruits of the Earth.* London: Vintage, 2002.

Gilgamesh. Edited by S. Mitchell. New York: Simon & Schuster, 2004.

Gill, A. A. "Daylesford Organic." *The Times,* 15 March, 2009. Accessed at: http://www.timesonline.co.uk/tol/life_and_style/food_and_drink/eating_out/a_a_gill/article5880725.ece on 18 July, 2013.

Gillis, J. "Clouds' Effect on Climate Change Is Last Bastion for Dissenters." *New York Times,* 30 April, 2012.

Glover, J. *Humanity – A Moral History of the Twentieth Century.* New Haven: Yale University Press, 2001.

Glynn, I. *An Anatomy of Thought – The Origin and Machinery of the Mind.* Oxford: Oxford University Press, 1999.

Goldhagen, D. J. (1996). *Hitler's Willing Executioners – Ordinary Germans and the Holocaust.* London: Abacus, 1997.

Goldhagen, D. J. *Worse Than War: Genocide, Eliminationism, and the Ongoing Assault on Humanity.* New York: Perseus Books, 2009.

Gopnik, B. "Philadelphia's Reopened Barnes Foundation Puts Its Masterpieces in a Better Light." *The Daily Beast,* 18 May, 2012.

Gore, A. *The Assault on Reason.* New York: Penguin Press, 2007.

Griffin, N. *Caucasus: Mountain Men and Holy Wars.* New York: St. Martin's Press, 2001.

Hamilton, W. D. "The Genetical Evolution of Social Behaviour." *Journal of Theoretical Biology,* 1964, 7 (1): 1–16.

Hancock, I. "The Romanies and the Holocaust: A Re-evaluation and an Overview." In: *The Historiography of the Holocaust,* edited by D. Stone, pp 383–396. Basingstoke/New York: Palgrave-Macmillan, 2005.

Hedge Fund Research. *HFR Global Hedge Fund Industry Report – Second Quarter 2013.* Accessed at: https://www.hedgefundresearch.com/?fuse=products-irglo on 18 July, 2013.

Helliwell, H., Layard, R. and Sachs, J., eds. *World Happiness Report.* Columbia University. Accessed at: http://www.earth.columbia.edu/sitefiles/file/Sachs%20Writing/2012/World%20Happiness%20Report.pdf on 18 July, 2013.

Hersh, S. "The Massacre at Mai Lai." In: *Tell Me No Lies: Investigative Journalism That Changed the World.* edited by J. Pilger. London: Jonathan Cape, 2005.

Higham, S. and Stephens, J. "New Details of Prison Abuse Emerge." *Washington Post,* 21 May, 2004. Accessed at: http://www.washingtonpost.com/wp-dyn/articles/A43783-2004May20.html on 18 July, 2013.

Hitler, A. *Mein Kampf*. Translated by Ralph Manheim (1943). Accessed at: http://www.nazi.org.uk/political%20pdfs/AdolfHitler-MeinKampf-ManheimTrans.pdf on 18 July, 2013.

Hobbes, T. *Leviathan*. London: Penguin Classics, 1968.

Hume, D. *A Treatise of Human Nature*. London: Penguin Classics, 1969.

Javers, E. "A Subprime Bet for Paulson?" *Business Week*, 12 October, 2007.

Kamm, H. "End of Communism Worsens Anti-Gypsy Racism." *New York Times*, 17 November, 1993.

Kane, R. *Free Will and Values*. Albany: State University of New York, 1985.

Kierkegaard, S. *Works of Love*. Translated and edited by Hong, H V and Hong, E H. Princeton NJ: Princeton University Press, 1998.

Klebnikov, P. *Godfather of the Kremlin: Boris Berezovsky and the looting of Russia*. Orlando: Harcourt, 2000.

Koestler, A. *The Sleepwalkers*. London: Pelican, 1970.

Krantz, M. and Hansen, B. "CEO Pay Soars While Workers' Pay Stalls." *USA Today*, 4 April, 2011.

Krishnamsetty, M. "Best Hedge Funds: Jim Simons Medallion Fund's Returns and Alpha." *Insider Monkey*, 30 December, 2010. Accessed at: http://www.insidermonkey.com/blog/best-hedge-funds-jim-simons-medallion-fund%E2%80%99s-returns-and-alpha-1679/ on 18 July, 2013.

Kundera, M. *The Unbearable Lightness of Being*. London: Faber & Faber, 1984.

Laertius, D. *Lives of Eminent Philosophers*. Translated by R. D. Hicks. Harvard: Loeb Classical Library, 1925.

Lao-Tsu. *Tao te Ching*. Translated by D. C. Lau. London, New York, Toronto: Everyman's Library, 1963.

Lawson, N. *An Appeal to Reason: A Cool Look at Global Warming*. London: Duckworth Overlook, 2008.

Leibniz. *The Monadology*. Translated by R. Latta. Oxford: Oxford University Press, 1923.

Leising, M. "Morgan Stanley Sues Peak Ridge Over $40.6 Million Loss." *Bloomberg News*, 30 November, 2010. Accessed at: http://www.bloomberg.com/news/2010-11-09/morgan-stanley-sues-peak-ridge-fund-over-40-3-million-gas-loss.html on 18 July, 2013.

Leonhardt, D. "Maybe money does buy happiness after all." *New York Times*, 16 April, 2008.

Lettvin, J. Y., Maturana, H. R., McCulloch, W. S. and Pitts, W. H. "What the Frog's Eye Tells the Frog's Brain." *Proceedings of the IRE*. In: *The Mind: Biological Approaches to its Function*, edited by W. C. Corning and M. Balaban, pp 233–258. New York: John Wiley & Sons Inc, 1968.

Levi, P. *If this is a Man*. Translated by S. Woolf. New York: Little, Brown, 1947.

Levi, P. *The Periodic Table.* Translated by R. Rosenthal. New York: Schocken Books, New York, 1975.

Levi, P. *The Drowned and the Saved.* Translated by R. Rosenthal. New York: Little, Brown, 1989.

Levi, P. *The Voice of Memory.* Edited by M. Belpoliti and R. Gordon. New York: The New Press, 1990.

Lewental, Z. "Memoir." In: *Auschwitz – the residence of death*, edited by A. Bujak, H. Swiebocki and T. Swiebocki. Auschwitz-Birkenau State Museum: Bialy Kruk, 2003.

Lewy, G. *The Nazi Persecution of the Gypsies.* Oxford: Oxford University Press, 2000.

Liptak, A. "Inmate Count in US Dwarfs Other Nations." *New York Times,* 23 April, 2008.

Locke, J. *An Essay Concerning Human Understanding.* Edited by P. H. Niddich. Oxford: Oxford University Press, 1975.

Luard, T. *China rethinks peasant "apartheid"*, BBC News, 2005. Accessed at: http://news.bbc.co.uk/2/hi/asia-pacific/4424944.stm on 18 July, 2013.

Macpherson, C. B. "Sir William Temple, Political Scientist?", *The Canadian Journal of Economics and Political Science / Revue canadienne d'Economique et de Science politique*, Vol. 9, No. 1 (February, 1943), pp. 39–54.

McCarthy, J. *Death and Exile: The Ethnic Cleansing of the Ottoman Muslims, 1821-1922.* Princeton: Darwin Press, 1996.

Monk, R. *Wittgenstein, The Duty of Genius.* London: Jonathan Cape, 1990.

Morgensen, G. and Story, L. "Investor Who Made Billions Is Not Target Of Suit." *New York Times,* 16 April, 2010.

Nagel, T. *What is it Like to be a Bat?* Philosophical Review 83, p435-450. In: Chalmers, D J. (ed.). *Philosophy of Mind, Classical and Contemporary Readings.*, edited by D. J. Chalmers, chapter 25. Oxford: Oxford University Press, 2002.

Naipaul, V S. *India: An Area of Darkness.* London: André Deutsch, 1964.

Naipaul, V S. *India: A Wounded Civilisation.* London: André Deutsch, 1977.

Naipaul, V S. *Among the Believers: An Islamic Journey.* London: André Deutsch, 1981.

Naipaul, V S. *Beyond Belief: Islamic Excursions Among the Converted People.* New York: Random House, 1988.

Naipaul, V S. *India: A Million Mutinies Now.* London: Heinemann, 1990.

Nassar, S. *A Beautiful Mind.* New York: Simon & Schuster, 1998.

New York Times. "2007, A Vintage Year For Mortgage Bears." DealBook column (author unknown), 8 April, 2008.

New York Times. "The Land of Denial." Editorial, 7 September, 2011.

Novitch, M. "Half a Million Gypsy Victims of the Nazi Terror." *Unesco*

Courier ,October 1984. Accessed at: http://www.questia.com/library/ 1G1-3455609/half-a-million-gypsies-victims-of-the-nazi-terror on 18 July, 2013.

O'Hara, K. and Scutt, T. "There is no Hard Problem of Consciousness." In: *Explaining Consciousness, the Hard Problem*, edited by J. Shear, pp 69–82. Cambridge, MA: Bradford Books, 1996.

Oreskes, N. and Conway, E. M. *Merchants of Doubt: How a Handful of Scientists Obscured the Truth on Issues from Tobacco Smoke to Global Warming*. New York: Bloomsbury Press, 2010.

Orwell, G. "Politics and the English Language." In: *Essays*, with an introduction by John Carey. London, New York, Toronto: Everyman's Library, 2002.

Oswald, A. "The hippies were right all along about happiness." *Financial Times*, 19 January, 2006.

Packard, V. *The Hidden persuaders*. 2nd edition. New York: Pocket Books, 1980.

Pearce, F. *The Climate Files – the battle for the truth about global warming*. London: Guardian Books, 2010.

Pew Center on the States. *One in 100: behind bars in America in 2008*. 28 February, 2008. Accessed at: http://www.pewstates.org/uploadedFiles/ PCS_Assets/2008/one%20in%20100.pdf on 18 July, 2013.

Pew Center on the States. *One in 31, the Long Reach of American Corrections*. 2 March, 2009. Accessed at: http://www.pewstates.org/uploaded Files/PCS_Assets/2009/PSPP_1in31_report_FINAL_WEB_3-26-09.pdf on 18 July, 2013.

Pew Center on the States. *Modest Rise in Number Saying There Is 'Solid Evidence' of Global Warming*. 1 December, 2011. Accessed at: http:// www.people-press.org/files/legacy-pdf/12-1-11%20Global%20warming %20release.pdf on 18 July, 2013.

Pickett, K. and Wilkinson, R. *The Spirit Level: Why Greater Equality Makes Societies Stronger*. London: Allen Lane, 2009.

Pinker, S. *The Language Instinct – How the Mind Creates Language*. New York: William Morrow, 1994.

Pinker, S. *The Blank State – The Modern Denial of Human Nature*. New York: Viking Penguin, 2002.

Plato. *Charmides*. In: *Plato, Complete Works*, edited by J. M. Cooper and D. S. Hutchison. Cambridge: Hackett, 1997.

Plato. *Clitophon*. In: *Plato, Complete Works*, edited by J. M. Cooper and D. S. Hutchison. Cambridge: Hackett, 1997.

Plato. *The Republic*. In: *Plato, Complete Works*, edited by J. M. Cooper and D. S. Hutchison. Cambridge: Hackett, 1997.

Popper, K. *Conjectures and Refutations: The Growth of Scientific Knowledge*.

London: Routledge & Keagan Paul, 1963.

Popper, K. and Eccles, J C. *The Self and Its Brain*. London/New York: Routledge & Keegan Paul, 1977.

Pravda. *3,000 Russian recruits die of army hazing every year*. 22 February, 2005. Accessed at: http://english.pravda.ru/hotspots/crimes/22-02-2005/7782-hazing-0/ on 18 July, 2013.

Public Relations Museum. *I was positively uninterested in the dance* (profile of Edward Bernays). Accessed at: http://www.prmuseum.com/bernays/bernays_1915.html on 18 July, 2013.

Ricardo, D. *The Principals of Political Economy and Taxation*. London: John Murray, 1817.

Ritter, K. "Climate Goal May Spell End For Some Coral Reefs." *Associated Press*, 7 December, 2010.

Rousseau, J-J. "Discourse on Moral Effects of the Arts and Sciences." In: *The Social Contract and the Discourses*, edited by A. Ryan and translated by G. D. H. Cole, pp 1–30. London, New York, Toronto: Everyman's Library, 1993.

Rousseau, J-J. "Discourse on the Origin and Basis of Inequality Amongst Men." In: *The Social Contract and the Discourses*, edited by A. Ryan and translated by G. D. H. Cole, pp 31–126. London, New York, Toronto: Everyman's Library, 1993.

Rousseau, J-J. "The Social Contract or Principals of Political Right." In: *The Social Contract and the Discourses*, edited by A. Ryan and translated by G. D. H. Cole, pp 181–198. London, New York, Toronto: Everyman's Library, 1993.

Rousseau, J-J. *Confessions*. (Translator unknown). London, New York, Toronto: Everyman's Library, 1992.

Russell, B. *A History of Western Philosophy*. London: George Allen & Unwin, 1945.

Russell, B. *History as an Art*. London: Hand and Flower Press, 1954.

Russell, B. *War Crimes in Vietnam*. London: George Allen & Unwin, 1967.

Ryle, G. *The Concept of Mind*. London: Penguin (Peregrine Books), 1976.

Said, E W. *Orientalism*. London: Vintage Books, 1978.

Schifferes, S. *The end of the American Dream?* BBC. 4 September, 2006. Accessed at: http://news.bbc.co.uk/2/hi/business/5303590.stm on 18 July, 2013.

Shephard, B. *A War of Nerves; Soldiers and Psychiatrists, 1914–1994*. Cambridge, MA: Harvard University Press, 2003.

Shirer, W L. *Berlin Diary: The Journal of a Foreign Correspondent, 1934–1941*. New York: Alfred A. Knopf, 1941.

Smith, A. *An Enquiry into the Nature and Causes of the Wealth of Nations*. London, New York, Toronto: Everyman's Library, 1991.

Smith, G. "Why I am leaving Goldman Sachs." *New York Times* Op-Ed. 14 March, 2012.

Smith, S. *Allah's Mountains: The Battle for Chechnya.* London: I.B.Tauris, 2006.

Spector, M. and McGinty, T. "The CEO Bankruptcy Bonus." *Wall Street Journal*, 27 January, 2012.

Steele, M. A., Halkin, S. L., Smallwood, P. D., McKenna, T. J., Mitsopoulos, K. and Beam, M. "Cache protection strategies of a scatter-hoarding rodent: do tree squirrels engage in behavioral deception?" *Animal Behavior*, volume 75. 2 February, 2008.

Stephens, J. "Nature Conservancy faces potential backlash from ties to BP." *Washington Post*, 24 May, 2010.

Stevenson, B. and Wolfer, J. "Economic Growth and Subjective Well-Being, Reassessing the Easterlin Paradox." *Brookings Papers on Economic Activity*, Spring 2008. Wharton, University of Pennsylvania.

Stevenson, B. and Wolfer, J. "Subjective Well-Being and Income: Is There Any Evidence of Satiation?" *American Economic Review: Papers & Proceedings*, 2013, 103(3): 598–604.

Strasbourg, J. "Long-Term Capital's Rosenfeld Opens Fund, Person Says." *Bloomberg News*, 9 May, 2007. Accessed at: http://www.bloomberg.com/apps/news?pid=newsarchive&sid=aCz8EcJBd5RA on 18 July, 2013.

Taylor, T. *Nuremberg and Vietnam, an American Tragedy.* New York: Quadrangle Books, 1970.

Teismann, M. "A study of verbal interaction and labelling of jealousy among dating couples involved in jealousy improvisations." Doctoral dissertation, New London: University of Connecticut, 1975.

Toland, J. *Adolf Hitler, The Definitive Biography.* New York: Anchor Books, 1976.

Tolstoy, L. *War and Peace.* Translated by C. C. Garnett. London: Everyman's Library, 1939.

Trader Monthly. "Top 100 Traders list for 2005." April/May 2006.

Trader Monthly. "Top 100 Traders list for 2006." April/May 2007.

Trivers, R. *Social Evolution.* Menlo Park CA: Benjamin Cummings, 1985.

United Nations. *General Assembly Resolution, 1948 260 (III) "Prevention and Punishment of the Crime of Genocide".* 9 December 1948. Accessed at: http://daccess-dds-ny.un.org/doc/RESOLUTION/GEN/NR0/044/31/IMG/NR004431.pdf?OpenElement on 18 July, 2013.

United Nations. *World population to 2300.* 2004. Accessed at: http://www.un.org/esa/population/publications/longrange2/WorldPop2300final.pdf on 18 July, 2013.

U.S. Department of Justice, Office of Justice Programs, Bureau of Justice Statistics. *One in 34 U.S. Adults Under Correctional Supervision in 2011,*

Lowest Rate Since 2000. 29 November, 2012. Accessed at: http://www.ojp.usdoj.gov/newsroom/pressreleases/2012/ojppr112912.pdf on 18 July, 2013.

Valéry, P. *Aesthetics.* Translated by R. Manheim. London: Routledge & Keegan Paul, 1964.

Voltaire. Letter to Rousseau in response to The Social Contract, 30 August, 1755. Accessed at: http://www.whitman.edu/VSA/letters/8.30.1755.html on 18 July, 2013.

von Bingen, H. *The Book of the Rewards of Life: Liber Vitae Meritorum.* Translated by B. W. Hozeski. New York, Garland Publishing, 1994.

von Neumann, J and Morgenstern, O. *The Theory of Games and Economic Behaviour.* Princeton: Princeton University Press, 1944.

von Neumann, J. "The Mathematician." *Works of the Mind* Vol. I no. 1. Chicago: University of Chicago Press, 1947.

Wang Jian Shou. home.wangjianshuo.com. 10 June 2006. Accessed at: http://home.wangjianshuo.com/archives/20060610_hukou_system_in_china.htm on 18 July, 2013.

Weiner, E. *The Geography of Bliss: One Grump's Search for the Happiest Places in the World.* New York: Hachette Book Group, 2008.

Whitworth, D. "China's colossus." *The Times,* 30 August, 2007.

Wilcox, B., Kunkel, D., Cantor, J., Dowrick, P., Linn, S. and Palmer, E. *Report of the APA Task Force on Advertising and Children,* American Psychological Association. 20 February, 2004. Accessed at: http://www.apa.org/pi/families/resources/advertising-children.pdf on 18 July, 2013.

Williams, B G. *The Crimean Tartars – The Diaspora Experience and the Forging of a Nation.* Boston, MA: Brill's Inner Asian Library, 2001.

Williams, J. *The Compleat Strategyst.* New York: Macgraw Hill, 1954.

Wittgenstein, L. *Tractatus Logico-Philosophicus.* Translated by C. K. Ogden. London: Routledge & Keegan Paul, 1922.

Wittgenstein, L. *Philosophical Investigations.* Translated by G. E. M. Anscombe. Oxford: Basil Blackwell, 1953.

Wittgenstein, L. *Lectures & Conversations on Aesthetics, Psychology and Religious Beliefs.* Oxford: Blackwell Publishing, 1966.

World Database of Happiness. Accessed at: http://worlddatabaseofhappiness.eur.nl on 18 July, 2013.

Zeeb, F. D., Robbins, T. W. and Winstanley, C. A. "Serotonergic and Dopaminergic Modulation of Gambling Behavior as Assessed Using a Novel Rat Gambling Task." *Journal of Neuropsychopharmacology,* September, 2009, 34(10):2329-43.

Zhisui, L. *The Private Life of Chairman Mao.* New York: Random House, 1994.

ACKNOWLEDGEMENTS

Becky Ferriera and Kyle Beaver were my editors. Leo Hollis also provided editorial feedback through The Literary Consultancy in London. Stephen Cashmore was my proofreader. Kristen Harrington of the Curved House designed my website and my cover. Eric J Henderson was my photographer.

Noam Chomsky gave valuable time to discuss some of the ideas behind the book. Ian Hancock of the University of Texas provided guidance and material on the Romany Holocaust and provided feedback on draft chapters.

Dawn Carrington, Sylvia Hesse, Andrea Kail, Tina Nole, Tim Sultan, Elizabeth Weaver and Brian Glyn Williams all reviewed drafts and provided feedback. Brian also inspired my interest in genocide and terrorism.

INDEX